MATHEMATICAL TOOLS FOR MACHINE TECHNOLOGY

MATHEMATICAL TOOLS FOR MACHINE TECHNOLOGY

JOHN D. POPOWSKI

**Dakota County Area
Vocational-Technical Institute**

**Breton Publishers
North Scituate, Massachusetts**

Breton Publishers
A Division of Wadsworth, Inc.

Library of Congress Cataloging in Publication Data

Popowski, John D., 1945–
   Mathematical tools for machine technology.

   Includes index.
   1. Shop mathematics.   I. Title.
TJ1165.P68   513′132   81–15531
ISBN 0–534–01096–2   AACR2

Mathematical Tools for Machine Technology was prepared for publication by the following people: **M.N. Lewis**, copy editor; **Amy Ullrich**, production editor and art coordinator; **Trisha Hanlon**, interior text designer; **Stephen Wm. Snider**, cover designer; **lepi graphics**, illustrator. Sylvia Dovner supervised production. The sponsoring editor was **George J. Horesta**. The book was set in Times Roman and Avant Garde by **Modern Graphics, Inc.**; printing and binding was by **ZBR Publications, Inc.**

Printed in the United States of America
1 2 3 4 5 6 7 8 9 – 86 85 84 83 82

In Memory of My Father

CONTENTS

CHAPTER 2

CHAPTER 3

CHAPTER 4
RATIOS AND PROPORTIONS

CHAPTER 5

CHAPTER 6

CHAPTER 7
MEASUREMENT OF ANGLES

CHAPTER 8
TRIANGLES

CHAPTER 9

CIRCLES

CHAPTER 10

TRIGONOMETRY

Appendix

Answers

Index

PREFACE

Mathematical Tools for Machine Technology presents the mathematical concepts required for success on the job in the machine trades. It is designed for individuals preparing for machine trades occupations, from the machine operator level up through the journeyman machinist level.

Beginning with the fundamentals of fractions and decimals, coverage progresses through linear measurement, ratios and proportions, formula calculations, and the basics of the metric system. A strong emphasis on geometry is maintained as the presentation continues with angular measurement and plane figures through trigonometry.

The mathematical concepts in the book are well illustrated and are supported with a variety of realistic, shop-related examples and problems. Review terms and comprehensive exercise sections appear at the end of each chapter.

Each exercise section begins with fairly simple exercises designed to reinforce the basic math concepts presented within the chapter. These are followed by problems incorporating the concepts into shop situations. Because the problems represent actual shop situations, the accompanying illustrations are drawn according to standard drafting practices. In many cases the instructor may need to review, or even define, drafting symbols and conventions in order for students to work the related math problems.

In the machinist occupations, machined parts are unacceptable unless all specifications are correct. Similarly, the solution to a problem in mathematics is unacceptable unless it's correct. As they work through this book, students should thus be encouraged to develop the habits of accuracy and precision that will be expected of them when working in the shop. All testing conducted with this text should emphasize the correctness required in the machine trades.

Very successful student performance has resulted from the use of the material in this book. It was developed and classroom tested during an eight-year period for a two-year machine trades program offered at a vocational-technical school. The text's approach is flexible enough to allow its use in either self-paced or traditional class situations.

Mathematical Tools for Machine Technology is equally applicable for use in both secondary and postsecondary machine trades programs. In secondary programs the basic skills presented in the early chapters would constitute the primary emphasis of the course. The remaining chapters could then be used for advanced, independent study at the option of the instructor. In postsecondary programs the beginning chapters could be used as a review, with the later chapters constituting the major part of the course.

CHAPTER 1

FRACTIONS

Learning Objectives

After studying this chapter, you should be able to:

— Indicate fractional amounts for a given fraction
— Identify proper (1/2, 3/4) and improper fractions (5/4, 17/8) and mixed numbers (1-1/2, 3-5/8)
— Calculate equal fractions of higher or lower terms
— Calculate equal improper fractions and mixed numbers
— Compare fractions for value
— Add and subtract like and unlike fractions and mixed numbers
— Multiply and divide whole numbers, fractions, and mixed numbers

As what we call civilization developed, the need for a system of mathematics increased. A system of *whole numbers* was devised to keep track of whole amounts. The number system used today is called the Arabic system because it was developed in that part of the world. We are all familiar with this system of whole numbers, which includes:

0, 1, 2, 3, 4, 5, 6, 7, 8, 9, . . .

But whole numbers did not fill the need for indicating all amounts. Another system was needed to represent parts of a whole. The fractional number system (or fractions) was developed to keep track of parts of a whole amount.

Fractions are numbers used to express the parts of a whole. *Fractional amounts* are parts of a whole. Some examples of fractions are:

$$\frac{1}{2}, \quad \frac{3}{4}, \quad 1\frac{3}{8}, \quad \frac{28}{16}, \quad \cdots$$

A machinist needs to have a thorough knowledge of fractions. Fractions are used in the shop in working with tools, handling materials, and reading dimensions. It would be very difficult to be a good machinist without having a good knowledge of fractions.

INTERPRETATION OF FRACTIONS

As we saw above, fractions, like whole numbers, are a means of showing amounts. However, fractions differ from whole numbers in having two parts and in representing the value of an amount in the form of a comparison. For example, if someone shared an apple with you by merely cutting off a piece, you would not know precisely how much of the apple you had been given. But if that person first cut the apple into 4 equal pieces and then gave you 1 of the pieces, you could tell how much of the apple you had received. That is, you could compare your piece with the 4 equal pieces of the whole apple:

$$\frac{1}{4} \quad \frac{\text{number of pieces of apple given to you}}{\text{number of equal pieces into which the apple was divided}}$$

The two parts of a fraction are the *numerator* (on top) and the *denominator* (below):

$$\frac{5}{8} \quad \frac{\text{numerator (tells how many equal parts are being considered)}}{\text{denominator (tells how many equal parts make up the whole)}}$$

If you spend 8 hours a day at work, you can express this time as part of a day by comparing it to the 24 hours that make a day. That is, you work 8/24 of a day.

Each inch on a 6″ rule is divided into 8 equal parts. Suppose you measure an object and find that its length is equal to 5 of those parts, as shown in Figure 1.1. You know what part of an inch the length of the object is. The object is 5/8" long.

Fractions are of great value because they are very versatile. We can divide a whole into as many equal parts as we deem necessary, and we can represent any part of the whole by a fraction.

From our own experiences, we are familiar with many different standardized divisions of whole quantities. Many of these divisions are standard throughout the world, while some are standard only to us. These divisions include:

— A week is divided into 7 days
— A day is divided into 24 hours
— An hour is divided into 60 minutes
— A pound is divided into 16 ounces
— A gallon is divided into 4 quarts
— A foot is divided into 12 inches
— An inch is divided into 2, 4, 8, 16, 32, and 64 parts

In the machine trades, fractional dimensioning is encountered continually. The most common twist drills are found in fractionally dimensioned series, as are end mills; fasteners; steel, aluminum, and brass stock; and many other tools and materials used by machinists.

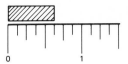

Figure 1.1

Types of Fractions

Proper fractions are fractions in which the numerator is smaller than the denominator. The value of a proper fraction is always less than 1, as in the following examples:

$$\frac{3}{4}, \frac{5}{8}, \frac{7}{8}, \frac{9}{16}, \frac{15}{32}$$

Like fractions are fractions that have a *common* (the same) *denominator*. For example, the following are like fractions:

$$\frac{5}{16}, \frac{11}{16}, \frac{8}{16}, \frac{1}{16}, \frac{15}{16}$$

Unlike fractions are fractions that do not have a common denominator. For example, the following are unlike fractions:

$$\frac{3}{4}, \frac{5}{8}, \frac{11}{16}, \frac{9}{32}, \frac{1}{2}$$

Improper fractions are fractions in which the numerator is larger than the denominator. The value of an improper fraction is always greater than 1, as in the following examples:

$$\frac{11}{2}, \frac{5}{4}, \frac{21}{16}, \frac{54}{32}, \frac{10}{8}$$

NOTE: Improper fractions are not used to express the value of an amount except during calculations. We use them to handle awkward situations that sometimes exist during arithmetic operations with fractions.

Mixed numbers are numbers used to express amounts that are greater than a whole and have a fractional part. Mixed numbers have two parts, the whole part and the fractional part. The following are examples of mixed numbers:

$$4\frac{5}{16}, \quad 11\frac{3}{8}, \quad 6\frac{3}{4}, \quad 3\frac{7}{8}$$

PROCEDURES FOR FINDING EQUAL FRACTIONS

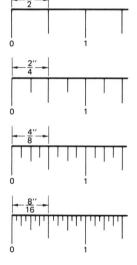

Figure 1.2

A unique property of fractions is that many fractions can be used to represent the same amount. For example, the illustration in Figure 1.2 shows that 1/2 of an inch is the same as 2/4 of an inch, as 4/8 of an inch, and as 8/16 of an inch.

Fractions that represent the same amount have the same value, and we call them *equal fractions*. The value of the fractions 1/2, 2/4, 4/8, and 8/16 is the same. They are equal. The fractions are written differently, but their implied values are the same. A machinist should be able to recognize quickly that 12/16 of an inch is the same as 3/4 of an inch, or that 17/16 of an inch is the same as 1-1/16 of an inch.

When working with fractions, machinists are often required to find equal fractions. The following rules and procedures can be used to find equal fractions. The most common equal fraction problems encountered by machinists require finding equal fractions of higher or lower terms.

Raising a Fraction to Higher Terms

Raising a fraction to *higher terms* means determining an equal fraction with a larger denominator.

RULE

To raise a fraction to higher terms, multiply the numerator and the denominator of the fraction by a common multiplier.

A *common multiplier* is a number used to multiply both the numerator and the denominator of a fraction to raise it without changing the value. For example, the fraction 1/4 can be raised to any number of equal fractions:

$$\frac{1 \times 2}{4 \times 2} = \frac{2}{8} \quad \text{or} \quad \frac{1 \times 3}{4 \times 3} = \frac{3}{12} \quad \text{or} \quad \frac{1 \times 4}{4 \times 4} = \frac{4}{16} \quad \text{and so on}$$

In order to raise a fraction to specific higher terms, the common multiplier is found by dividing the higher denominator by the lower. For example, to express 5/8 in the higher terms of 16ths, the required common multiplier is 2, because $16 \div 8 = 2$. Therefore, both 5 and 8 must be multiplied by 2:

$$\frac{5 \times 2}{8 \times 2} = \frac{10}{16}$$

Thus, $5/8 = 10/16$ in value. Here, the value expressed by the fraction 5/8 is being equated to 10/16, an equal fraction of higher terms of 16ths.

The problem of raising a fraction to an equal fraction of higher terms is illustrated in the following example.

EXAMPLE

Problem

Express the fraction shown on the ruler in Figure 1.3a in the higher terms shown on the ruler in Figure 1.3b.

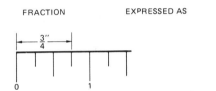
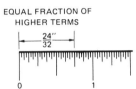

Figure 1.3a   Figure 1.3b

Analysis

Express 3/4″ as a fraction of 32nds.

Solution

Step 1:   Find the common multiplier required to raise 4ths to 32nds

$$32 \div 4 = 8$$

Step 2:   Multiply the numerator and the denominator by the common multiplier

$$\frac{3 \times 8}{4 \times 8} = \frac{24}{32}$$

Answer

$$\frac{3''}{4} = \frac{24''}{32}$$

Reducing a Fraction to Lower Terms

Reducing a fraction to *lower terms* means determining an equal fraction with a smaller denominator.

RULE

To reduce a fraction to lower terms, divide both the numerator and denominator of the fraction by a common factor.

Common factors are numbers that will evenly divide both the numerator and the denominator. In many cases, we can find more than one common factor. The largest number that will divide both the numerator and the denominator evenly is called the *largest common factor*. When we cannot find any common factors to divide the numerator and denominator any further, the fraction is expressed in its lowest terms.

For example, to reduce 40/64 to its lowest terms, we must first determine the common factors of 40 and 64. The number 40 can be evenly divided by 2, 4, 5, 8, 10, and 20. The number 64 can be evenly divided by 2, 4, 8, 16, and 32. We know that 5, 10, and 20 are not factors of 64 and that 16 and 32 are not factors of 40. We see that 2, 4, and 8 are common factors of 40 and 64 and that 8 is the largest. Therefore, we divide by 8 because no larger number will evenly divide 40 and 64:

$$\frac{40 \div 8}{64 \div 8} = \frac{5}{8}$$

Thus, 40/64 = 5/8 in value. Here, the value expressed by the fraction 40/64 is being equated to 5/8, an equal fraction of the lowest terms.

The following example shows how to express a fraction in lowest terms.

EXAMPLE

Problem

Express the fraction shown on the ruler in Figure 1.4a in the lowest terms shown on the ruler in Figure 1.4b.

FRACTION   EXPRESSED AS   EQUAL FRACTION OF LOWEST TERMS

Figure 1.4a   Figure 1.4b

Analysis

Divide both the numerator and the denominator by the largest common factor.

Solution

Step 1a: Determine all the numbers that will evenly divide 28

2, 4, 7, 14

Step 1b: Determine all the numbers that will evenly divide 32

2, 4, 8, 16

Step 2: Compare the answers and choose the largest common factor

$$\begin{matrix} 2 & 4 & 7 & 14 \\ & \updownarrow & & \\ 2 & 4 & 8 & 16 \end{matrix}$$

Step 3: Divide both the numerator and the denominator by the largest common factor

$$\frac{28 \div 4}{32 \div 4} = \frac{7}{8}$$

Answer

$$\frac{28''}{32} = \frac{7''}{8}$$

Changing a Mixed Number to an Equal Improper Fraction

Changing a mixed number to an equal improper fraction involves calculating the total parts represented by the whole and fractional part of the mixed number.

RULE

To change a mixed number to an equal improper fraction, restate the whole number as a fraction and add it to the fractional part of the mixed number.

NOTE: A whole number can always be stated as a fraction without changing its value by putting the number over 1.

For example, to express 2-3/8 as an equal improper fraction, we first state the whole number as a fraction, $2 = 2/1$, and restate it in terms of 8ths by multiplying:

$$\frac{2}{1} \times \frac{8}{8} = \frac{2 \times 8}{1 \times 8} = \frac{16}{8}$$

We then add the restated fraction to the fractional part of the mixed number:

$$\frac{16}{8} + \frac{3}{8} = \frac{19}{8}$$

Thus, the total parts represented by 2-3/8 is 19/8.

The same procedure is used to change 3-5/16″ to an equal improper fraction. The whole number is first stated in terms of 16ths:

$$\frac{3}{1} \times \frac{16}{16} = \frac{3 \times 16}{1 \times 16} = \frac{48}{16}$$

The restated fraction is then added to the fractional part of the mixed number:

$$\frac{48}{16} + \frac{5}{16} = \frac{53}{16}$$

Thus, 3-5/16″ = 53/16″ in value.

Measurements like the one shown on the ruler illustrated in Figure 1.5 are usually read as mixed numbers (five and three-fourths inches). The following example demonstrates how to change this mixed number to an equal improper fraction.

EXAMPLE

Problem

Determine an equal improper fraction for the mixed number shown on the ruler in Figure 1.5.

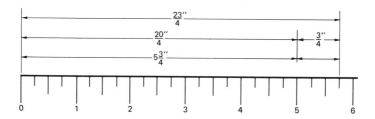

Figure 1.5

Analysis

Change 5-3/4″ to an equal improper fraction.

Solution

Step 1:   State the whole number in terms of 4ths by multiplying

$$\frac{5}{1} \times \frac{4}{4} = \frac{5 \times 4}{1 \times 4} = \frac{20}{4}$$

Step 2:   Add the fractions

$$\frac{20}{4} + \frac{3}{4} = \frac{23}{4}$$

Answer

$$5\frac{3''}{4} = \frac{23''}{4}$$

NOTE: A simple way to remember how to calculate the total parts in a mixed number is to multiply the whole number by the denominator and add the results to the numerator. For example, to determine the total parts in 5-3/4, multiply 5 × 4 and then add the results to 3:

$$5 \times 4 = 20 \quad \text{and} \quad 20 + 3 = 23$$

Thus, the total parts in 5-3/4 = 23 parts, or 23/4.

Changing an Improper Fraction to an Equal Mixed Number

Changing an improper fraction to an equal mixed number involves calculating how many whole and fractional parts are represented in the improper fraction.

RULE

To change an improper fraction to an equal mixed number, divide the numerator by the denominator to determine the whole number and place any remainder over the denominator to express the fractional parts.

For example, to express 13/4 as an equal mixed number, we divide the numerator by the denominator:

$$13 \div 4 = 3, \text{ with 1 remainder}$$

As a result of the division, we have 3 whole parts and 1 fractional part left over (the *remainder*). We place the remainder over the denominator and add it to the whole number:

$$3 + \frac{1}{4} = 3\frac{1}{4}$$

Thus, the whole and fractional parts represented by 13/4 are 3-1/4.

The same procedure is used to change 45/16″ to an equal mixed number. First the numerator is divided by the denominator:

$$45 \div 16 = 2, \text{ with 13 remainder}$$

The remainder is expressed as fractional parts and added to the whole number:

$$2 + \frac{13}{16} = 2\frac{13}{16}$$

Thus, 45/16″ = 2-13/16″ in value.

The following example shows how to change an improper fraction to an equal mixed number.

EXAMPLE

Problem

Determine an equal mixed number for the improper fraction shown on the ruler in Figure 1.6.

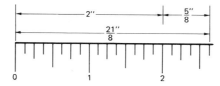

Figure 1.6

Analysis

Change 21/8″ to a mixed number.

Solution

Step 1:   Divide the numerator by the denominator

$$21 \div 8 = 2, \text{ with 5 remainder}$$

Step 2:   Express the remainder as a fractional part and add it to the whole number

$$2 + \frac{5}{8} = 2\frac{5}{8}$$

Answer

$$\frac{21″}{8} = 2\frac{5″}{8}$$

PROCEDURES FOR COMPARING FRACTIONS

Machinists spend a great deal of time computing and taking measurements. The faster we can accomplish these tasks, the more efficient we become. One of our computing tasks is to make simple comparisons of the measurements we take.

Generally, we can make these comparisons mentally. For example, we can quickly tell that a piece of round stock that is 2″ in diameter will not fit into a hole that is 1″ in diameter because we know that 2 is greater than 1. But in working with fractional measurements, how efficiently we make the comparison between two or more fractions depends on how familiar we are with the value of the fractional parts.

RULE

To compare fractions for their value, express the fractions in like terms.

Fractions that are expressed in *like terms* are fractions that have common denominators. For example, the value of the denominators of 1/4 and 3/4 is the same: a fourth of a whole. Because these two fractions are in like terms, we can easily compare 1 fourth with 3 fourths to determine that 1/4 is less than 3/4.

When the denominators of the fractions to be compared are not the same, we must change one or more of the fractions so that they are expressed in like terms. Each fraction that is changed must be changed to an equal fraction.

In some instances, expressing fractions in like terms for comparison means raising one of the fractions to an equal fraction of higher terms that are the same as those of the comparison fraction. For example, to compare 2/3 and 5/6, we must raise 2/3 to an equal fraction expressed in terms of 6ths:

$$\frac{2 \times 2}{3 \times 2} = \frac{4}{6}$$

Thus, 2/3 = 4/6 in value, and 4/6 can now be easily and accurately compared with 5/6.

In other instances, expressing fractions in like terms for comparison means changing both fractions to equal fractions with the same denominator. The new denominator for both fractions is the product of the two original denominators. For example, to compare 4/5 and 7/8, we first find a new denominator by multiplying the two original denominators:

$$5 \times 8 = 40$$

We then raise each fraction to be compared to the higher terms of 40ths:

$$\frac{4 \times 8}{5 \times 8} = \frac{32}{40} \quad \text{and} \quad \frac{7 \times 5}{8 \times 5} = \frac{35}{40}$$

Thus, 4/5 = 32/40 and 7/8 = 35/40 in value. Now the two like fractions 32/40 and 35/40 can be compared.

Similarly, the fractions 2/10″ and 3/8″ can be compared by expressing them in like terms. First the new denominator is obtained:

$$10 \times 8 = 80$$

Then the fractions are changed to equal fractions with the same denominator:

$$\frac{2 \times 8}{10 \times 8} = \frac{16}{80} \quad \text{and} \quad \frac{3 \times 10}{8 \times 10} = \frac{30}{80}$$

Thus, 2/10″ = 16/80″ and 3/8″ = 30/80″ in value. The like fractions 16/80″ and 30/80″ can now be compared.

A typical problem in comparing fractions is shown in the following example.

EXAMPLE

Problem

If a rough cut on a lathe leaves a diameter of 15/32″ on a part, how much more can be taken off in the finishing cut if the print specifies a 1/2″ diameter?

Analysis

Express the fractions in like terms for comparison.

Solution

Step 1:   Change 1/2 to an equal fraction that is in the like terms of 32

$$\frac{1 \times 16}{2 \times 16} = \frac{16}{32}$$

Step 2:   Compare the two like fractions

$$\frac{16}{32} \quad \text{and} \quad \frac{15}{32}$$

Answer

The comparison shows that since 1/2″ = 16/32″, the diameter after the rough cut, 15/32″, is already too small to meet the specified diameter of 1/2″. The part will have to be discarded.

ARITHMETIC OPERATIONS

Performing the operations of addition, subtraction, multiplication, and division with fractional numbers is fairly simple. However, machinists are often required to calculate equal fractions before arithmetic operations can be performed. Further, we are also often required to simplify answers after the operations have been performed.

NOTE: To *simplify* answers means to reduce proper fractions to their lowest terms and to change improper fractions to mixed numbers. A good understanding of the procedures for finding equal fractions is a must for understanding this section.

Addition

When dealing with the operations of addition and subtraction, we must keep in mind that all the fractions being added or subtracted must be expressed in like terms. In other words, only like fractions can be used. A common (the same) denominator must be used for each fraction involved in an operation of addition or subtraction.

RULE

To add like fractions, add the numerators and simplify the answer if possible.

The following example shows how to add like fractions.

EXAMPLE

Problem

Find the length of the arbor shown in Figure 1.7.

Analysis

$$\frac{13''}{16} + \frac{8''}{16} + \frac{9''}{16} = ?$$

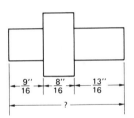

Figure 1.7

Solution

Step 1:   Add the numerators

$$\frac{13}{16} + \frac{8}{16} + \frac{9}{16} = \frac{13 + 8 + 9}{16} = \frac{30}{16}$$

Step 2:   Change to an equal mixed number

$$\frac{30}{16} = 30 \div 16 = 1, \text{ remainder } 14 = 1\frac{14}{16}$$

Step 3:   Simplify by reducing to lowest terms

$$1\frac{14}{16} = 1\frac{14 \div 2}{16 \div 2} = 1\frac{7}{8}$$

Answer

$$\frac{13''}{16} + \frac{8''}{16} + \frac{9''}{16} = 1\frac{7''}{8}$$

RULE

To add unlike fractions, express all fractions in like terms. Then add the numerators and simplify the answer if possible.

The following example demonstrates addition of unlike fractions.

EXAMPLE

Problem

Find the length of the bracket shown in Figure 1.8.

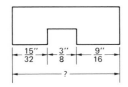

Figure 1.8

Analysis

$$\frac{15''}{32} + \frac{3''}{8} + \frac{9''}{16} = ?$$

Solution

Step 1a: Find the common multipliers needed to raise 3/8 and 9/16 to the higher terms of 32nds

$$32 \div 16 = 2 \quad \text{and} \quad 32 \div 8 = 4$$

Step 1b: Express the fractions in higher terms of 32nds

$$\frac{3 \times 4}{8 \times 4} = \frac{12}{32} \quad \text{and} \quad \frac{9 \times 2}{16 \times 2} = \frac{18}{32}$$

Step 2: Add the numerators of all fractions

$$\frac{15}{32} + \frac{12}{32} + \frac{18}{32} = \frac{15 + 12 + 18}{32} = \frac{45}{32}$$

Step 3: Simplify by changing to an equal mixed number

$$\frac{45}{32} = 1\frac{13}{32}$$

Answer

$$\frac{15''}{32} + \frac{3''}{8} + \frac{9''}{16} = 1\frac{13''}{32}$$

RULE

To add mixed numbers, express the fractional parts of the mixed numbers in like terms. Then add the fractional parts together and the whole parts together and simplify the answer if possible.

The procedure for adding mixed numbers is illustrated in the following example.

EXAMPLE

Problem

Find the length of the support strap shown in Figure 1.9.

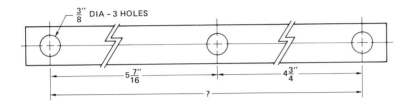

Figure 1.9

Analysis

$$4\frac{3''}{4} + 5\frac{7''}{16} = ?$$

Solution

Step 1:   Express the fractional parts of the mixed number in like terms by changing 3/4 to the higher terms of 16ths

$$\frac{3 \times 4}{4 \times 4} = \frac{12}{16}$$

Step 2a: Add the numerators of the fractional parts

$$\frac{12}{16} + \frac{7}{16} = \frac{12 + 7}{16} = \frac{19}{16}$$

Step 2b: Add the whole parts

$$4 + 5 = 9$$

Step 3:   Add the results of Steps 2a and 2b

$$9 + \frac{19}{16} = 9\frac{19}{16}$$

Step 4:   Simplify by changing the improper fraction to a mixed number and adding it to the whole number

$$\frac{19}{16} = 1\frac{3}{16}$$

$$9 + 1\frac{3}{16} = 10\frac{3}{16}$$

Answer

$$4\frac{3''}{4} + 5\frac{7''}{16} = 10\frac{3''}{16}$$

Subtraction

RULE

To subtract like fractions, subtract the numerators and simplify the answer if possible.

The following example demonstrates subtraction of like fractions.

EXAMPLE

Problem

Find the missing measurement of the pin shown in Figure 1.10.

Analysis

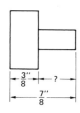

Figure 1.10

$$\frac{7''}{8} - \frac{3''}{8} = ?$$

Solution

Step 1:   Subtract the numerators

$$\frac{7}{8} - \frac{3}{8} = \frac{7 - 3}{8} = \frac{4}{8}$$

Step 2:   Simplify by reducing to lowest terms

$$\frac{4 \div 4}{8 \div 4} = \frac{1}{2}$$

Answer

$$\frac{7''}{8} - \frac{3''}{8} = \frac{1''}{2}$$

RULE

To subtract unlike fractions, first express all fractions in like terms. Then subtract the numerators and simplify the answer if possible.

Unlike fractions are subtracted in the following example.

EXAMPLE

Problem

Find the length of the missing measurement of the bearing cap shown in Figure 1.11.

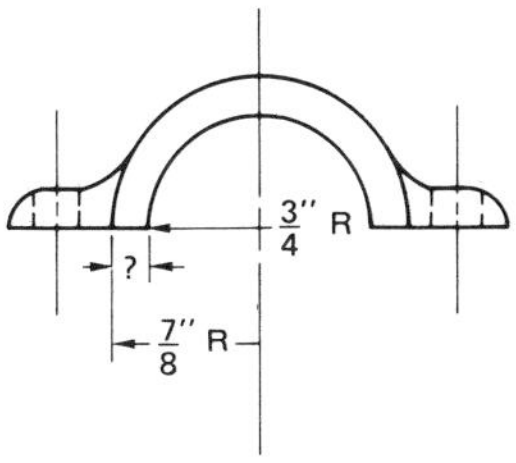

Analysis

$$\frac{7''}{8} - \frac{3''}{4} = ?$$

Solution

Step 1: Express fractions in like terms by changing 3/4 to the higher terms of 8ths

$$\frac{3 \times 2}{4 \times 2} = \frac{6}{8}$$

Step 2: Subtract the numerators of the like fractions

$$\frac{7}{8} - \frac{6}{8} = \frac{7 - 6}{8} = \frac{1}{8}$$

Answer

$$\frac{7''}{8} - \frac{3''}{4} = \frac{1''}{8}$$

Figure 1.11

RULE

To subtract mixed numbers, express the fractional parts of the mixed numbers in like terms. Subtract the fractional parts and then the whole parts and simplify the answer if possible.

The subtraction of mixed numbers is shown in the following example.

EXAMPLE

Problem

Find the missing measurement of the trip cam shown in Figure 1.12.

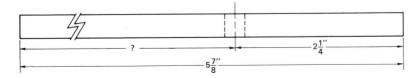

Figure 1.12

Analysis

$$5\frac{7''}{8} - 2\frac{1''}{4} = \; ?$$

Solution

Step 1:   Express the fractional parts of the mixed number in like terms by changing 1/4 to the higher terms of 8ths

$$\frac{1 \times 2}{4 \times 2} = \frac{2}{8}$$

Step 2a: Subtract the numerators of the fractional parts

$$\frac{7}{8} - \frac{2}{8} = \frac{7 - 2}{8} = \frac{5}{8}$$

Step 2b: Subtract the whole parts

$$5 - 2 = 3$$

Step 3:   Add the results of Steps 2a and 2b

$$3 + \frac{5}{8} = 3\frac{5}{8}$$

Answer

$$5\frac{7''}{8} - 2\frac{1''}{4} = 3\frac{5''}{8}$$

Sometimes, after expressing the fractional parts in like terms, we are faced with subtracting a larger fraction from a smaller fraction of like terms. This situation requires making the smaller fraction into an improper fraction by *borrowing* from the whole part of that number.

NOTE: In borrowing in a mixed number, 1 is borrowed from the whole number and added to the fractional part of the mixed number to make an improper fraction. For example, in the mixed number 7-2/8, 1 may be borrowed from the 7. The 1 is then restated as a fraction, 1 = 8/8, and added to the fractional part of the mixed number: 8/8 + 2/8 = 10/8. Therefore, 7-2/8 = 6-10/8.

The problem in the following example requires borrowing since the fractional parts cannot be subtracted as stated.

Example

Problem

Find the missing measurement of the tuning fork shown in Figure 1.13.

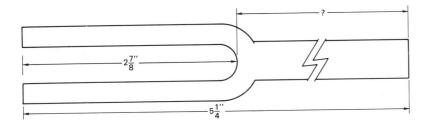

Figure 1.13

Analysis

$$5\frac{1}{4}'' - 2\frac{7}{8}'' = ?$$

Solution

Step 1: Express the fractional parts of the mixed number in like terms by changing 1/4 to the higher terms of 8ths in order to subtract

$$5\frac{2}{8} - 2\frac{7}{8}$$

Step 2: Since 7/8 cannot be subtracted from 2/8, express 5-7/8″ as an equivalent (equal) mixed number by borrowing

$$5\frac{2}{8} = 4 + 1 + \frac{2}{8} = 4 + \frac{8}{8} + \frac{2}{8} = 4\frac{10}{8}$$

Step 3: Restate the problem using the equivalent mixed number

$$4\frac{10}{8} - 2\frac{7}{8}$$

Step 4a: Subtract the numerators of the fractional parts

$$\frac{10}{8} - \frac{7}{8} = \frac{10 - 7}{8} = \frac{3}{8}$$

Step 4b: Subtract the whole parts

$$4 - 2 = 2$$

Step 5: Add the results of Steps 4a and 4b

$$2 + \frac{3}{8} = 2\frac{3}{8}$$

Answer

$$5\frac{1}{4}'' - 2\frac{7}{8}'' = 2\frac{3}{8}''$$

Multiplication

Machinists do not use multiplication and division as often as addition and subtraction when they work with fractions. When we do perform these operations, we should keep in mind that we do not need to express fractions in like terms when we multiply or divide. To do so would only create additional work for no purpose. The procedures that we use to multiply and divide fractions and mixed numbers apply to many different types of problems. However, some of these problems are seldom worked in practical applications. These types of problems are identified as being optional at the end of this section.

As we have already seen in earlier sections, the basic procedure for multiplying two fractions is to multiply the numerators by the numerators and the denominators by the denominators. The following rules and examples demonstrate how to apply this basic procedure when multiplying fractions, whole numbers, and mixed numbers.

RULE

To multiply a fraction by a whole number, restate the whole number as a fraction. Multiply the numerators by the numerators and the denominators by the denominators and simplify the answer if possible.

The following example shows how to multiply a proper fraction by a whole number.

EXAMPLE

Problem

Find the length of the bracket shown in Figure 1.14.

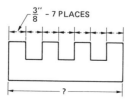

Figure 1.14

Analysis

$$7 \times \frac{3}{8} = ?$$

Solution

Step 1:   Restate the whole number as a fraction and multiply

$$\frac{7}{1} \times \frac{3}{8} = \frac{7 \times 3}{1 \times 8} = \frac{21}{8}$$

Step 2:   Simplify by changing to an equal mixed number

$$\frac{21}{8} = 2\frac{5}{8}$$

Answer

$$7 \times \frac{3''}{8} = 2\frac{5''}{8}$$

NOTE: A simple way to remember how to multiply a fraction by a whole number is to multiply the whole number by the numerator and put the results over the denominator. For example, to multiply $7 \times 3/8$, multiply: $7 \times 3 = 21$. Then put the results over the denominator: $21/8$.

RULE

To multiply a whole number by a mixed number, multiply the whole number by the whole part of the mixed number. Then multiply the whole number by the fractional part of the mixed number. Add the results and simplify the answer if possible.

A mixed number is multiplied by a whole number in the following example.

EXAMPLE

Problem

Find the length of the drill press jig shown in Figure 1.15.

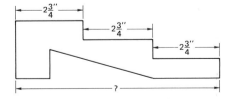

Figure 1.15

Analysis

$$3 \times 2\frac{3}{4}'' = ?$$

Solution

Step 1a: Multiply the whole number by the whole part of the mixed number

$$3 \times 2 = 6$$

Step 1b: Restate the whole number 3 as a fraction and multiply by the fractional part of the mixed number

$$\frac{3}{1} \times \frac{3}{4} = \frac{3 \times 3}{1 \times 4} = \frac{9}{4}$$

Step 2: Add the results of Steps 1a and 1b

$$6 + \frac{9}{4} = 6\frac{9}{4}$$

Step 3: Simplify by reducing to lowest terms

$$6\frac{9}{4} = 8\frac{1}{4}$$

Answer

$$3 \times 2\frac{3}{4}'' = 8\frac{1}{4}''$$

RULE

To multiply a mixed number by a fraction, change the mixed number to an equal improper fraction. Then multiply the two fractions and simplify the answer if possible.

For example, to multiply 5-3/8 by 1/4, we first express the mixed number as an equal improper fraction:

$$5\frac{3}{8} = \frac{5 \times 8}{1 \times 8} + \frac{3}{8} = \frac{40}{8} + \frac{3}{8} = \frac{40 + 3}{8} = \frac{43}{8}$$

We next multiply the two fractions:

$$\frac{43}{8} \times \frac{1}{4} = \frac{43 \times 1}{8 \times 4} = \frac{43}{32}$$

Then we simplify the answer:

$$\frac{43}{32} = 1\frac{11}{32}$$

Thus, 5-3/8 × 1/4 = 1-11/32.

To multiply 2-3/4″ by 3-5/8″, each mixed number is expressed as an equal improper fraction:

$$2\frac{3}{4} = \frac{11}{4} \quad \text{and} \quad 3\frac{5}{8} = \frac{29}{8}$$

The two fractions are then multiplied:

$$\frac{11}{4} \times \frac{29}{8} = \frac{11 \times 29}{4 \times 8} = \frac{319}{32}$$

Finally the answer is simplified:

$$\frac{319}{32} = 9\frac{31}{32}$$

Thus, 2-3/4″ × 3-5/8″ = 9-31/32″.

Division

Solving division problems in which fractions are involved requires changing the problem into a multiplication problem by inverting the divisor of the division problem. The *divisor* is the number by which another number (the dividend) is divided:

dividend ÷ divisor = quotient

To *invert* the divisor is to exchange the numerator and the denominator:

$$\frac{3}{4} \text{ inverted is } \frac{4}{3}$$

$$\frac{7}{16} \text{ inverted is } \frac{16}{7}$$

In dividing a fraction by a whole number, the whole number is restated as a fraction and then inverted:

$$5 = \frac{5}{1}$$

$$\frac{5}{1} \text{ inverted is } \frac{1}{5}$$

RULE

To divide a fraction by a fraction, invert the divisor and multiply.

For example, in the problem 5/8 ÷ 2/3, 2/3 is the divisor. We change the problem to a multiplication problem by inverting the divisor:

$$\frac{5}{8} \div \frac{2}{3} = \frac{5}{8} \times \frac{3}{2}$$

We then multiply the numerators and denominators

$$\frac{5}{8} \times \frac{3}{2} = \frac{5 \times 3}{8 \times 2} = \frac{15}{16}$$

Thus, 5/8 ÷ 2/3 = 15/16.
   The same procedure is used to divide 3/4″ by 2. The divisor is the whole number 2, which must be restated as a fraction: 2/1. The division problem is changed to a multiplication problem by inverting the divisor and multiplying:

$$\frac{3}{4} \div \frac{2}{1} = \frac{3}{4} \times \frac{1}{2}$$

Next the numerators and denominators are multiplied:

$$\frac{3}{4} \times \frac{1}{2} = \frac{3 \times 1}{4 \times 2} = \frac{3}{8}$$

Thus, 3/4 ÷ 2 = 3/8.

RULE

To divide a mixed number by a whole number, express the mixed number as an improper fraction and restate the whole number as a fraction. Then invert the divisor and multiply.

Problems that require the division of a mixed number by a whole number are common in the machine shop. The following example illustrates a typical problem.

EXAMPLE

Problem
Find the missing measurement of the sine bar shown in Figure 1.16.

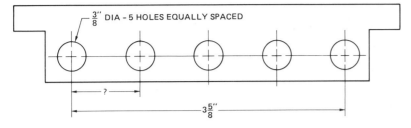

Figure 1.16

Analysis

$$3\frac{5}{8} \div 4 = ?$$

Solution

Step 1:   Express the mixed number as an improper fraction and restate the whole number as a fraction

$$3\frac{5}{8} = \frac{29}{8} \quad \text{and} \quad 4 = \frac{4}{1}$$

Step 2:   Change the division problem to a multiplication problem by inverting the divisor

$$\frac{29}{8} \div \frac{4}{1} = \frac{29}{8} \times \frac{1}{4}$$

Step 3:   Multiply the numerators and the denominators

$$\frac{29}{8} \times \frac{1}{4} = \frac{29 \times 1}{8 \times 4} = \frac{29}{32}$$

Answer

$$3\frac{5}{8} \div 4 = \frac{29}{32}$$

Division of a Mixed Number by a Fraction (Optional)

Here we look at some examples of how to divide a mixed number by a fraction. The procedure is similar to the one we followed in dividing a mixed number by a whole number.

RULE

To divide a mixed number by a fraction, express the mixed number as an improper fraction. Then invert the divisor and multiply.

For example, if we want to divide 4-3/4 by 2/3, we first express the mixed number as an improper fraction:

$$4\frac{3}{4} = \frac{19}{4}$$

We then change the division problem to a multiplication problem by inverting the divisor:

$$\frac{19}{4} \div \frac{2}{3} = \frac{19}{4} \times \frac{3}{2}$$

Multiply the numerators and the denominators:

$$\frac{19}{4} \times \frac{3}{2} = \frac{19 \times 3}{4 \times 2} = \frac{57}{8}$$

Simplify the answer by changing the improper fraction to a mixed number:

$$\frac{57}{8} = 7\frac{1}{8}$$

Thus, 4-3/4 ÷ 2/3 = 7-1/8.

If we want to divide 7-3/8 by 1/4, we first express the mixed number as an improper fraction:

$$7\frac{3}{8} = \frac{59}{8}$$

Change the division problem to a multiplication problem by inverting the divisor:

$$\frac{59}{8} \div \frac{1}{4} = \frac{59 \times 4}{8 \times 1}$$

Multiply the numerators and the denominators:

$$\frac{59}{8} \times \frac{4}{1} = \frac{59 \times 4}{8 \times 1} = \frac{236}{8}$$

Simplify the answer:

$$\frac{236}{8} = 29\frac{4}{8} = 29\frac{1}{2}$$

Thus, 7-3/8 ÷ 1/4 = 29-1/2.

TERMS FOR REVIEW

- — whole numbers
- — fractions
- — fractional amounts
- — numerator
- — denominator
- — proper fractions
- — like fractions
- — common denominator
- — unlike fractions
- — improper fractions
- — mixed numbers

- — equal fractions
- — higher terms
- — common multiplier
- — lower terms
- — common factor
- — largest common factor
- — remainder
- — like terms
- — simplify borrowing
- — divisor
- — invert

EXERCISES

Exercise 1.1: Interpretation of Fractions

A.   Express each of the following parts as a fraction.

1.   5 inches is what part of a foot?

2.   7 ounces is what part of a pound?

3.   73 cents is what part of a dollar?

4.   8 cents is what part of a quarter?

5.   9 inches is what part of a foot?

6.   1 foot is what part of a yard?

7.   3 quarts is what part of a gallon?

1. _____

2. _____

3. _____

4. _____

5. _____

6. _____

7. _____

Exercise 1.2: Types of Fractions

A.   List the following as proper fractions (P), improper fractions (I), or mixed numbers (M).

1.   3/8 _____

2.   5/16 _____

3.   11/5 _____

4.   9/12 _____

5.   4-3/8 _____

6.   3-11/16 _____

7.   12/8 _____

8.   9/8 _____

9.   1-5/8 _____

10.   15/64 _____

11.   17-3/4 _____

12.   15/32 _____

13.   1/3 _____

14.   8-1/2 _____

15.   6-1/4 _____

16.   21/4 _____

17.   5/32 _____

18.   19/16 _____

19.   2-3/4 _____

20.   12/16 _____

Exercise 1.3: Finding Equal Fractions

A.   Reduce the following fractions to their lowest terms.

1.   6/8 = _____

2.   5/10 = _____

3.   6/10 = _____

4.   2/12 = _____

5.   55/100 = _____

6.   24/64 = _____

7.   15/50 = _____

8.   12/32 = _____

9.   16/32 = _____

10.   22/36 = _____

11.   45/60 = _____

12.   6/8 = _____

13.   600/2000 = _____

14.   9/12 = _____

15.   360/5200 = _____

16.   60/365 = _____

B.   Express each of the following parts as a fraction of the lowest terms.

1.   4 inches is what part of a foot?

2.   40 minutes is what part of an hour?

3.   11 ounces is what part of a pound?

1. _____

2. _____

3. _____

4. 8 months is what part of a year?   4. _____

5. 20 hours is what part of a day?   5. _____

6. 55 minutes is what part of an hour?   6. _____

C. Express the following fractions in the higher terms indicated.

1. 3/4 = _____ /12   **2.** 1/6 = _____ /36   **3.** 11/12 = _____ /48

4. 7/15 = _____ /60   **5.** 1/8 = _____ /64   **6.** 1/3 = _____ /9

7. 3/5 = _____ /20   **8.** 3/4 = _____ /16   **9.** 2/3 = _____ /12

10. 2/3 = _____ /15   **11.** 3/8 = _____ /16   **12.** 5/8 = _____ /16

D. Change the following mixed numbers to improper fractions.

1. 2-1/4 = _____   **2.** 3-5/8 = _____   **3.** 9-3/4 = _____

4. 8-1/2 = _____   **5.** 6-9/10 = _____   **6.** 17-5/8 = _____

7. 5-1/4 = _____   **8.** 15-1/2 = _____   **9.** 5-3/4 = _____

E. Express the following improper fractions as mixed numbers.

1. 7/3 = _____   **2.** 19/8 = _____   **3.** 24/16 = _____

4. 49/16 = _____   **5.** 71/4 = _____   **6.** 23/16 = _____

7. 92/32 = _____   **8.** 15/8 = _____   **9.** 35/32 = _____

Exercise 1.4: Equal Fractions and Fraction Comparisons

A. State the equal fractions for the following parts of an inch.

1. 1/8 = _____ /16   **2.** 3/4 = _____ /8   **3.** 1/2 = _____ /4

4. 1/4 = _____ /8   **5.** 1/16 = _____ /32   **6.** 3/8 = _____ /16

7. 5/16 = _____ /32   **8.** 7/8 = _____ /16

B. Arrange the following twist drill sizes from smallest to largest:

7/32,   3/8,   17/64,   1/8,   7/16,   13/32,   1/2,   3/16,   5/16,   5/32.

___   ___   ___   ___   ___   ___   ___   ___   ___   ___

C. Find the lowest common denominator (smallest denominator) that can be used to express each set of fractions in like terms.

1. 1/2 and 1/8 _____   **2.** 1/3 and 1/4 _____   **3.** 2/3 and 3/5 _____

4. 3/4 and 5/16 _____   **5.** 7/8 and 3/32 _____   **6.** 3/4 and 2/10 _____

7. 3/10, 1/5, and 3/25 _____   **8.** 3/4, 1/2, and 7/16 _____   **9.** 3/4, 1/4, and 7/8 _____

10. 7/8, 3/32, and 1/4 _____   **11.** 4/25, 1/50, and 3/5 _____ **12.** 3/4, 1/8, and 3/32 _____

D.   Answer the following shop-related problems.

1.   If a print specifies a measurement of 3/4″ and the part measures 48/64″, is the part machined properly? If not, is the part too small or too large?

1. _____

2.   Can a 7/8″ bolt pass freely through a 57/64″ hole?

2. _____

3.   A part measures 60/64″. What is the measurement of this part expressed in lowest terms?

3. _____

4.   The computed diameter of an arbor is 45/32″. What is this measurement as an equal mixed number?

4. _____

5.   If a print specifies a measurement of 5/16 ± 1/64″, and during inspection the part measures 19/64″, is the part within tolerance?

5. _____

6.   The specified nominal diameter on a threaded shaft is given as 9/16″. What is this measurement in 32nds?

6. _____

7.   The following measurements are on a ring gage:
29/64″, 17/32″, 33/64″, 1/2″, 9/16″, 31/64″, 35/64″, 15/32″, and 7/16″.
Match these measurements to the letters on the following diagram.

7a. A = _____

7b. B = _____

7c. C = _____

7d. D = _____

7e. E = _____

7f. F = _____

7g. G = _____

7h. H = _____

7i. I = _____

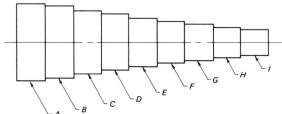

Exercise 1.5: Addition and Subtraction

A.   Add the following fractions and mixed numbers. Reduce answers to lowest terms.

1.   5/8 + 7/8 = _____

2.   21/32 + 15/32 = _____

3.   5/16 + 9/16 + 3/16 = _____

4.   3/8 + 1/2 + 1/4 = _____

5.   3/4 + 5/16 + 29/32 = _____

6.   5/8 + 11/16 + 3/4 = _____

7.   5/16 + 3/8 + 1/4 = _____

8.   2/25 + 7/10 + 3/4 = _____

9.   1-3/8 + 2-3/4 + 1-11/16 = _____

10.   5-7/8 + 3-5/8 + 2-11/16 = _____

11.   8-3/4 + 2-9/16 + 6-5/8 = _____

12.   20-1/4 + 8-3/10 + 2-2/25 = _____

B.   Subtract the following fractions and mixed numbers. Reduce answers to lowest terms.

1.   15/16 − 9/16 = _____

2.   27/32 − 15/32 = _____

3.   3/4 − 5/8 = _____

4.   13/16 − 3/8 = _____

5.   11/16 − 3/8 = _____

6.   4/5 − 7/25 = _____

7.   17/20 − 2/10 = _____

8.   3/4 − 19/64 = _____

9.   5-7/8 − 2-1/2 = _____

10. 8-11/32 − 3-3/8 = _____   **11.** 3-3/5 − 2-7/25 = _____   **12.** 4-11/32 − 2-6/8 = _____

13. 5-2/25 − 3-33/100 = ____   **14.** 19-3/4 − 17-9/16 = _____   **15.** 17-1/8 − 7-1/4 = _____

C. Solve the following addition problems.

1. What is the overall length (*A*) of the plug gage illustrated?

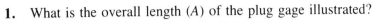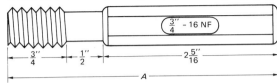

1. _____

2. Find the outside diameter (*A*) of the bushing illustrated.

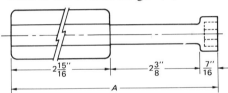

2. _____

3. What is the overall length (*A*) of the hex driver illustrated?

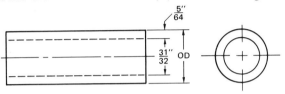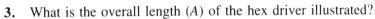

3. _____

4. Find dimensions *A* and *B* of the bracket illustrated.

4a. *A* = _____
4b. *B* = _____

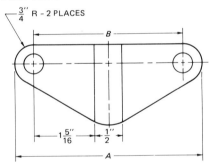

5. Find dimensions *A*, *B*, and *C* of the figure illustrated.

5a. *A* = _____
5b. *B* = _____
5c. *C* = _____

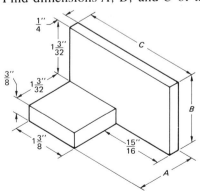

6. Find dimensions *A*, *B*, and *C* of the arbor illustrated.

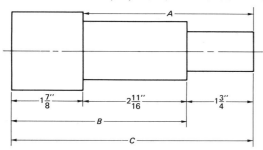

    6a. *A* = _____

    6b. *B* = _____

    6c. *C* = _____

7. Find dimensions *A*, *B*, *C*, *D*, and *E* of the figure illustrated.

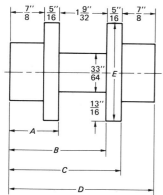

    7a. *A* = _____

    7b. *B* = _____

    7c. *C* = _____

    7d. *D* = _____

    7e. *E* = _____

8. Find dimensions *A*, *B*, and *C* of the bracket illustrated.

    8a. *A* = _____

    8b. *B* = _____

    8c. *C* = _____

9. Find dimensions *A*, *B*, *C*, and *D* of the pin illustrated.

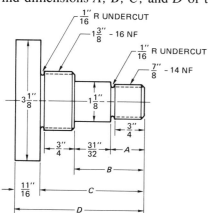

    9a. *A* = _____

    9b. *B* = _____

    9c. *C* = _____

    9d. *D* = _____

10. Find dimensions *A*, *B*, *C*, *D*, *E*, and *F* of the step gage illustrated.

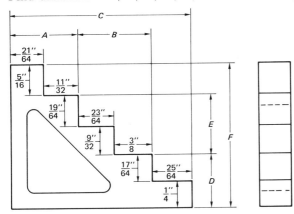

10a. *A* = _____

10b. *B* = _____

10c. *C* = _____

10d. *D* = _____

10e. *E* = _____

10f. *F* = _____

11. Find dimensions *A*, *B*, *C*, *D*, *E*, *F*, *G*, and *H* of the idler pin illustrated.

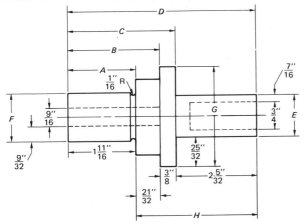

11a. *A* = _____

11b. *B* = _____

11c. *C* = _____

11d. *D* = _____

11e. *E* = _____

10f. *F* = _____

10g. *G* = _____

10h. *H* = _____

D. Solve the following subtraction problems.

1. Find dimension *A* of the drill press vise illustrated.

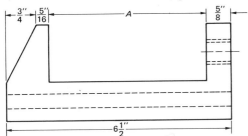

1. _____

2. What are dimensions *A* and *B* of the bushing illustrated?

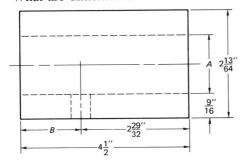
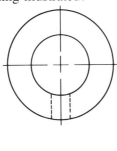

2a. *A* = _____

2b. *B* = _____

3. What is the depth (*A*) of the keyway of the shaft illustrated?

3. _____

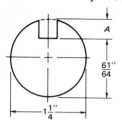

4. Find dimensions *A*, *B*, and *C* of the part illustrated.

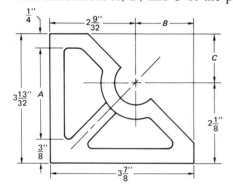

4a. *A* = _____

4b. *B* = _____

4c. *C* = _____

5. Determine dimension *A* of the Go–No Go gage illustrated.

5. _____

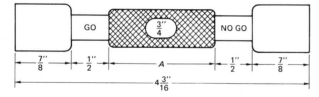

6. Find dimensions *A*, *B*, *C*, *D*, *E*, and *F* of the milling machine arbor illustrated.

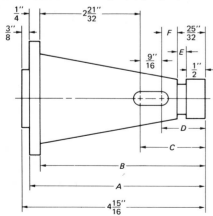

6a. *A* = _____

6b. *B* = _____

6c. *C* = _____

6d. *D* = _____

6e. *E* = _____

6f. *F* = _____

7. Find dimensions *A*, *B*, *C*, *D*, *E*, and *F* of the pin illustrated.

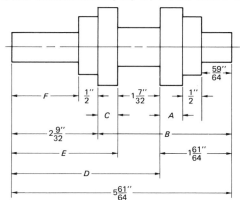

7a. *A* = _____

7b. *B* = _____

7c. *C* = _____

7d. *D* = _____

7e. *E* = _____

7f. *F* = _____

8. Find dimensions *A*, *B*, *C*, *D*, *E*, *F*, *G*, *H*, and *I* of the plate illustrated.

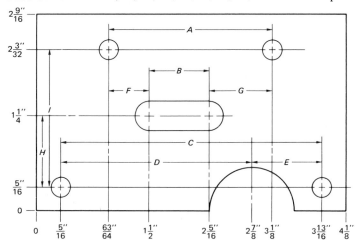

8a. *A* = _____

8b. *B* = _____

8c. *C* = _____

8d. *D* = _____

8e. *E* = _____

8f. *F* = _____

8g. *G* = _____

8h. *H* = _____

8i. *I* = _____

Exercise 1.6: Multiplication and Division

A. Solve the following common multiplication and division problems.

1. 5 × 3/4 = _____

2. 4 × 11/32 = _____

3. 3 × 2-5/8 = _____

4. 5 × 6-1/4 = _____

5. 2 × 8-11/32 = _____

6. 2/3 × 1/2 = _____

7. 27/32 × 1/3 = _____

8. 5-3/8 × 1/4 = _____

9. 2-1/2 × 3/4 = _____

10. 5/16 × 3/4 = _____

11. 3/4 ÷ 2 = _____

12. 9/16 ÷ 4 = _____

13. 4-3/8 ÷ 6 = _____

14. 9-11/16 ÷ 8 = _____

15. 2-1/4 ÷ 5 = _____

B. Optional. Solve the following less-common multiplication and division problems.

1. 3-1/2 × 4-1/3 = _____

2. 4-3/8 × 2-5/10 = _____

3. 2-3/4 × 6-2/3 = _____

4. 3/4 ÷ 1/2 = _____

5. 21/32 ÷ 3/4 = _____

6. 5-3/4 ÷ 2/3 = _____

7. 7-3/8 ÷ 1/5 = _____

8. 3-3/4 ÷ 2-1/2 = _____

C. Solve the following shop-related problems.

1. Determine dimension *A* of the part illustrated.

1. _____

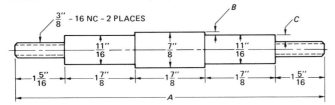

2. Determine dimensions *A*, *B*, and *C* of the arbor illustrated.

2a. *A* = _____

2b. *B* = _____

2c. *C* = _____

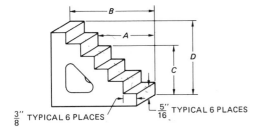

3. Determine dimensions *A*, *B*, *C*, and *D* of the step block illustrated.

3a. *A* = _____

3b. *B* = _____

3c. *C* = _____

3d. *D* = _____

4. How many 8-3/4″ pieces can be cut from 12′ of stock? Allow 1/16″ waste for each cut, as shown in the illustration.

4. _____

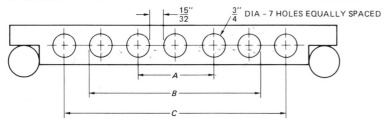

5. Determine dimensions *A*, *B*, and *C* of the sine bar illustrated.

5a. *A* = _____

5b. *B* = _____

5c. *C* = _____

6. The holes of each of the *A*, *B*, *C*, and *D* series in the part illustrated are equally spaced. Determine the following distances.

6a. _____

6b _____

6c. _____

6d. _____

a. Distance between centers of *A* holes.

b. Distance between centers of *B* holes.

c. Distance between centers of *C* holes.

d. Distance between centers of *D* holes.

7. Determine dimensions *A*, *B*, *C*, and *D* of the part illustrated.

7a. *A* = _____

7b. *B* = _____

7c. *C* = _____

7d. *D* = _____

8. The pitch of a thread is the distance between a point on one thread and the corresponding point on the adjacent threads, as illustrated below on a V-thread. The number of threads found over any given length may therefore be found by dividing that length by the pitch of the thread. Find the number of full threads over the following lengths.

8a. _____

8b. _____

8c. _____

8d. _____

a. Number of 1/8″ pitch threads over 1-3/4″.

b. Number of 1/12″ pitch threads over 7/8″.

c. Number of 1/13″ pitch threads over 1-1/8″.

d. Number of 1/32″ pitch threads over 11/16″.

CHAPTER 2

DECIMALS

Learning Objectives

After studying this chapter, you should be able to:

— State decimal fractions as decimals
— State decimals as decimal fractions
— Compare decimals for their value
— Round off decimals to required place values
— Add, subtract, multiply, and divide decimals
— Convert decimals to equal fractions and fractions of a given base
— Convert fractions to decimals rounded to required place values

In Chapter 1, we worked with fractions. In this chapter, we cover another system used to indicate fractional amounts—the decimal system. As we will see, decimals are really fractions in a different form. Machinists use decimals even more often than they use standard fractions. Decimals are used because advances in technology have required ever more accurate measurements. Since decimals are a simple way to indicate accurate measurements, they have become the primary number system used in machine technology today. For example, precision measuring tools such as micrometers and vernier calipers, which the machinist uses daily, are read in decimals. In fact, many tools that were once referred to in terms of fractions are now being referred to by equivalent decimals. For example, what was usually called a 3/4″ drill is now more and more often known as a 0.750″ drill.

INTERPRETATION OF DECIMALS

Although we usually think of decimals as being numbers that are different from fractions, in fact, they are not. *Decimals* are really a simplified means of representing a special group of fractions called decimal fractions. *Decimal fractions* are fractions whose denominators are powers of 10—for example, 10, 100, 1000, 10,000, and so on.

> **NOTE:** When 10 is multiplied by itself any number of times, the product is called a *power* of 10. For example:
>
> $10 \times 10 = 100$
>
> $10 \times 10 \times 10 \times 10 = 10,000$

The following are examples of decimal fractions:

$$\frac{3}{10}, \quad \frac{9}{10}, \quad \frac{75}{100}, \quad \frac{8}{100}, \quad \frac{142}{1000}, \quad \frac{4255}{10,000}$$

When decimal fractions are expressed as decimals, only the numerators are written. The denominators of the decimal fractions are not written. Instead, their value is indicated by the position of the decimal point (.) in the numerator. Thus, the decimals that are equal to the decimal fractions indicated above are:

0.3, 0.9, 0.75, 0.08, 0.142, 0.4255

The position of each digit of the numerator in relation to the decimal point is its *place value*. The following are the first four place-value positions:

Tenths Hundredths Thousandths Ten-thousandths

. ___ ___ ___ ___

Any decimal fraction of tenths is represented as a decimal having a digit one place to the right of the decimal point—in the tenths position. Some examples are:

$\dfrac{3}{10}$ becomes 0.3 and is read as "three tenths"

$\dfrac{9}{10}$ becomes 0.9 and is read as "nine tenths"

Any decimal fraction of hundredths is represented as a decimal having digits two places to the right of the decimal point—in both the tenths and hundredths positions. Some examples are:

$\dfrac{35}{100}$ becomes 0.35 and is read as "thirty-five hundredths"

$\dfrac{7}{100}$ becomes 0.07 and is read as "seven hundredths"

In the second case, a zero is placed between the decimal point and the 7 to keep the 7 in the hundredths position.

Any decimal fraction of thousandths is represented as a decimal having digits three places to the right of the decimal point—in the tenths through the thousandths positions. A few examples follow:

$\dfrac{125}{1000}$ becomes 0.125 and is read as "one hundred twenty-five thousandths"

$\dfrac{75}{1000}$ becomes 0.075 and is read as "seventy-five thousandths"

$\dfrac{5}{1000}$ becomes 0.005 and is read as "five thousandths"

In the second and third cases, zeros are again placed between the decimal points and the digits to keep the digits in the thousandths position.

Any decimal fraction of ten-thousandths is represented as a decimal having digits four places to the right of the decimal point—in the tenths through the ten-thousandths position. An example follows:

$\dfrac{1284}{10,000}$ becomes 0.1284 and is read as "one hundred twenty-eight thousandths and four tenths"

Note that the "four tenths" indicates four-tenths of a thousandth, or four ten-thousandths. Machinists often read a decimal in this manner because the number is easier to say. Another example of a decimal fraction of ten-thousandths follows:

$\dfrac{60}{10,000}$ becomes 0.0060 and is read as "six thousandths and zero tenths"

$\dfrac{2}{10,000}$ becomes 0.0002 and is read as "two ten-thousandths"

Again, zeros are placed between the decimal points and the digits to keep the digits in the ten-thousandths position.

Types of Decimals

There are two types of decimals: pure and mixed decimals. *Pure decimals* represent only quantities less than 1. Examples of pure decimals are:

0.3,   0.82,   0.83,   0.975,   0.8755

Mixed decimals are decimals that have a whole number combined with a pure decimal. Examples of mixed decimals are:

9.3,   7.50,   2.375,   6.6255

ASSOCIATED PROCEDURES
Comparing Decimals

When comparing the value of various decimals, we must first express the decimals to the same place value. The same place value means that the decimals are written out to the same number of places. We write out decimals to the same number of places by *annexing zeros,* or placing additional zeros to the right. Annexing zeros to a decimal does not change its value. For example, 0.4 becomes 0.40 by annexing one zero, but its value is not changed:

$$0.4 \ = \ 0.40 \quad \text{or} \quad \frac{4}{10} \ = \ \frac{40}{100}$$

0.4 becomes 0.400 by annexing two zeros:

$$0.4 \ = \ 0.400 \quad \text{or} \quad \frac{4}{10} = \frac{400}{1000}$$

Comparing decimals is really very simple. In fact, we seldom have to actually rewrite the decimals. Instead, we can visualize them. For example, let us consider a comparison of the following:

0.6,   0.58,   0.576

Since we see that 0.576 has three places, we must visualize the other decimals as having the same number of places:

$$0.6 \ = \ 0.600$$
$$0.58 \ = \ 0.580$$

We can now easily compare the decimals 0.600, 0.580, and 0.576:

0.600 is the largest (600 thousandths)

0.580 is the next largest (580 thousandths)

0.576 is the smallest (576 thousandths)

Thus, 0.6, 0.58, and 0.576 are clearly arranged from largest to smallest.

Rounding Off Decimals

When making calculations with decimals, we are often required to round off decimals. Basically, *rounding off decimals* is the procedure of simplifying decimals to a desired place value. Decimals like 0.4875329 or 2.6255893 are impractical for use in the machine shop. Since the precision these large decimals show is not necessary and not used in most machine shop work, we need to simplify them, or round them off, to a more practical form. The place value to which we round off is determined by the accuracy each situation calls for. For the machine trades, this place value is, in most cases, the thousandths or ten-thousandths position.

The policies for rounding off decimals are varied. They vary because of the different measurement situations that exist in the machine trades. Types of measurement will be discussed in Chapter 5. For now, we consider the most common policy. This policy is the one followed throughout this text.

Rounding-Off Policy

In rounding off a decimal number, we look at the digit to the right of the place-value position that is being rounded off to. We then apply one of the following two options:

1. If the digit is 5 or greater, we increase the digit in the desired place-value position by 1 and drop all remaining digits to the right of it.
2. If the digit is less than 5, we leave the digit in the desired place-value position as it is and drop all remaining digits to the right of it.

Examples of numbers rounded off to the nearest tenth are as follows:

3.45 becomes 3.5

43.333 becomes 43.3

19.082 becomes 19.1

Examples of numbers rounded off to the nearest hundredth are as follows:

7.177 becomes 7.18

18.133 becomes 18.13

9.006 becomes 9.01

Examples of numbers rounded off to the nearest thousandth are as follows:

45.2545 becomes 45.255

2.79019 becomes 2.790

3.12592 becomes 3.126

ARITHMETIC OPERATIONS

Adding, subtracting, multiplying, and dividing decimals are part of a machinist's daily routine. The procedures for these operations are the same we use with whole numbers. However, we are also concerned with properly locating the decimal point in the answers. Proper location of the decimal point during arithmetic operations with decimals is considered in the following sections. Hand calculators have greatly simplified decimal calculations.

Addition

RULE

To add decimals, line up the decimal points of the numbers being added to insure that like place-value digits of the numbers are being added together.

After the alignment, we add the decimal numbers without giving any further consideration to the decimal points. We locate the decimal point in the answer directly in line with the decimal points of the numbers being added.

While decimals of different place values may be added together, for convenience's sake we can annex zeros to lower place-value decimals as an aid in assuring that the decimals are lined up. For example, if we want to add 0.25, 0.370, and 0.8, we may annex zeros as necessary:

$$
\begin{array}{ll}
0.250 & \text{(one zero annexed)} \\
0.370 & \\
\underline{+\ 0.800} & \text{(two zeros annexed)} \\
1.420 &
\end{array}
$$

Addition of decimal numbers is illustrated in the following example.

EXAMPLE

Problem

Find measurements *A* and *B* of the pin shown in Figure 2.1.

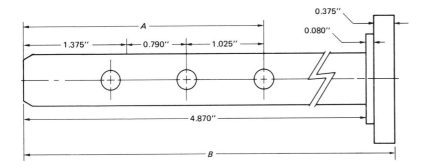

Figure 2.1

Analysis

Arrange the numbers to be added in columns so that the decimal points line up.

Solution

Step 1:   Add the three parts of measurement *A*

$$
\begin{array}{r}
1.375 \\
0.790 \\
+\ 1.025 \\
\hline
3.190
\end{array}
$$

Step 2:   Add the three parts of measurement *B*

$$
\begin{array}{r}
4.870 \\
0.080 \\
+\ 0.375 \\
\hline
5.325
\end{array}
$$

Answer

$A = 3.190''$

$B = 5.325''$

Subtraction

RULE

To subtract decimals, line up the decimal points of the numbers being sub-tracted to insure that like place-value digits of the numbers are being sub-tracted.

After the alignment, we subtract the decimals without giving any further consideration to the decimal points. We locate the decimal point in the answer directly in line with the decimal points of the numbers being subtracted.

As is the case in adding decimals, for convenience's sake, we may want to annex zeros when subtracting a lower place-value decimal from a higher place-value decimal. For example, if we want to subtract 0.35 from 0.687, we may annex one zero:

$$\begin{array}{r} 0.687 \\ -\ 0.350 \\ \hline 0.337 \end{array}$$

NOTE: When we are subtracting a higher place-value decimal from a lower place-value decimal, we must annex zeros in order to subtract. For example, to subtract 1.375 from 3.5, we must annex two zeros to 3.5:

$$\begin{array}{r} 3.500 \quad \text{(two zeros annexed)} \\ -\ 1.375 \\ \hline 2.125 \end{array}$$

The following example illustrates subtraction of decimal numbers.

EXAMPLE

Problem

Find measurements A and B of the V-block shown in Figure 2.2.

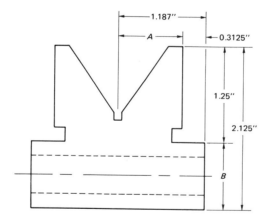

Figure 2.2

Analysis

Arrange the numbers to be subtracted in columns so that the decimal points line up.

Solution

Step 1:   Annex one zero to 1.187 and subtract to find measurement A

$$\begin{array}{r} 1.1870 \\ -\ 0.3125 \\ \hline 0.8745 \end{array}$$

Step 2:   Annex one zero to 1.25 and subtract to find measurement B

$$
\begin{array}{r}
2.125 \\
-\ 1.250 \\
\hline
0.875
\end{array}
$$

Answer

$$A\ =\ 0.8745''$$

$$B\ =\ 0.875''$$

Multiplication

Multiplication of decimals is exactly the same as multiplication of whole numbers, with the exception of locating the decimal point in the answer. We locate the decimal point by following a simple rule.

RULE

To multiply decimals, make the number of digits to the right of the decimal point in the answer equal to the sum of the number of digits to the right of the decimal points of the decimals being multiplied.

For example, in multiplying 2.135 by 0.2, four decimal places are required in the answer:

$$
\begin{array}{rl}
2.13\,5 & \text{(3 digits)} \\
\times\quad 0.2 & \text{(+ 1 digit)} \\
\hline
0.4\,27\,0 & \text{(4 digits)}
\end{array}
$$

In multiplying 4.605 by 3.73, five decimal places are required in the answer:

$$
\begin{array}{rl}
4.6\,05 & \text{(3 digits)} \\
\times\quad 3.73 & \text{(+ 2 digits)} \\
\hline
13\,8\,15 & \\
3\,22\,3\,5 & \\
13\,81\,5 & \\
\hline
17.17\,6\,65 & \text{(5 digits)}
\end{array}
$$

NOTE: When we are multiplying decimals, we often encounter situations where the numbers being multiplied do not generate enough digits in the answer for the correct placement of the decimal point. In such cases, we need to add zeros to the left of the existing digits of the answer. For example, to multiply 0.12 by 0.03, we must add two zeros to the existing digits of the answer in order to locate the decimal point correctly:

$$
\begin{array}{rl}
0.12 & \text{(2 digits)} \\
\times\ 0.03 & \text{(+ 2 digits)} \\
\hline
0.0036 & \text{4 digits}
\end{array}
$$

Division

Division of decimals is a process that is exactly like the process for division of whole numbers with, again, the added concern of properly locating the decimal point in the answer. In division, the location of the decimal point in the answer is determined before we actually divide. The process is called *clearing the decimal point*.

> **NOTE:** The number to be divided is called the *dividend*. The number by which it is to be divided is called the *divisor*. The result of the division is known as the *quotient:*
>
> $$\text{divisor } \overline{)\ \text{dividend}}^{\text{quotient}}$$

RULE

To clear the decimal point in a division problem: (1) Move the decimal point to the right of all the digits in the divisor. (2) Then move the decimal point to the right the same number of places in the dividend. (3) Locate the decimal point in the quotient directly above the new location.

Once the decimal point in a division problem has been cleared to the correct position in the quotient, we carry out the division process without giving any further consideration to the decimal point. For example, in order to divide 3.6 by 1.2, we must take the three steps to clear the decimal point. First, we move the decimal point to the right of all digits in the divisor:

$$1.2\,\overline{)\ 3.6}$$

Then, we move the decimal point the same number of places in the dividend:

$$12.\,\overline{)\ 3.6}$$

Finally, we locate the decimal point in the quotient directly above the new location:

$$12.\,\overline{)\ 36.}$$

Once the decimal point has been cleared, we divide to solve the problem:

$$12.\,\overline{)\ 36.}^{\,3.}$$

In some cases, clearing the decimal point in a division problem requires annexing zeros in the dividend. An example is the problem of dividing 6.4 by 0.16. First, the decimal point is moved to the right of the digits in the divisor:

$$0.16\,\overline{)\ 6.4}$$

Then, one zero is annexed in order to move the decimal point the same number of places in the dividend:

$$16. \overline{)6.40}$$

Finally, the decimal point is located in the quotient directly above the new location:

$$16. \overline{)640.}^{\;.}$$

Once the decimal point is cleared, the division problem may be solved:

$$16. \overline{)640.}^{\;40.}$$

Since the majority of answers to division problems do not come out even, we often need to divide at least one place beyond what we require in the answer and then round off. For example, to obtain an answer in hundredths, we need to divide out three places (thousandths position) and then round off.

To find the answer in hundredths to the problem of dividing 130.89 by 32.58, we proceed by taking the three steps to clear the decimal point. We first move the decimal point to the right of the digits in the divisor:

$$32.58 \overline{)130.89}$$

We then move the decimal point the same number of places in the dividend:

$$3258. \overline{)130.89}$$

We next locate the decimal point in the quotient directly above the new location and annex zeros in order to divide out to three places beyond the decimal:

$$3258. \overline{)13089.000}^{\;.}$$

We divide out to three places beyond the decimal:

```
          4.017
3258. ) 13089.000
        13032
           57 00
           32 58
           24 420
           22 806
            1 614
```

We can now round off the answer to the nearest hundredth:

$$4.017 = 4.02$$

Finding the answer in thousandths to the problem of dividing 1.38 by 0.085 requires annexing five zeros in the dividend: one zero to clear the decimal point and four additional zeros to divide out to four places (ten-thousandths position). To clear the decimal point, the decimal point is first moved to the right of the digits in the divisor:

$$0.085 \overline{)\,1.38}$$

Next, one zero is annexed in the dividend in order to move the decimal point the same number of places:

$$85. \overline{)\,1.380}$$

Then, the decimal point is located in the quotient directly above the new location:

$$85. \overline{)\,1380.}$$

To divide out to four places beyond the decimal, four additional zeros are annexed to the right of the decimal:

$$
\begin{array}{r}
16.2352 \\
85. \overline{)\,1380.0000} \\
85 \\
\overline{530} \\
510 \\
\overline{20\,0} \\
17\,0 \\
\overline{3\,00} \\
2\,55 \\
\overline{450} \\
425 \\
\overline{250} \\
170 \\
\overline{80}
\end{array}
$$

The answer is then rounded off to the nearest thousandth:

$$16.2352 = 16.235$$

CONVERSIONS

Fraction-Decimal Conversions

We have seen that decimals are a simplified means of representing decimal fractions. However, we will also need to convert other fractions to decimals, or vice versa. In many cases, only an approximately equal value can be obtained by conversion. In these cases, a rounding-off process will be necessary. During these calculations, again, keep in mind that we are only restating a value in a new way.

RULE

To convert a fraction to a decimal, divide the numerator by the denominator. If rounding off is necessary, round off to the position of accuracy required.

For example, to convert 3/4 to a decimal, divide 3 by 4:

4. ÷ 3.

Locate the decimal point properly in the quotient and annex zeros in order to divide out beyond the decimal point:

```
        0.75
   4. ) 3.00
        2 8
         20
         20
```

Thus, 3/4 = 0.75.

To convert 5/8 to a decimal, divide 5 by 8:

```
        0.625
   8. ) 5.000
        4 8
         20
         16
          40
          40
```

Thus, 5/8 = 0.625.

To convert 4/7 to a decimal, divide 4 by 7:

```
      0.571428
7. ) 4.000000
     3 5
      50
      49
      10
       7
       30
       28
       20
       14
        60
        56
         4
```

Thus, 4/7 = 0.57 to the nearest hundredth, 0.571 to the nearest thousandth, or 0.5714 to the nearest ten-thousandth. Each of these decimal answers is only approximately equal to the fraction 4/7. Since 4/7 cannot be represented by an exact decimal, we must choose a rounding-off position. This position is decided by the degree of accuracy needed.

RULE

To convert a mixed number to a decimal, ignore the whole number and convert the fraction as above.

For example, to convert 2-3/8 to a decimal, we ignore the whole number, 2, and divide 3 by 8:

```
      0.375
8. ) 3.000
     2 4
      60
      56
      40
      40
```

Thus, 2-3/8 = 2.375.

To convert 8-5/16 to a decimal, we ignore the whole number, 8, and divide 5 by 16:

$$
\begin{array}{r}
0.3125 \\
16. \overline{)\,5.0000} \\
\underline{4\;8} \\
20 \\
\underline{16} \\
40 \\
\underline{32} \\
80 \\
\underline{80}
\end{array}
$$

Thus, 8-5/16 = 8.3125.

Decimal-Fraction Conversions

The procedure we use to convert a decimal to a fraction depends on whether we want an exact equal fraction or an approximate fraction of a specific denominator. For example, for the decimal 0.58:

$\dfrac{29}{50}$ is an exact equal fraction

$\dfrac{19}{32}$ is an approximate fraction to the nearest 32nd

RULE

To convert a decimal to an exact equal fraction, express the decimal as its decimal fraction and reduce to lowest terms.

Some examples of decimals converted to exact equal fractions are:

$$0.58 \;=\; \frac{58}{100} \;=\; \frac{29}{50}$$

$$0.75 \;=\; \frac{75}{100} \;=\; \frac{3}{4}$$

$$0.02 \;=\; \frac{2}{100} \;=\; \frac{1}{50}$$

$$0.50 \;=\; \frac{50}{100} \;=\; \frac{1}{2}$$

A decimal can be converted to an approximate fraction of a desired denominator when specific fractions are needed. Such is the case with linear measurement, where fractions of 8ths, 16ths, 32nds, and 64ths are used.

RULE

To convert a decimal to an approximate fraction with a specific denominator, first multiply the decimal by the desired denominator. Then round off the answer to the nearest whole number to obtain the numerator of the desired fraction.

For example, to convert 0.58 to the nearest 32nd, we first multiply 0.58 by 32:

```
    0.58
  ×   32
    1 16
   17 4
   18.56
```

We then round off 18.56 to the nearest whole number to obtain a numerator of 19. Thus, $0.58 \cong 19/32$. Note that the symbol $\cong$ means "approximately equal."

To convert 0.635 to the nearest 64th, 0.635 is first multiplied by 64:

```
    0.635
  ×    64
    2 540
   38 10
   40.640
```

40.64 is rounded off to the nearest whole number to obtain a numerator of 41. Thus, $0.635 \cong 41/64$.

TERMS FOR REVIEW

— decimals
— decimal fractions
— place value
— pure decimals
— mixed decimals
— annexing zeros

— rounding off decimals
— clearing the decimal point
— divisor
— dividend
— quotient

EXERCISES

Exercise 2.1: Interpretation of Decimals

A. Express the following decimal fractions as decimals.

1. 3/10 = _____

2. 92/100 = _____

3. 9/10 = _____

4. 182/1000 = _____

5. 6/100 = _____

6. 92/1000 = _____

7. 18/100 = _____

8. 4/1000 = _____

9. 1475/10,000 = _____

10. 3-5/10 = _____

11. 20-15/100 = _____

12. 6-149/1000 = _____

13. 8-2/10 = _____

14. 7-7/100 = _____

15. 1-8/1000 = _____

B. Express the following decimals as decimal fractions.

1. 0.7 = _____

2. 0.35 = _____

3. 0.09 = _____

4. 0.002 = _____

5. 0.19 = _____

6. 0.1865 = _____

7. 6.3 = _____

8. 8.07 = _____

9. 17.468 = _____

10. 2.006 = _____

11. 118.5 = _____

12. 1.0125 = _____

Exercise 2.2: Comparing Decimals

A. Match the following drill sizes with their decimal equivalents.

1. Arrange the following decimal equivalents of the fractional-size drills from smallest to largest size, and match them with the fractional sizes:
0.5625″, 0.5312″, 0.5″, 0.6094″, 0.5937″, 0.625″, 0.5156″, 0.5781″, 0.5469″

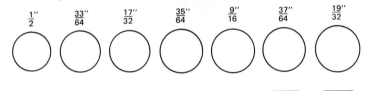

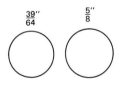

2. Arrange the following decimal equivalents of the letter-size drills, from smallest to largest size, and match them with the letter sizes:
0.261″, 0.234″, 0.250″, 0.242″, 0.266″, 0.257″, 0.238″, 0.246″

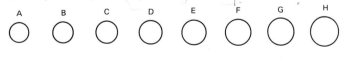

3. Arrange the following decimal equivalents of the wire-size drills from largest to smallest size, and match them with the wire sizes:
0.0995″, 0.1285″, 0.104″, 0.116″, 0.11″, 0.111″, 0.113″, 0.1065″, 0.12″, 0.1015″, 0.0980″

30	31	32	33	34	35	36	37
○	○	○	○	○	○	○	○

_____ _____ _____ _____ _____ _____ _____ _____

38	39	40
○	○	○

_____ _____ _____

B. Round off the following decimals to the position indicated.

1. 8.1584 to the nearest thousandth.   1. _____

2. 0.3856 to the nearest hundredth.   2. _____

3. 18.5395 to the nearest thousandth.   3. _____

4. 237.052 to the nearest tenth.   4. _____

5. 7.5358 to the nearest thousandth.   5. _____

6. 11.7348 to the nearest hundredth.   6. _____

7. 7.0052 to the nearest thousandth.   7. _____

8. 5.99983 to the nearest ten-thousandth.   8. _____

9. 2.185 to the nearest tenth.   9. _____

10. 5.71878 to the nearest ten-thousandth.   10. _____

Exercise 2.3: Arithmetic Operations

A. Add the following sets of decimals.

1. 23.89 + 4.8 + 0.75 + 18.1   1. _____

2. 0.9563 + 0.051 + 0.127 + 0.42   2. _____

3. 1849.5 + 15.625 + 243.76 + 1.082   3. _____

4. 3.25 + 0.2 + 0.6 + 1.5 + 1.05   4. _____

5. 4.52 + 0.752 + 67 + 3.024 + 138.72   5. _____

6. 0.089 + 0.57 + 0.0031 + 98 + 0.30801   6. _____

7. 37 + 831 + 402.95 + 0.00206 + 5.86   7. _____

B. Subtract the following sets of decimals.

1. 9.82 − 3.05 = _____   2. $728.00 − $163.73 = _____

3. $117.03 − $52.18 = _____   4. 84.33 − 16.58 = _____

5. 2.45 − 0.5308 = _____   6. 11.625 − 2.08 = _____

7. 2 − 0.085 = _____   8. 200 − 100.001 = _____

C. Multiply the following sets of decimals.

1. $16.92 \times 8 = $ _____

2. $5.95 \times 1.5 = $ _____

3. $0.432 \times 0.57 = $ _____

4. $1.125 \times 0.003 = $ _____

5. $0.3 \times 1.2 \times 5.05 = $ _____

D. Divide the following sets of decimals. Round off to three decimal places.

1. $205.8 \div 37 = $ _____

2. $118 \div 3.5 = $ _____

3. $3.985 \div 0.42 = $ _____

4. $1.32 \div 0.873 = $ _____

5. $37 \div 0.83 = $ _____

6. $483.5 \div 0.85 = $ _____

7. $183.5 \div 0.25 = $ _____

8. $0.8758 \div 0.152 = $ _____

E. Solve the following problems.

1. Find the length (A) of the twist drill illustrated.

1. $A = $ _____

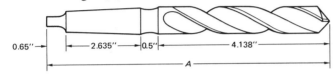

2. (a) Find the overall length (A) of the following stop block. (b) What is the difference in diameters?

2a. $A = $ _____

2b. _____

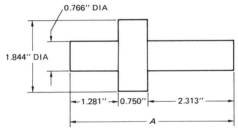

3. Find the overall length (A) of the thread gage illustrated.

3. $A = $ _____

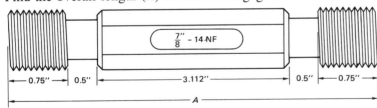

4. Determine dimensions A, B, C, and D of the cylindrical shaft illustrated.

4a. $A = $ _____

4b. $B = $ _____

4c. $C = $ _____

4d. $D = $ _____

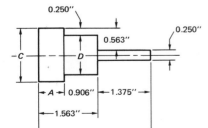

5. Determine dimensions *A* and *B* of the following bracket.

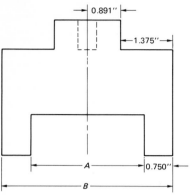

5a. *A* = _____

5b. *B* = _____

6. Determine dimensions *A*, *B*, and *C* of the casting illustrated.

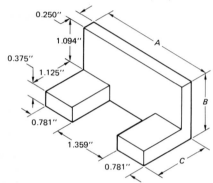

6a. *A* = _____

6b. *B* = _____

6c. *C* = _____

7. Determine the inside diameter (ID) of the washer illustrated.

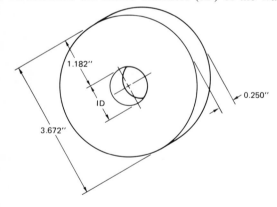

7. ID = _____

8. Determine dimensions *A*, *B*, *C*, *D*, *E*, and *F* of the following pin.

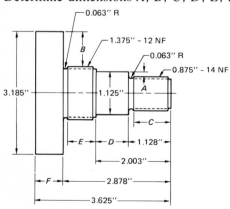

8a. *A* = _____

8b. *B* = _____

8c. *C* = _____

8d. *D* = _____

8e. *E* = _____

8f. *F* = _____

9. Determine dimensions *A*, *B*, *C*, *D*, *E*, *F*, *G*, *H*, *I*, *J*, *K*, and *L* of the mounting bracket illustrated.

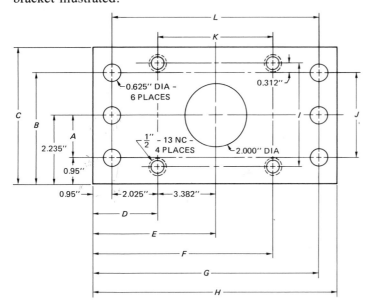

9a. *A* = _____

9b. *B* = _____

9c. *C* = _____

9d. *D* = _____

9e. *E* = _____

9f. *F* = _____

9g. *G* = _____

9h. *H* = _____

9i. *I* = _____

9j. *J* = _____

9k. *K* = _____

9l. *L* = _____

10. Determine the number of threads for the following lengths of the illustrated thread: (a) for 1.25″, (b) for 4.8″, (c) for 3.375″, and (d) for 1″. Round off answers to the nearest tenth.

10a. _____

10b. _____

10c. _____

10d. _____

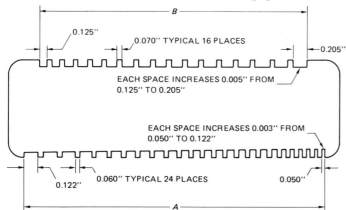

11. Determine the dimensions *A* and *B* of the gage illustrated.

11a. *A* = _____

11b. *B* = _____

12. Determine dimensions *A*, *B*, and *C* of the following narrowing die plate.

12a. *A* = _____

12b. *B* = _____

12c. *C* = _____

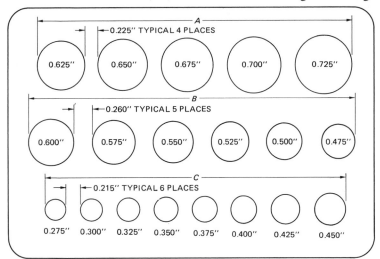

Exercise 2.4: Conversions

A. Convert the following fractions to decimals. If necessary, round answers off to the nearest ten thousandth.

1. 3/4 = _____   **2.** 11/50 = _____   **3.** 3/8 = _____

4. 5/16 = _____   **5.** 5/64 = _____   **6.** 1/8 = _____

7. 1/32 = _____   **8.** 1/16 = _____   **9.** 1/64 = _____

10. 49/64 = _____   **11.** 25-5/8 = _____   **12.** 2-2/3 = _____

13. 18-5/16 = _____   **14.** 3-17/32 = _____   **15.** 5-7/8 = _____

16. 7-11/16 = _____

B. Convert the following decimals to equal fractions of the lowest terms.

1. 3.7 = _____   **2.** 8.54 = _____   **3.** 0.250 = _____

4. 2.3125 = _____   **5.** 0.125 = _____   **6.** 0.783 = _____

7. 4.33 = _____   **8.** 2.875 = _____   **9.** 5.1875 = _____

10. 1.480 = _____   **11.** 3.75 = _____   **12.** 4.88 = _____

C. Convert the following decimals to the fraction indicated.

1. 0.875 to the nearest 16th = _____   **2.** 0.573 to the nearest 32nd = _____

3. 0.730 to the nearest 60th = _____   **4.** 0.35 to the nearest 12th = _____

5. 0.058 to the nearest 64th = _____   **6.** 0.333 to the nearest 8th = _____

7. 4.82 to the nearest 8th = _____   **8.** 11.78 to the nearest 16th = _____

9. 7.258 to the nearest 32nd = _____   **10.** 6.932 to the nearest 12th = _____

CHAPTER 3

LINEAR MEASUREMENT

Learning Objectives

After studying this chapter, you should be able to:

— Interpret the tolerances, limits, clearances, and interferences of dimensioned parts
— Read fractional and decimal scales of steel rules
— Use steel rules properly
— Read 0.001″, 0.0001″, and depth micrometers
— Use outside micrometers properly
— Read vernier calipers
— Use gage blocks

Since the beginning of modern mass production, the ability to make accurate linear measurements has become increasingly important. Today, precision measurement is a must. Without it, interchangeable parts of high quality could not exist.

Linear measurement is the measurement between two points. For example, in Figure 3.1, the length of the block is the linear measurement between its two ends. The width of the block is the linear measurement between its two sides. The center-to-center distance of the two holes is the linear measurement between the centers of the two holes.

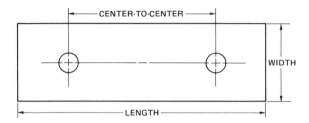

Figure 3.1

Machinists deal with many different linear dimensions as well as various means of expressing them. We therefore need to know how to interpret dimensions properly. We also need to be able to use the measuring tools found in the shop so that required dimensions are properly maintained during the machining process. Since the degree of precision required varies, different measuring tools are used.

DIMENSIONING

In industry, many terms apply to the dimensioning of parts. To insure that we interpret the measurement requirements correctly, we need to understand the meaning of dimensioning terms.

Nominal dimensions are general classifications used primarily to designate sizes of manufactured products. The nominal dimension does not necessarily indicate the true size of the product or item. Some very common examples of the use of nominal dimensions are the sizes of washers and construction lumber. Figure 3.2 shows how their nominal sizes differ from their true sizes.

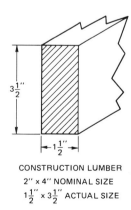

CONSTRUCTION LUMBER
2″ x 4″ NOMINAL SIZE
$1\frac{1}{2}″$ x $3\frac{1}{2}″$ ACTUAL SIZE

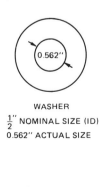

WASHER
$\frac{1}{2}″$ NOMINAL SIZE (ID)
0.562″ ACTUAL SIZE

Figure 3.2

Actual dimensions are the true measured dimensions. Again in Figure 3.2, note the actual or true size of the lumber and the washer.

Basic dimensions are the dimensions specified for a part. Basic dimensions represent the most desirable actual dimensions for a part after the machining is completed. In Figure 3.3a, 1.750″ and 1.876″ are the basic dimensions. In Figure 3.3b, 2.250″ is the basic dimension. Basic dimensions are the dimensions that produce the best results for the mating of parts. The determinations of tolerances and limits are made from the basic dimensions.

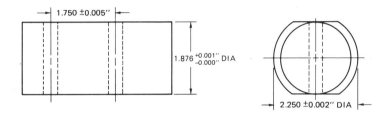

Figure 3.3a   **Figure 3.3b**

Tolerance is the maximum variation permitted from the basic dimension. Tolerance indicates how much larger or smaller than the basic dimension the actual dimension can be after machining for the part to fit and work properly with other parts. In Figure 3.3a, the basic dimension 1.750″ has a total tolerance of 0.010″ (+0.005″ and −0.005″ variation from 1.750″). The basic dimension 1.876″ has a total tolerance of 0.001″ (*only* a +0.001″ variation from 1.876″—it may not be any smaller). In Figure 3.3b, the basic dimension 2.250″ has a total tolerance of 0.004″ (+0.002″ and −0.002″ variation from 2.250″).

Bilateral tolerance is a tolerance in which variation is permissible above (+) and below (−) the basic dimension. Bilateral tolerance is illustrated in Figure 3.4a and is indicated by the sign ± (plus or minus). *Unilateral tolerance* is a tolerance in which variation is permissible in only one direction (*either* above or below) from the basic dimension, as illustrated in Figure 3.4b.

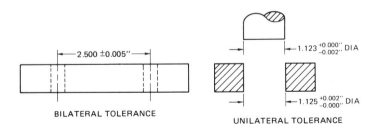

Figure 3.4a   **Figure 3.4b**

Limits are the acceptable maximum and minimum measurements. In Figure 3.5, limit dimensions (the maximum limit is placed over the minimum limit) are used to define the largest and smallest dimensions that will still permit proper location of the holes. These dimensions are called the upper and lower limits. Limits are calculated by adding the plus tolerance to the basic dimension and by subtracting the minus tolerance from the basic dimension.

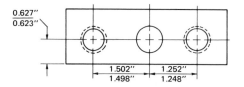

Figure 3.5

Clearance is the total maximum or minimum tolerance between two working surfaces. This term is commonly applied to the mating of OD and ID parts, such as bearings and journals or bolts and holes, as shown in Figure 3.6.

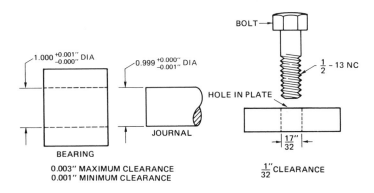

Figure 3.6

Interference is the amount of overlap between two mating parts. In Figure 3.7, the maximum interference between the shaft and bearing race is 0.0030″, and the minimum interference is 0.0015″. Mating parts that have an interference fit require force to mate the parts.

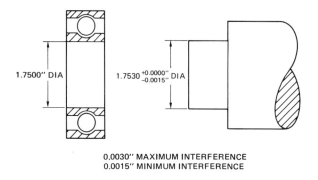

Figure 3.7

STEEL RULES

The *steel rule* is a straight edge accurately graduated to form a measuring scale. It is the simplest measuring tool that we use in the shop. The 6″ pocket rule, shown in Figure 3.8, is the most common steel rule used in a machine shop. In fact, most machinists carry one in their shirt pockets.

Figure 3.8a

Figure 3.8b

Most 6″ rules are marked on both edges of both sides, as illustrated in Figure 3.8. In this case, all the scales are fractional. The decimal scales illustrated in Figure 3.9 are also quite common.

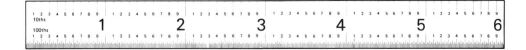

Figure 3.9

The steel rule is the least accurate measuring tool of the machine shop. It is generally used to measure stock material and for rough measurements of parts during the machining process. The steel rule is also probably the most abused tool of the shop. The steel rule should not be used as a scraper or screwdriver.

Reading Fractional Scales

The fractional scales on steel rules are graduated in 8ths and 16ths, as shown in Figure 3.8a, or 32nds and 64ths, as shown in Figure 3.8b. Usually the scales are labeled accordingly.

In order to read these fractional scales, we must first understand how the scales are marked. Counting the markings is impractical. We should be aware that the smaller the graduation, the shorter the line marking the graduation. We can see in

Figure 3.10 that, for example, the 1/8″ markings are shorter than the 1/4″ markings, and the 1/64″ markings are shorter than the 1/32″ markings. The smallest graduations on a steel rule are in sixty-fourths (1/64) of an inch.

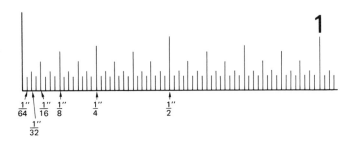

Figure 3.10

The scales commonly show the number of 32nds and 64ths at all the 1/8″ graduations, as shown in Figure 3.8b. This marking makes these finer scales easier to read.

Reading Decimal Scales

The two common decimal scales found on steel rules are the tenths (0.1) and hundredths (0.01) graduations, shown in Figure 3.9. On both scales, the tenths graduations are numbered to make the scales easier to read. On the hundredths scale, all the smaller, unnumbered graduations are equal to hundredths of an inch. By counting the markings between every tenths mark in Figure 3.11, we can see how the system works.

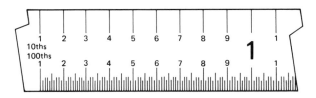

Figure 3.11

Proper Use of Steel Rules

The following procedures should be followed for measuring with a steel rule.

1. Whenever possible, measure from an inch mark, as shown in Figure 3.12, rather than the end of the rule. This procedure is common practice because the ends of the rule could be damaged, burred, rounded, or even worn. Remember, however, to adjust the reading according to the inch mark used.

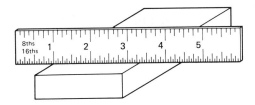

Figure 3.12

2. Always try to keep the scale edge of the rule perpendicular to the surface of the part being measured, as Figure 3.13 shows.

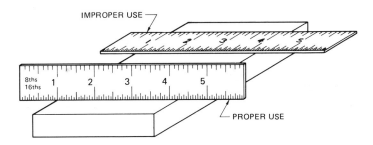

Figure 3.13

3. When measuring flat surfaces, make sure the rule is at right angles to the edges of the surface being measured, as shown in Figure 3.14.

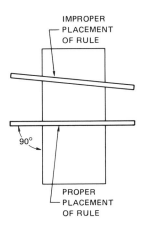

Figure 3.14

4. When measuring inside or outside diameters, make sure that the rule is directly across the center of the part. Keep one end of the scale edge stationary and move the rule back and forth in a small arc to find the maximum reading. Figure 3.15 shows how to measure a diameter.

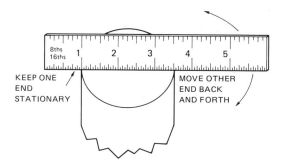

Figure 3.15

5. Always use the scale of the precision required. If a precision of 32nds is required, use the 32nds scale. If a precision of 64ths is required, use the 64ths scale.

MICROMETERS

The *micrometer* is the most common and widely used precision measuring tool of the machine shop. There are many different types of micrometers. We use specialized micrometers for measuring flat surfaces, curved surfaces, V-surfaces, and depths. The principle of each micrometer, however, is the same.

The principle of the micrometer is simple. A high-precision screw (spindle) is rotated through a fixed nut in the barrel of the instrument. This screw controls the distance between the face of the anvil and the face of the spindle. Figure 3.16 shows the parts of the 1″ micrometer.

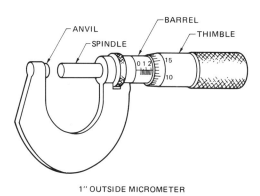

1″ OUTSIDE MICROMETER

Figure 3.16

Reading and using a micrometer takes skill and practice. Measurements taken with a micrometer are stated as decimals and are accurate to the thousandths (0.001) and ten-thousandths (0.0001) of an inch.

Reading 0.001″ Micrometers

The most common micrometer is the 1″ (or thousandths-inch) outside micrometer, shown in Figure 3.16. We take readings of the 0.001″ micrometer from two scales, the barrel scale and the thimble scale. We combine the readings from these two scales to get the total micrometer reading.

A typical barrel scale looks like the magnified scale illustrated in Figure 3.17. The scale is 1″ long and has ten major graduations. These graduations are numbered. We do not, however, read each graduation as a tenth (0.1) of an inch, but rather as a hundred-thousandth (0.100) of an inch. The values shown with arrows in Figure 3.17 are the hundred-thousandths readings of the tenths graduations.

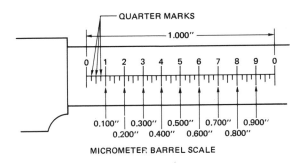

Figure 3.17

Each hundred-thousandth (0.100) graduation is divided into four equal smaller graduations of twenty-five thousandths (0.025) of an inch. The marks of these graduations are called *quarter marks*. These graduations, too, are shown in Figure 3.17.

To read the scale on the barrel, we read the number of hundred-thousandths marks that are not covered by the thimble. As illustrated in Figure 3.18, the micrometer reading is the combined number of exposed hundred-thousandths (0.100) and twenty-five thousandths (0.025) graduations. Thus, in Figure 3.18a, the reading is 0.400 (4 hundred-thousandths marks) plus 0.025 (1 quarter mark) for a total barrel reading of 0.425″. In Figure 3.18b, the reading is 0.200 (2 hundred-thousandths marks) plus 0.050 (2 quarter marks) for a total barrel reading of 0.250″. In Figure 3.18c, the reading is 0.000 (no hundred-thousandths marks exposed) plus 0.075 (3 quarter marks) for a total barrel reading of 0.075″.

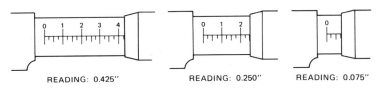

Figure 3.18a   **Figure 3.18b**   **Figure 3.18c**

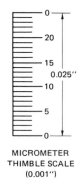

MICROMETER
THIMBLE SCALE
(0.001″)

Figure 3.19

A typical *thimble scale* is illustrated in Figure 3.19. The thimble is divided into twenty-five graduations, each representing a thousandth (0.001) of an inch. The total length of the thimble scale is therefore twenty-five thousandths (0.025) of an inch.

To read the thimble scale, we read each thousandth mark most nearly in line with the center line on the barrel scale, as illustrated in Figure 3.20. This reading on the thimble scale is to the nearest thousandth of an inch. Thus, in Figure 3.20a, the thimble reading is 0.018″ because the 0.018 mark of the thimble lines up with the center line on the barrel. In Figure 3.20b, the thimble reading is 0.007″ because the 0.007 mark of the thimble is most nearly in line with the barrel center line. The actual reading, however, is a little more than 0.007″. In Figure 3.20c, the thimble reading is 0.012″ because the 0.012 mark of the thimble is most nearly in line with the barrel center line. The actual reading, however, is a little less than 0.012″.

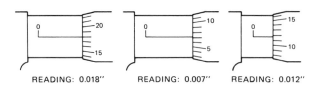

READING: 0.018″   READING: 0.007″   READING: 0.012″

Figure 3.20

The total micrometer reading, then, is the combined reading obtained from the barrel and the thimble. For example, in Figure 3.21a:

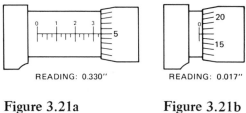

READING: 0.330″   READING: 0.017″

Figure 3.21a   **Figure 3.21b**

READING: 0.821″

Figure 3.21c

$$
\begin{array}{rl}
0.325 & \text{(barrel reading)} \\
+\ 0.005 & \text{(thimble reading)} \\
\hline
0.330 & \text{(total micrometer reading)}
\end{array}
$$

We read this total as ''three hundred thirty thousandths of an inch.'' In Figure 3.21b:

0.000   (barrel reading)
+ 0.017   (thimble reading)
0.017   (total micrometer reading)

We read this total as "seventeen thousandths of an inch." In Figure 3.21c:

0.800   (barrel reading)
+ 0.021   (thimble reading)
0.821   (total micrometer reading)

We read this total as "eight hundred twenty-one thousandths of an inch."

Reading 0.0001″ Micrometers

The 0.0001″ (ten-thousandths-inch) micrometer is, for the most part, identical to the 0.00l″ micrometer. The difference is that a third scale—the *vernier scale*—is added to the barrel to provide a precision of ten-thousandths (0.0001) of an inch. The vernier scale and the barrel scale are shown in Figure 3.22.

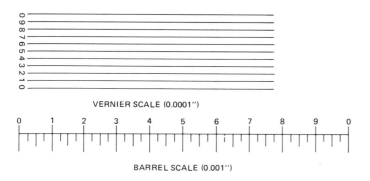

Figure 3.22

The 0.0001″ micrometer is read just as the 0.001″ micrometer is read, with the additional step of reading the *vernier scale*. The vernier reading is added to the barrel and thimble readings. To read the vernier scale, we select the vernier mark that lines up with a mark on the thimble. If the vernier mark "4" lines up with a thimble mark, we add 4 ten-thousandths of an inch (0.0004″). If the vernier mark "5" lines up, we add 5 ten-thousandths of an inch (0.0005″). In Figure 3.23, the

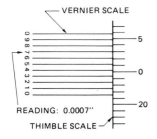

Figure 3.23

vernier mark ''7'' lines up with a thimble mark, so we add 0.0007″ to the micrometer reading.

For example, we find the total micrometer reading shown in Figure 3.24a as follows:

READING 0.4573″

Figure 3.24a

Figure 3.24b

READING: 0.2878″

0.450	(barrel reading)
0.007	(thimble reading)
+ 0.0003	(vernier reading)
0.4573	(total micrometer reading)

We find the total reading of the micrometer shown in Figure 3.24b as follows:

0.275	(barrel reading)
0.012	(thimble reading)
+ 0.0008	(vernier reading)
0.2878	(total micrometer reading)

Proper Use of Outside Micrometers

Micrometers are precision measuring tools. We cannot get accurate measurements if we do not use and care for them properly. The following suggestions will help to insure accurate measurements.

1. Check the micrometer before use to make sure it is *zeroed*. A 0-to-1″ micrometer can be checked by closing it completely. If, when the micrometer is closed, the thimble zero coincides with the zero point of the center line of the barrel, as shown in Figure 3.25, the micrometer is zeroed. We can check 1-to-2″, 1-to-3″, and larger micrometers by completely closing the micrometer onto the properly dimensioned test plugs, called standards, supplied with them.

2. Occasionally check the micrometer with gage blocks to make sure that it is properly calibrated. Calibration is especially important if the micrometer has been dropped.

3. Always keep the faces of the anvil and spindle clean. Since fingers are acidic, keep them off these faces.

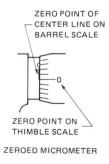

ZERO POINT OF CENTER LINE ON BARREL SCALE

ZERO POINT ON THIMBLE SCALE

ZEROED MICROMETER

Figure 3.25

4. Hold the anvil stationary when measuring parts. Make all movement of the micrometer at the spindle end. At times, rocking the spindle end back and forth in an arc is advisable, to make certain that the proper closure is being made. This procedure is illustrated in Figure 3.26.

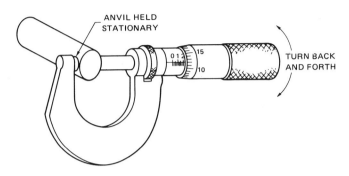

Figure 3.26

5. When taking readings with micrometers, always obtain a snug fit with the part being measured. Fitting the micrometer correctly takes practice and is a skill acquired only through experience.

Reading Depth Micrometers

The depth micrometer, shown in Figure 3.27, is used to measure the depth of holes and slots. A rod is extended from the base of the depth micrometer. The rods come in various lengths to allow for various depth-measurement situations. They vary in length by 1″.

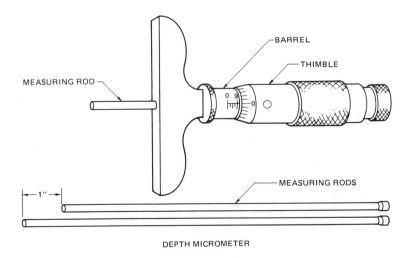

DEPTH MICROMETER

Figure 3.27

The depth micrometer also has barrel and thimble scales from which readings are taken. But, while the values are the same, these scales are the reverse of the scales on an outside micrometer. Scales for a depth micrometer are shown in Figure 3.28.

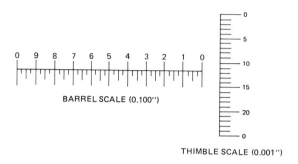

BARREL SCALE (0.100″)

THIMBLE SCALE (0.001″)

Figure 3.28

Because the barrel scale is reversed, we read the part of the scale that is covered by the thimble. Even though the thimble scale is also reversed, it is read in the same way as the thimble scale of outside micrometers. The reading is taken from the thousandth mark that most nearly lines up with the barrel center line.

For example, the depth micrometer scales shown in Figure 3.29a are read as follows:

      0.850   (barrel reading)
    + 0.007   (thimble reading)
      0.857   (total micrometer reading)

The scales shown in Figure 3.29b are read as follows:

      0.525   (barrel reading)
    + 0.015   (thimble reading)
      0.540   (total micrometer reading)

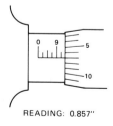

READING: 0.857″

Figure 3.29a

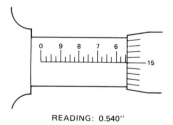

READING: 0.540″

Figure 3.29b

VERNIER CALIPERS

The *vernier caliper,* shown in Figure 3.30, is a very versatile tool. It is used to make inside, outside, and depth measurements. The precision of the vernier caliper, however, is only 0.001″, and it is a little more difficult to read than the micrometer.

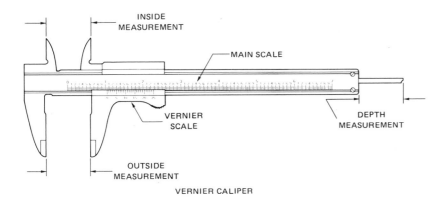

VERNIER CALIPER

Figure 3.30

Reading Vernier Calipers

Like the 0.001″ micrometer, the vernier caliper has two scales, a stationary main scale and a sliding vernier scale. The readings from these two scales are combined to obtain the total reading of the caliper.

The stationary main scale looks like a rule with graduations similar to those on a micrometer barrel. Inches are divided into tenths (hundred-thousandths) and then subdivided by quarter marks (twenty-five thousandths). The main scale and vernier scale are shown in Figure 3.31. The main scale is read at the quarter mark to the left of the zero mark of the vernier scale on the sliding jaw. The main-scale reading in Figure 3.31, for example, is 2.350″ (2.000 plus 0.300, plus 0.050).

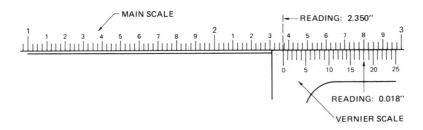

Figure 3.31

The vernier scale is similar to the thimble scale on a micrometer and is read by finding the vernier graduation that most nearly aligns with a mark of the main scale. If the vernier mark "10" lines up, the reading is 0.010″. In Figure 3.31, the vernier-scale reading is 0.018″. Thus, the total reading of the vernier caliper shown in Figure 3.31 is 2.368″ (2.350 main-scale reading plus 0.018 vernier-scale reading).

We read the scales shown in Figure 3.32a as follows:

$$
\begin{array}{ll}
2.450 & \text{(main-scale reading)} \\
+\ 0.008 & \text{(vernier reading)} \\
\hline
2.458 & \text{(total vernier caliper reading)}
\end{array}
$$

We read the scales shown in Figure 3.32b as follows:

$$
\begin{array}{ll}
3.675 & \text{(main-scale reading)} \\
+\ 0.017 & \text{(vernier reading)} \\
\hline
3.692 & \text{(total vernier caliper reading)}
\end{array}
$$

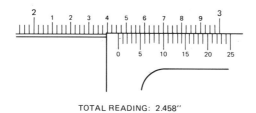

TOTAL READING: 2.458″

Figure 3.32a

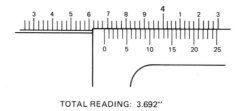

TOTAL READING: 3.692″

Figure 3.32b

GAGE BLOCKS

Gage blocks are standards of length, usually square or rectangular in shape. They are made of high-quality steel that is ground and polished to a high degree of precision. Gage blocks are used in the machine shop to calibrate precision measuring tools, to inspect and lay out work, and to set up machines. Gage blocks come in sets of eighty-one, grouped into the four series shown in Table 3.1.

Reading Gage Blocks

The first series of gage blocks is graduated in ten-thousandths (0.0001) of an inch, the second series in thousandths (0.001) of an inch, the third in fifty-thousandths

Table 3.1 Gage Blocks

First Series (0.0001″ — 9 Blocks)

.1001   .1002   .1003   .1004   .1005   .1006   .1007   .1008   .1009

Second Series (0.001″ — 49 Blocks)

.101 .102 .103 .104 .105 .106 .107 .108 .109 .110 .111 .112 .113
.114 .115 .116 .117 .118 .119 .120 .121 .122 .123 .124 .125 .126
.127 .128 .129 .130 .131 .132 .133 .134 .135 .136 .137 .138 .139
.140 .141 .142 .143 .144 .145 .146 .147 .148 .149

Third Series (0.050″ — 19 Blocks)

.050 .100 .150 .200 .250 .300 .350 .400 .450 .500 .550 .600 .650
.700 .750 .800 .850 .900 .950

Fourth Series (1.000″ — 4 Blocks)

1.000   2.000   3.000   4.000

(0.050) of an inch, and the fourth in inches (1.0). These graduated gage blocks can be combined to make up any specific dimension desired.

In combining the blocks, we always start with the ten-thousandths series and work to the inch series. Figure 3.33 shows how to build a combination of gage blocks for the measurement 4.8534″. To obtain a zero in the ten-thousandths position, select gage block 0.1004″ from the first series and subtract it from the desired measurement:

$$
\begin{array}{r}
4.8534 \\
-\ 0.1004 \\
\hline
4.7530
\end{array}
$$

We then select gage block 0.103″ from the second series and subtract it from the remaining measurement:

$$
\begin{array}{r}
4.753 \\
-\ 0.103 \\
\hline
4.650
\end{array}
$$

Note that we could have chosen other gage blocks. Use of the 0.103″ block leaves a ''5'' in the hundredths position and makes our selection of the next block easier. We next select the 0.650″ block from the third series and subtract it from the remaining measurement:

$$
\begin{array}{r}
4.650 \\
-\ 0.650 \\
\hline
4.000
\end{array}
$$

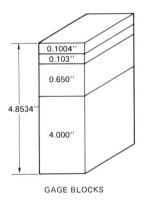

GAGE BLOCKS

Figure 3.33

Our final selection is, therefore, the 4.000″ gage block from the fourth series. Combined, these gage blocks give a total measurement of 4.8534″:

$$
\begin{array}{r}
0.1004 \\
0.1030 \\
0.6500 \\
+\ 4.0000 \\
\hline
4.8534
\end{array}
$$

When using gage blocks, we need to keep in mind that they are very precise. Therefore, they should be kept clean, and we should be especially careful not to scratch them.

The 6″ steel rule, the 0.001″ and 0.0001″ outside micrometers, the depth micrometer, the vernier caliper, and gage blocks are just a few of the precision tools used by machinists. They are, however, the most common ones. Knowing how to read and use these instruments is very important to the machinist.

TERMS FOR REVIEW

— linear measurement
— nominal dimensions
— actual dimensions
— basic dimensions
— tolerance
— bilateral tolerance
— unilateral tolerance
— limits
— clearance

— interference
— steel rule
— micrometer
— quarter marks
— thimble scale
— vernier scale
— zeroed
— vernier caliper
— gage blocks

EXERCISES

Exercise 3.1: Dimensioning

A. State the upper and lower limits of the following basic dimensions and tolerances. (Example: 1.375 ±0.005 = 1.380/1.370)

1. 0.250 ±0.002 = _____

2. 8.705 ±0.015 = _____

3. 3.085 $\begin{array}{l}+0.003\\-0.000\end{array}$ = _____

4. 1.873 $\begin{array}{l}+0.000\\-0.002\end{array}$ = _____

5. 0.7500 ±0.0015 = _____

6. 2.0458 ±0.0012 = _____

7. 0.0655 $\begin{array}{l}+0.0010\\-0.0000\end{array}$ = _____

8. 1.893 ±0.010 = _____

9. 8-5/8 ±1/64 = _____

10. 2-11/16 ±1/32 = _____

B. State the maximum and minimum clearance between the following mating parts.

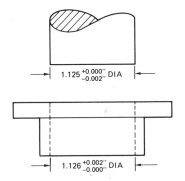

1.125 $^{+0.000''}_{-0.002''}$ DIA

1.126 $^{+0.002''}_{-0.000''}$ DIA

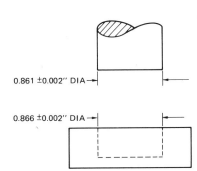

0.861 ±0.002″ DIA

0.866 ±0.002″ DIA

1a. maximum clearance = _____

1b. minimum clearance = _____

2a. maximum clearance = _____

2b. minimum clearance = _____

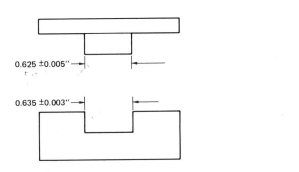

0.625 ±0.005″

0.635 ±0.003″

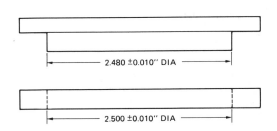

2.480 ±0.010″ DIA

2.500 ±0.010″ DIA

3a. maximum clearance = _____

3b. minimum clearance = _____

4a. maximum clearance = _____

4b. minimum clearance = _____

C. State the maximum and minimum interference between the following mating parts.

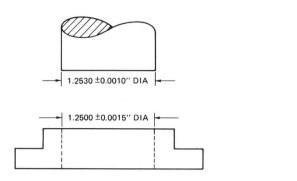

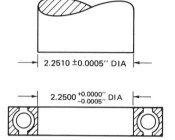

1a. maximum interference = _____   **2a.** maximum interference = _____

1b. minimum interference = _____   **2b.** minimum interference = _____

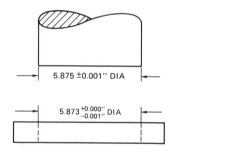

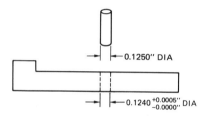

3a. maximum interference = _____   **4a.** maximum interference = _____

3b. minimum interference = _____   **4b.** minimum interference = _____

Exercise 3.2: Reading Fractional and Decimal Scales

A. State the measurement indicated by points *A* through *L* on the 8ths and 16ths scales of the following 6″ rule.

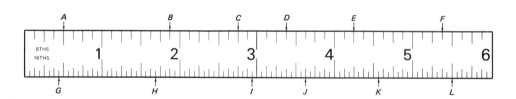

1. *A* = _____   **2.** *B* = _____   **3.** *C* = _____

4. *D* = _____   **5.** *E* = _____   **6.** *F* = _____

7. *G* = _____   **8.** *H* = _____   **9.** *I* = _____

10. *J* = _____   **11.** *K* = _____   **12.** *L* = _____

B. State the measurements indicated by points *A* through *L* on the 32nds and 64ths scales of the following 6″ rule.

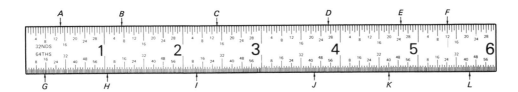

1. *A* = _____   2. *B* = _____   3. *C* = _____

4. *D* = _____   5. *E* = _____   6. *F* = _____

7. *G* = _____   8. *H* = _____   9. *I* = _____

10. *J* = _____   11. *K* = _____   12. *L* = _____

C. State the measurements indicated by points *A* through *L* on the tenths and hundredths scales of the following 6″ rule.

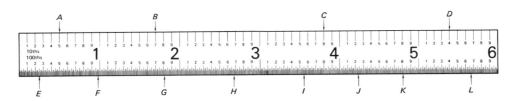

1. *A* = _____   2. *B* = _____   3. *C* = _____

4. *D* = _____   5. *E* = _____   6. *F* = _____

7. *G* = _____   8. *H* = _____   9. *I* = _____

10. *J* = _____   11. *K* = _____   12. *L* = _____

Exercise 3.3: Reading Scales from Inch Marks

A. State the measurements indicated by points *A* through *F* of the following scale. Take readings from the 1″ mark.

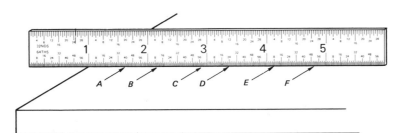

1. *A* = _____   2. *B* = _____   3. *C* = _____

4. *D* = _____   5. *E* = _____   6. *F* = _____

B.   State the measurements indicated by points *A* through *F* of the following scale.
Take readings from the 4″ mark in reverse of the scale.

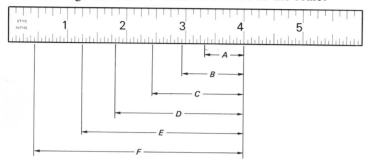

1. *A* = _____   2. *B* = _____   3. *C* = _____
4. *D* = _____   5. *E* = _____   6. *F* = _____

Exercise 3.4: Micrometers

A.   Read the following 0.001″ micrometers to the nearest thousandths of an inch.

   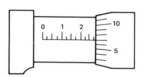

1. _____   2. _____   3. _____

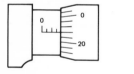   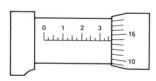   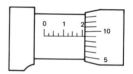

4. _____   5. _____   6. _____

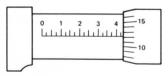

7. _____   8. _____   9. _____

B.   Read the following 0.0001″ micrometers to the nearest ten-thousandths of an
inch.

      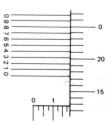

1. _____   2. _____   3. _____

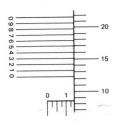 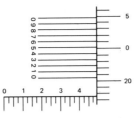 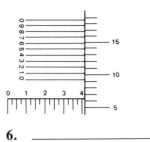

4. _____   **5.** _____   **6.** _____

Exercise 3.5: Depth Micrometers

A. Determine the readings of the following depth micrometers.

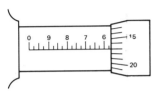 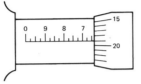 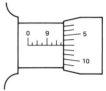

1. _____   **2.** _____   **3.** _____

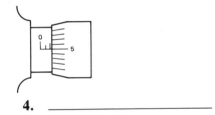 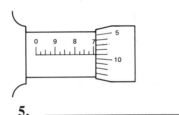 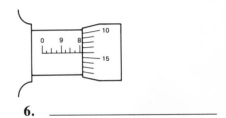

4. _____   **5.** _____   **6.** _____

Exercise 3.6: Vernier Calipers

A. Determine the readings of the following vernier calipers.

1. 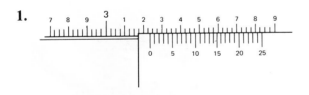   **1.** _____

2. 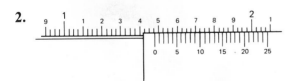   **2.** _____

3. 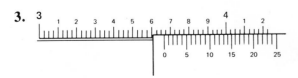   **3.** _____

4.   4. _____

5.   5. _____

6.   6. _____

7.   7. _____

8.   8. _____

Exercise 3.7: Gage Blocks

A. Determine a combination of gage blocks to represent each of the following measurements.

1. 1.3582″ _____   **2.** 3.5766″ _____

3. 7.5491″ _____   **4.** 6.1895″ _____

5. 4.9982″ _____   **6.** 2.0513″ _____

CHAPTER 4

RATIOS AND PROPORTIONS

Learning Objectives

After studying this chapter, you should be able to:

— State a ratio between two values

— Express ratios in their simplest form

— Calculate the unknown term of a proportion

— Calculate percent, percentage, and base of percent problems

— Calculate the taper, TPF, TPI, and the diameter of the small and large ends of tapered pieces

— Calculate size ratios between two gears or pulleys

— Calculate RPM and gear or pulley sizes of gear or pulley systems

— Calculate RPM ratios of simple and compound systems

We make many comparisons in our daily lives. We compare this car to that car, we compare one person to another person, and often our work is compared to the work of someone else.

RATIOS

A *ratio* is a mathematical comparison of one value with another value. The comparisons known as ratios exist in vast numbers throughout our society. They are very common in the machine trades. Feed ratios, speed ratios, gear ratios, tapers, and indexing solutions are just a few examples of the ratios a machinist will encounter.

Interpretation of Ratios

At one time, the exchange rate between the German mark and the American dollar was 4 marks for 1 dollar, or simply 4 to 1. In Chapter 1, we defined a *fraction* as a comparison between two values. Thus, fractions are really ratio expressions. Saying that the ratio of marks to dollars is 4 to 1 is the same as saying that the ratio of marks to dollars is 4/1. Since decimals are another way of writing fractions, they, too, are ratio expressions. Perhaps without realizing it, we often use the concept of ratios in our daily lives.

Ratios may be written in a number of different ways. Consider, for example, the ratio of the length of piece *A* to the length of piece *B* in Figure 4.1. The ratio comparing the lengths may be written in any of the following ways:

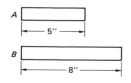

Figure 4.1

> 5 to 8
>
> 5:8
>
> 5/8 (fractional expression)

Each of these ratios is read as ''five to eight.'' The ratio may also be stated as 0.625, a decimal expression, since 0.625 is the decimal equivalent of the fraction 5/8.

A great deal of the information used in the machine trades is given in ratio form. Therefore, in order to obtain the correct information, machinists must know how to interpret ratios. First, we need to know what measurements are being compared by the ratios. Second, we need to know the direction of comparison between those measurements.

Consider, for example, two gears used in a mechanical system that has a gear ratio of 2 to 1. First of all, what measurement of the gears are we talking about—the size of the gears, the number of teeth, or the RPM relationships of the two gears? Not knowing which measurement relationship is being considered could result in drastic changes in the design of the system.

In this example, the term *gear ratio* implies that we are relating the RPM measurements. Second, what is the direction of comparison between the measurements? Gear ratios are stated in the direction in which power is transmitted—that is, from the driver gear to the driven gear. Thus, the ratio of 2 to 1 gives the relationship of the RPM of the driver gear to the RPM of the driven gear. We should now be able to picture two gears, like those shown in Figure 4.2, where a smaller driver gear turns two times every time the larger driven gear turns once.

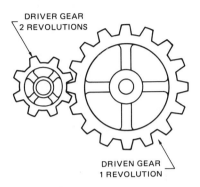

Figure 4.2

Reducing Ratios to Simplest Form

In general, ratio relationships are expressed in their simplest form, such as:

1/2.5,   0.45/1,   7.49/1,   0.86438,   2.7693

As can be seen from these examples, the simplest form of a ratio is an expression in which either one term is reduced to 1 or the ratio is stated as a decimal.

Reducing ratios means that the ratio is simplified so that one term is reduced to 1.

RULE

To reduce a ratio, divide through the ratio by the term to be reduced to 1.

For example, to reduce the ratio 10/50 so that the first term is 1, divide through the ratio by the first term, 10:

$$\frac{10 \div 10}{50 \div 10} = \frac{1}{5}$$

The ratio is thus 1 to 5.

To reduce the ratio 10/50 so that the second term is 1, divide through the ratio by the second term, 50:

$$\frac{10 \div 50}{50 \div 50} = \frac{0.2}{1}$$

The ratio is thus 0.2 to 1.

Decimal Ratios

The same procedure used to express a ratio as a decimal is the same procedure used to convert fractions to decimals. The result of this procedure is a *decimal ratio*.

RULE

To express a ratio as a decimal, divide the first term by the second term and round off the decimal if necessary.

For example, to express the ratio 9.5/11.5 as a decimal, divide 9.5 by 11.5:

$$9.5 \div 11.5 = 0.8261 \text{ (rounded off to four places)}$$

To express the ratio 5.698/3.275 as a decimal, divide 5.698 by 3.275:

$$5.698 \div 3.275 = 1.73985 \text{ (rounded off to five places)}$$

PROPORTIONS

Ratios are useful mathematical tools. However, they can be put together into even more useful mathematical tools called proportions. In the following sections and in later chapters, we will see how useful a thorough knowledge of proportions can be for machinists.

Interpretation of Proportions

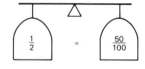

Figure 4.3

A *proportion* is an expression stating that two ratios are equal, as illustrated in Figure 4.3. In this figure, we can see that the ratio 1 to 2 is the same as 50 to 100, or 1/2 = 50/100. The following are other examples of proportions:

$$\frac{3}{4} = \frac{9}{12}, \quad \frac{1}{2} = \frac{10}{20}, \quad \frac{5}{8} = 0.625$$

These proportions are the same equal relationships we worked with when equating fractions and decimals. We are really not looking at anything new. We are now merely calling these equal relationships what they really are—proportions.

Proportions are frequently used in the machine trades. For example, each dimension on a drawing of a part to be machined must be in proportion to each dimension of the actual part. If the width of the part is drawn at a scale of 6″ to 1″, then the length must also be drawn at the same scale of 6″ to 1″. Thus, an actual width of 6″ will be drawn as 1″, and an actual length of 12″ will be drawn as 2″. The dimensions on the drawing will be in proportion to the actual part because 6 is to 1 as 12 is to 2, or

$$\frac{6}{1} = \frac{12}{2}$$

NOTE: We can test whether two ratios are, in fact, a proportion by finding and comparing the cross products. The *cross products* of the terms of a proportion are always equal. We find the cross products when we *cross multiply* each numerator by the denominator on the other side of the equals sign. For example, we check the proportion 1/2 = 50/100 as follows:

$$\frac{1}{2} \bowtie \frac{50}{100} = \frac{1 \times 100}{2 \times 50} = \frac{100}{100}$$

Similarly, we can check the proportion 6/1 = 12/2:

$$\frac{6}{1} \bowtie \frac{12}{2} = \frac{6 \times 2}{1 \times 12} = \frac{12}{12}$$

Solving Proportion Problems

Solving a proportion problem means solving for one of the values—an unknown value—of the proportion. When we were solving for equal fractions, the problems looked like the following:

$$\frac{3}{4} = \frac{?}{16}, \quad \frac{5}{8} = \frac{?}{64}, \quad \frac{1}{2} = \frac{?}{32}$$

Now, we need to change the procedure we use to solve problems such as these. We are changing the procedure because in many proportion problems, the numbers are not so simple. We do, however, have a simple rule to follow in order to find an unknown value in a proportion.

RULE

To find an unknown value in a proportion, cross multiply the known numerator–denominator pair and then divide the product by the remaining known term.

For example, we want to solve for the unknown term in the following proportion:

$$\frac{3}{4} = \frac{?}{12}$$

First, we cross multiply the known numerator–denominator pair, 3 and 12:

$$3 \times 12 = 36$$

We then divide the product, 36, by the remaining known term, 4:

$$36 \div 4 = 9$$

Therefore, 3/4 = 9/12.

To check the answer, we find and compare cross products:

$$\frac{3}{4} \diagup\!\!\!\!\diagdown \frac{9}{12} \qquad \frac{3 \times 12}{4 \times 9} = \frac{36}{36}$$

The same procedure is used to solve for the unknown term in the following proportion:

$$\frac{5}{8} = \frac{?}{64}$$

First, the known numerator–denominator pair, 5 and 64, are cross multiplied:

$$5 \times 64 = 320$$

The product, 320, is then divided by the remaining known term, 8:

$$320 \div 8 = 40$$

Therefore, 5/8 = 40/64. This answer is checked by finding and comparing cross products:

$$\frac{5}{8} \diagup\!\!\!\!\diagdown \frac{40}{64} \qquad \frac{5 \times 64}{8 \times 40} = \frac{320}{320}$$

The rule of "cross multiply and divide" is used no matter which value of a proportion we are solving for, as illustrated in the following examples.

To solve the proportion problem 3/4 = 9/?, we cross multiply the known numerator–denominator pair and divide by the remaining known term:

$$\frac{\text{(cross multiply)}}{\text{(divide)}} \quad \frac{4 \times 9}{3} = \frac{36}{3} = 12$$

Therefore, 3/4 = 9/12.

To solve the proportion problem ?/3 = 10/15, we cross multiply the known numerator–denominator pair and divide by the remaining known term:

$$\frac{3 \times 10}{15} = \frac{30}{15} = 2$$

Therefore, 2/3 = 10/15.

To solve the proportion problem 3.5/? = 5/20, we cross multiply the known numerator–denominator pair and divide:

$$\frac{3.5 \times 20}{5} = \frac{70}{5} = 14$$

Therefore, 3.5/14 = 5/20.

PERCENTS

Both in the machine shop and in daily life, we often need to work with percents. Like decimals, percents are closely related to fractions. As we saw earlier, decimals are a simple way of writing fractions of tenths, hundredths, thousandths, and ten-thousandths. Similarly, percents are a simple means of writing fractions of hundredths. Percents are also a means of expressing ratios. In working with percents as ratios, we make the comparison against a base of 100.

Interpretation of Percents

Percent means "per one hundred." Percents written in fractional form have 100 as the base of comparison (denominator). The following are examples of percents written in fractional form:

$$\frac{3}{100}, \quad \frac{25}{100}, \quad \frac{63}{100}, \quad \frac{142}{100}$$

As we know, fractions of hundredths can be written in decimal form:

0.03, 0.25, 0.63, 1.42

We can also write fractions of hundredths as percents by using the percent symbol, %. Thus, in percent notation, these fractions are written:

3%, 25%, 63%, 142%

As ratio expressions, percents compare an amount to a base of 100. For example, 3% (3 per 100) is the same as the ratio 3 to 100:

$$3\% = \frac{3}{100} = 0.03 = 3:100$$

Since percents are ratio expressions, they can be used in stating proportions. In a proportion expression, the percent ratio (amount per 100) is equated with another ratio. The two values that form the other ratio are called the percentage and the base. The *percentage* is a number expressed as a percent of another number. The *base* is the value to which the percentage is being compared. For example, if we say that 20 is 50% of 40, 20 is the percentage, 40 is the base to which it is being compared, and 50 is the percent.

Thus, in percent proportions, the ratio of the percent to 100 is equal to the ratio of percentage to base:

$$\frac{percent}{100} = \frac{percentage}{base}$$

Solving Percent Problems

With the percent proportion in mind, we can now solve such problems as, What percent of 75 is 15? In other words:

$$\frac{?}{100} = \frac{15}{75}$$

Or, we can solve the problem, 30 is what percentage of 80?

$$\frac{30}{100} = \frac{?}{80}$$

We can also find the answer to the problem, 27 is 9% of what amount:

$$\frac{9}{100} = \frac{27}{?}$$

We solve percent problems as we would solve any other proportion problem. That is, we cross multiply the known numerator–denominator pair and divide. However, percent problems are easier to solve if we use this basic rule to make other rules for finding specific unknown values in percent problems.

RULE

To find the percent, multiply the percentage by 100 and divide by the base:

$$\text{percent} = \frac{100 \times \text{percentage}}{\text{base}}$$

For example, consider the problem, What percent of $72.00 is $8.50? The question is asking us to find a value that has the same relationship to 100 that $8.50 has to $72.00. The value wanted is the percent. We know that:

$8.50 = \text{percentage}$

$72.00 = \text{base}$

The rule for finding the percent is:

$$\text{percent} = \frac{100 \times \text{percentage}}{\text{base}}$$

We can substitute the known values to solve the problem:

$$\text{percent} = \frac{100 \times 8.50}{72.00}$$

We then multiply as indicated in the numerator:

$$\text{percent} = \frac{850.00}{72.00}$$

Finally, we divide to find the percent:

percent = 11.8, rounded off to the nearest tenth

Therefore, $8.50 is 11.8% of $72.00.

RULE

To find the percentage, multiply the percent by the base and divide by 100:

$$\text{percentage} = \frac{\text{percent} \times \text{base}}{100}$$

Suppose we are asked, What is 20% of $16.50? The question is asking us to find an amount that is part of $16.50. Also, the question states that the amount is to be proportionally 20% of $16.50. The value wanted is the percentage. We know that:

$16.50 = base

20 = percent

The rule for finding the percentage is:

$$\text{percentage} = \frac{\text{percent} \times \text{base}}{100}$$

We can substitute the known values to solve the problem:

$$\text{percentage} = \frac{20 \times 16.50}{100}$$

We next perform the multiplication in the numerator:

$$\text{percentage} = \frac{330.00}{100}$$

Finally, we divide to find the percentage:

percentage = 3.30

Therefore, 20% of $16.50 = $3.30.

RULE

To find the base, multiply the percentage by 100 and divide by the percent:

$$\text{base} = \frac{100 \times \text{percentage}}{\text{percent}}$$

Suppose we are asked, $3.50 is 5% of what amount? The question is asking us to find the value of which $3.50 is 5%. The value wanted is the base. We know that:

$$\$3.50 = \text{percentage}$$
$$5 = \text{percent}$$

The rule for finding the base is:

$$\text{base} = \frac{100 \times \text{percentage}}{\text{percent}}$$

We can substitute the known values to solve the problem:

$$\text{base} = \frac{100 \times 3.50}{5}$$

We then perform the multiplication in the numerator:

$$\text{base} = \frac{350.00}{5}$$

Finally, we divide to find the base:

$$\text{base} = 70.00$$

Thus, $3.50 is 5% of $70.00.

TAPERS

Machinists frequently need to apply their mathematical skills to tapers. Tapered shanks (shanks with one end larger in diameter than the other) have been used on tools for a long time in the machine trades. They have been used for tools such as twist drills, mandrells, end mills, lathe centers, and chucks. Some tapered tools are illustrated in Figure 4.4. Tapered shanks are used because of two very important characteristics. First, they permit a very tight grip for driving tools, yet the grip can be easily broken when removal is desired. Second, they provide an automatic, accurate alignment of the tool.

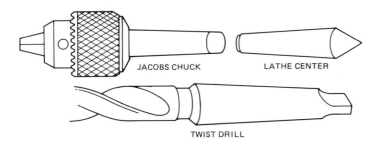

Figure 4.4

Interpretation of Tapers

We can all visualize what tapered pieces look like, but we probably would not know how to measure one. The measurement of a tapered piece is called its *taper*. The taper is the difference between the two end diameters or widths of a tapered piece.

Most tapered pieces encountered in the shop are commercially made and have standard tapers. Morse Standard, Jarno, and Brown & Sharpe are probably the most common series of standard tapers. Whenever a standard taper is specified on a print, we can find the correct dimensioning information in *Machinery's Handbook*. This specific information will not be given here. We will consider the rules for measuring tapers.

RULE

> *To find the taper, subtract the diameter of the small end from the diameter of the large end.*

For example, the piece of tapered round stock shown in Figure 4.5 has a large-end diameter of 0.875″ and a small-end diameter of 0.500″. To find the taper, subtract the smaller diameter from the larger:

Figure 4.5

$$\text{taper} = 0.875 - 0.500 = 0.375''$$

RULE

> *To find the small-end diameter of a tapered piece, subtract the taper from the large-end diameter; to find the large-end diameter, add the taper to the small-end diameter.*

For example, to find the diameter of the small end (*A*) of the tapered sleeve illustrated in Figure 4.6, subtract the taper from the diameter of the large end:

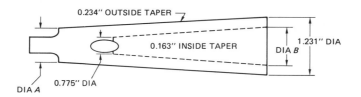

Figure 4.6

$$\text{diameter } A = 1.231 - 0.234 = 0.997''$$

To find the diameter of the large end (*B*) of the tapered hole, add the taper to the small-end diameter:

$$\text{diameter } B = 0.775 + 0.163 = 0.938''$$

Figure 4.7 shows two pieces of tapered round stock. One is 3″ long and the other is 2″ long. Both have a large-end diameter of 1.250″ and a small-end diameter of 0.750″. Both have the same taper:

Figure 4.7

$$\text{taper} = 1.250 - 0.750 = 0.500''$$

Even though both have the same taper, we can see from Figure 4.7 that the two pieces are tapered differently. Thus, we need to identify the length over which the taper occurs when we express a taper measurement. To do so, we express a ratio of taper to length. For the 3″ piece, the ratio is the 0.500″ taper to the 3″ length. For the 2″ piece, the ratio is the 0.500″ taper to the 2″ length. As we will see in the next section, these two ratios give us all the information needed to make the two tapered pieces.

Flat tapered pieces are handled the same way. Figure 4.8 shows an 8″ flat piece with a large-end width of 2.500″ and a small-end width of 1.750″. The taper of this piece is 0.750″ over a length of 8″.

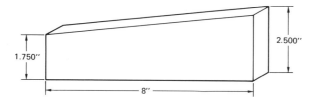

Figure 4.8

Solving TPF and TPI Problems

On a blueprint for a tapered surface, taper information is generally given as a TPF or TPI specification. *TPF* means taper per foot. The TPF ratio expresses the difference in end diameters or widths over the length of 1′. For example, 0.60235 TPF is the TPF specification for a Morse 3 taper. *TPI* means taper per inch. The TPI ratio expresses the difference in end diameters or widths over the length of 1″. For example, the TPI specification for a Morse 3 taper is 0.05019″.

The relationship between TPF, TPI, and the measured taper of a tapered piece is a proportional one (remember that 1′ = 12″). Thus, in proportional form, the relationship between TPF, TPI, and the measured taper is:

$$\frac{TPF}{12} = \frac{TPI}{1} = \frac{taper}{length\ of\ piece}$$

The following rules are really just the commonsense relationships of a proportion as found by the rule for cross multiplying and dividing. The basic rule for solving proportion problems are being used to make specific rules for working with tapers.

RULE

To find the TPI when the TPF is known, divide the TPF by 12:

$$TPI = \frac{TPF}{12}$$

EXAMPLE

Problem

Find the TPI of the tapered piece shown in Figure 4.9.

Analysis

Apply the rule for finding the TPI:

$$TPI = \frac{TPF}{12}$$

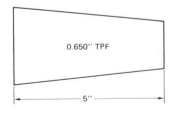

Figure 4.9

We know from Figure 4.9 that:

$$TPF = 0.650″$$

Solution

Step 1: Substitute the known value for TPF

$$TPI = \frac{0.650}{12}$$

Step 2: Divide to find TPI

Answer

$$TPI = 0.054''$$

RULE

To find the taper when the end diameters are unknown, multiply the TPI by the length of the tapered piece:

$$taper = TPI \times length$$

EXAMPLE

Problem

Find the taper of the tapered piece shown in Figure 4.9.

Analysis

Apply the rule for finding the taper:

$$taper = TPI \times length$$

We know from Figure 4.9 that:

$$TPF = 0.650''$$
$$length = 5''$$

Solution

Step 1a: Apply the rule for finding TPI

$$TPI = \frac{TPF}{12}$$

Step 1b: Substitute the known value for TPF and divide to find TPI

$$TPI = \frac{0.650}{12} = 0.054''$$

Step 2:   Substitute the found value for TPI into the rule for finding the taper

$$taper = TPI \times length$$
$$= 0.054 \times 5$$

Step 3:   Multiply to find the taper

Answer

$$taper = 0.270''$$

RULE

To find the TPI when the taper and length are known, divide the taper by the length (in inches) of the tapered piece:

$$TPI = \frac{taper}{length}$$

EXAMPLE

Problem

Find the TPI of the tapered piece shown in Figure 4.10.

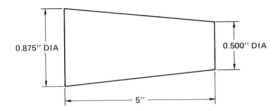

Figure 4.10

Analysis

Apply the rule for finding the TPI:

$$TPI = \frac{taper}{length}$$

We know from Figure 4.10 that:

$$length = 5''$$

Solution

Step 1a: Apply the rule for finding the taper

$$taper = large\text{-}end\ diameter\ -\ small\text{-}end\ diameter$$

Step 1b: Substitute the known values for the diameters and subtract to find the taper

$$taper = 0.875 - 0.500 = 0.375''$$

Step 2:   Substitute the known values into the rule for finding TPI

$$TPI = \frac{taper}{length} = \frac{0.375}{5}$$

Step 3:   Divide to find the TPI

Answer

$$TPI = 0.075''$$

RULE

To find the TPF, multiply the TPI by 12:

$$TPF = TPI \times 12$$

EXAMPLE

Problem

Find the TPF of the tapered piece shown in Figure 4.10.

Analysis

Apply the rule for finding the TPF:

$$TPF = TPI \times 12$$

We know from the previous example that.

$$TPI = \frac{0.875 - 0.500}{5} = 0.075''$$

Solution

Step 1:   Substitute the known value for TPI

$$TPF = 0.075 \times 12$$

Step 2:   Multiply to find the TPF

Answer

$$TPF = 0.900''$$

RULE

To find the length of a tapered piece, divide the taper by the TPI:

$$length = \frac{taper}{TPI}$$

EXAMPLE

Problem

Find the length of the tapered piece shown in Figure 4.11.

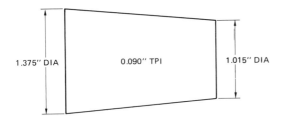

Figure 4.11

Analysis

Apply the rule for finding the length:

$$\text{length} = \frac{\text{taper}}{\text{TPI}}$$

We know from Figure 4.11 that:

$$\text{TPI} = 0.090''$$

Solution

Step 1a: Apply the rule for finding the taper

$$\text{taper} = \text{large-end diameter} - \text{small-end diameter}$$

Step 1b: Substitute the known values for the diameters and subtract to find the taper

$$\text{taper} = 1.375 - 1.015 = 0.360''$$

Step 2: Substitute the known values into the rule for finding length

$$\text{length} = \frac{\text{taper}}{\text{TPI}}$$

$$= \frac{0.360}{0.090}$$

Step 3: Divide to find the length

Answer

$$\text{length} = 4''$$

GEAR AND PULLEY SYSTEMS

Gears and pulleys are two means of transferring rotary power from a driver shaft to a driven shaft at which the power is needed. During this transfer of power, the output RPMs (revolutions per minute) of the driven shaft can be controlled by controlling the size of the gears or pulleys being used to provide the input RPMs. The difference in size between the driver and the driven gears or pulleys gives these systems their RPM ratios (sometimes referred to as speed ratios).

The *RPM ratio* of a system is the ratio of the input RPMs of the driver shaft to the output RPMs of the final driven shaft. The means of calculating these ratios for gear and for pulley systems are the same. However, gear systems have more flexibility, so we will emphasize them.

Interpretation of Gear and Pulley Systems

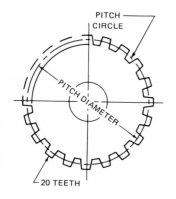

Figure 4.12

NOTE: In this chapter, the drawings of gears and pulleys are schematized. Part of the gear shown in Figure 4.12 is a schematic drawing. The dashed line represents the teeth. Part of the pulley shown in Figure 4.14 is a schematic drawing. The solid and dashed lines represent the pulley.

The sizes of the two gears shown in Figure 4.13 can be compared in two ways. We can compare the number of teeth on the driver gear to the number of teeth on the driven gear. In this case, the ratio is 32 to 16, or a 2-to-1 teeth ratio. Or, we can compare the pitch diameters of the two gears. The *pitch diameter* (P. Dia.) of a gear is the diameter of the gear's *pitch circle*. The pitch circle is an imaginary circle passing through the center of each gear tooth, as illustrated in Figure 4.12. In this case, the ratio is 4 to 2, or a 2-to-1 pitch-diameter ratio. The teeth ratio and the pitch-diameter ratio are always the same.

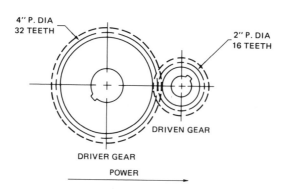

Figure 4.13

In pulley systems, there are two types of pulleys—flat and V-type. A flat pulley is shown in Figure 4.14. A V-type pulley is shown in Figure 4.15. The outside diameter (OD) is used to make size comparisons of flat pulleys. Thus, in

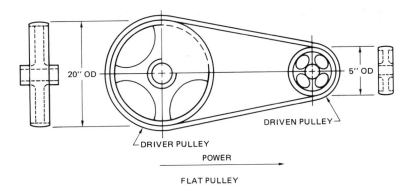

Figure 4.14

Figure 4.14, the size ratio between the driver and the driven pulley is 20 to 5, or 4 to 1 (the driver pulley is 4 times larger than the driven pulley). The outside diameter, as illustrated in Figure 4.15, can also be used to state size ratios of V-type pulleys (OD is how pulleys are usually dimensioned). However, slight errors are made when the OD dimension is used. Thus, to obtain the exact dimensions from which pulley ratios are determined, we need to consult *Machinery's Handbook*.

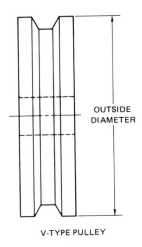

Figure 4.15

Solving Simple Gear and Pulley System Problems

We can use a proportion to express the size and RPM relationships between the driver gear or pulley and the driven gear or pulley in simple systems. *Simple gear and pulley systems* are those in which two gears are meshed or two pulleys are used to transmit power. This proportion is:

$$\frac{\text{size of driver}}{\text{size of driven}} = \frac{\text{RPM of driven}}{\text{RPM of driver}}$$

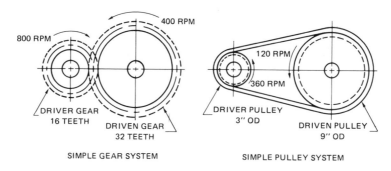

Figure 4.16a   **Figure 4.16b**

For the gears shown in Figure 4.16a, the relationship is:

$$\frac{16 \text{ teeth}}{32 \text{ teeth}} = \frac{400 \text{ RPM}}{800 \text{ RPM}}$$

For the pulleys shown in Figure 4.16b, the relationship is:

$$\frac{3''}{9''} = \frac{120 \text{ RPM}}{360 \text{ RPM}}$$

Notice that the RPM ratio of two gears or two pulleys is proportional to the inverse (reverse) of their size ratio. That is, the numerator of the RPM ratio corresponds to the denominator of the size ratio and vice versa. We say that the RPM ratios and size ratios are *inversely proportional*.

This inverse relationship, or proportion, is the basis for solving gear and pulley system problems. However, we can express the size–RPM relationship in a way that is, perhaps, easier to remember:

size of driver × RPM of driver = size of driven × RPM of driven

For the gears shown in Figure 4.16a, this relationship is:

$$16 \times 800 = 32 \times 400$$
$$12{,}800 = 12{,}800$$

For the pulleys shown in Figure 4.16b, the relationship is:

$$3 \times 360 = 9 \times 120$$
$$1080 = 1080$$

To solve gear and pulley problems, we can use the size–RPM proportional relationship to make rules for finding unknown sizes or RPMs of gears and pulleys within a simple system.

RULES

To find the size of the driver gear or pulley, use the rule:

$$\text{size of driver} = \frac{\text{size of driven} \times \text{RPM of driven}}{\text{RPM of driver}}$$

To find the input RPMs of the driver gear or pulley, use the rule:

$$\text{RPM of driver} = \frac{\text{size of driven} \times \text{RPM of driven}}{\text{size of driver}}$$

To find the size of the driven gear or pulley, use the rule:

$$\text{size of driven} = \frac{\text{size of driver} \times \text{RPM of driver}}{\text{RPM of driven}}$$

To find the output RPMs of the driven gear or pulley, use the rule:

$$\text{RPM of driven} = \frac{\text{size of driver} \times \text{RPM of driver}}{\text{size of driven}}$$

The following example shows how to use these rules for the size–RPM relationship to find the required driver gear for the meshed gear system shown in Figure 4.17.

EXAMPLE

Problem

Find the size of the driver gear required for the system of meshed gears shown in Figure 4.17.

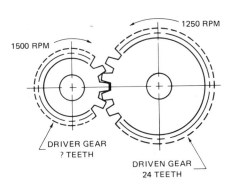

Figure 4.17

Analysis

Apply the rule for finding the size of the driver gear:

$$\text{size of driver gear} = \frac{\text{size of driven gear} \times \text{RPM of driven gear}}{\text{RPM of driver gear}}$$

We know from Figure 4.17 that:

$$\text{RPM of driver} = 1500$$
$$\text{RPM of driven} = 1250$$
$$\text{size of driven} = 24 \text{ teeth}$$

Solution

Step 1: Substitute the known values into the rule

$$\text{size of driver gear} = \frac{24 \times 1250}{1500}$$

Step 2: Perform the multiplication in the numerator

$$\text{size of driver gear} = \frac{30,000}{1500}$$

Step 3: Divide to find the size of the driver gear

Answer

$$\text{size of driver gear} = 20 \text{ teeth}$$

Note: The input-to-output RPM ratio is 1500 to 1250 (1500/1250), or 1.2 to 1.

Simple gear systems may use one or more *intermediate,* or *idler, gears,* as Figure 4.18 shows. Idlers do not effect the RPMs of a system, but they are very

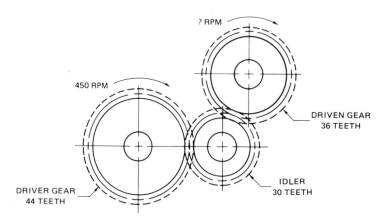

Figure 4.18

important. They serve to control the direction of rotation of the final driven shaft. They also serve as a means of transmitting power from the point of power to a point where the power is needed without the use of unmanageable large gears.

In simple systems with idler gears the input-to-output RPM ratio between the driver-shaft gear and the final driven-shaft gear is unaffected by the idler gears. The following example shows how to calculate the RPM ratio of a system with idler gears.

NOTE: To calculate the input-to-output RPM ratio between the driver gear and the final driven gear in a simple gear system, ignore the idler gear.

EXAMPLE

Problem

Calculate the output RPMs of the driven gear of the simple system shown in Figure 4.18.

Analysis

Apply the rule for finding the RPM of the driven gear:

$$\text{RPM of driven gear} = \frac{\text{size of driver gear} \times \text{RPM of driver gear}}{\text{size of driven gear}}$$

We know from Figure 4.18 that:

$$\text{size of driver gear} = 44 \text{ teeth}$$
$$\text{size of driven gear} = 36 \text{ teeth}$$
$$\text{RPM of driver gear} = 450$$

Solution

Step 1: Substitute the known values into the rule

$$\text{RPM of driven gear} = \frac{44 \times 450}{36}$$

Step 2: Perform the multiplication in the numerator

$$\text{RPM of driven gear} = \frac{19,800}{36}$$

Step 3: Divide to find the RPM of the driven gear

Answer

$$\text{RPM of driven gear} = 550$$

Note: The input-to-output RPM ratio of the system is 450 to 550 (450/550), or 1 to 1.22.

Solving Compound Gear and Pulley System Problems

Compound gear and pulley systems have two or more RPM ratios in the power train, all of which affect the final output RPMs. Figure 4.19 shows such a system. The first RPM ratio occurs when gear *A* drives the center shaft by driving gear *B*. The second RPM ratio results as gear *C*, which is keyed to the center shaft, drives the last gear, *D*. Since gear *B* and gear *C* are keyed together on the center shaft, the direction of rotation and the RPM of these two gears are therefore the same. Gear *A* provides the initial input RPMs, and gear *D* provides the final output RPMs.

A compound system is just a combination of two or more simple systems. Therefore, we can solve problems involving compound systems by using the same rules we used for simple systems. However, we will need to make more than one calculation.

The following example shows how to determine the final output RPMs of a compound gear system.

EXAMPLE

Problem

Determine the final output RPMs of the compound gear system shown in Figure 4.19.

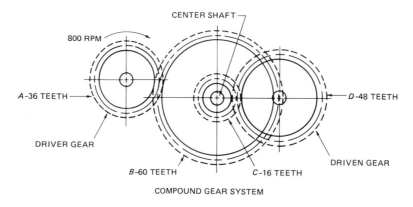

Figure 4.19

Analysis

Use the rule for finding the RPM of a driven gear:

$$\text{RPM of driven gear} = \frac{\text{size of driver gear} \times \text{RPM of driver gear}}{\text{size of driven gear}}$$

We know from Figure 4.19 that *A* and *C* are driver gears and *B* and *D* are driven gears where   RPM of gear A = 800

          size of driver gear A = 36 teeth

          size of driven gear B = 60 teeth

          size of driver gear C = 16 teeth

          size of driven gear D = 48 teeth

Since B and C are on the same shaft:

        RPM of gear B = RPM of gear C

Solution

Step 1a: Apply the rule for finding the RPM of a driven gear to find the RPM of the driven center-shaft gear (B)

$$\text{RPM of } B = \frac{\text{size of } A \times \text{RPM of } A}{\text{size of } B}$$

Step 1b: Substitute the known values into the rule

$$\text{RPM of } B = \frac{36 \times 800}{60}$$

Step 1c: Perform the multiplication in the numerator

$$\text{RPM of } B = \frac{28,800}{60}$$

Step 1d: Divide to find the RPM of driven gear B

$$\text{RPM of } B = 480$$

Note: The input-to-output RPM ratio between the initial driver gear (A) and the driven center-shaft gear (B) is 800 to 480 (800/480), or 1.67 to 1, rounded off.

Step 2a: Apply the same rule to find the RPM of the final driven gear (D)

$$\text{RPM of } D = \frac{\text{size of } C \times \text{RPM of } C}{\text{size of } D}$$

Step 2b: Substitute the known values into the rule

$$\text{RPM of } D = \frac{16 \times 480}{48}$$

Step 2c: Perform the multiplication in the numerator

$$\text{RPM of } D = \frac{7680}{48}$$

Step 2d: Divide to find the RPM of final driven gear D

Answer

$$\text{RPM of } D = 160$$

Note: The input-to-output RPM ratio between the center-shaft driver gear (C) and the final driven gear (D) is 480 to 160 (480/160), or 3 to 1.

RULE

To solve for the overall input-to-output RPM ratio of a compound system, use either of the following procedures:

1. State the *ratio of initial* input RPM to *final* output RPM as a reduced ratio
2. Multiply together all the RPM ratios affecting power transfer of the system

In the system shown in Figure 4.19, we found that when the input RPM is 800, the output RPM is 160. We can therefore state the ratio of the input RPM to the output RPM as a reduced ratio:

$$\text{overall RPM ratio} = 800 \text{ to } 160 = 5 \text{ to } 1$$

To find the overall input-to-output RPM ratio of the system, we can also multiply together all the RPM ratios affecting power transfer. We know that two RPM ratios exist: 1.67 to 1 between gears A and B and 3 to 1 between gears C and D. If we multiply these RPM ratios, we get:

$$\text{overall RPM ratio} = 1.67 \times 3 = 5.01 \text{ to } 1$$

Note that we have a slight error between the two answers because we used a rounded-off number (1.67). However, this error is not significant.

TERMS FOR REVIEW

— ratio
— gear ratio
— reducing ratios
— decimal ratio
— proportion

— cross products
— cross multiply
— percent
— percentage
— base

— taper
— TPF
— TPI
— RPM ratio
— pitch diameter

— pitch circle
— simple gear and pulley system
— inversely proportional
— intermediate or idler gears
— compound gear and pulley systems

EXERCISES

Exercise 4.1: Interpretation of Ratios

A. State the ratios between the illustrated line segments in fractional form. (Example: E to $A = 5/3$)

1. A to $B =$ _____
2. C to $E =$ _____
3. F to $G =$ _____
4. B to $E =$ _____
5. F to $H =$ _____
6. G to $A =$ _____

B. Draw two segmented lines whose lengths are in the following ratios. (Example: 2 to 3 =)

1. 1 to 2 =
2. 3 to 5 =
3. 6 to 1 =
4. 5 to 2 =
5. 7 to 3 =
6. 5 to 4 =

Exercise 4.2: Reducing Ratios

A. Reduce the following ratios to the indicated form. Give answers in three decimal places.

1. 79 to 5 = _____ to 1
2. 3.5 to 7.5 = 1 to _____
3. 6.3 to 19.8 = _____ to 1
4. 4.6 to 17.7 = 1 to _____
5. 18.5 to 92.8 = _____ to 1

B. Express the following ratios in decimal form. Round off to five decimal places where rounding off is necessary.

1. 3 to 5 = _____
2. 10:12 = _____
3. 4.5/8 = _____
4. 16.5 to 11.61 = _____
5. 8.432/7.586 = _____
6. 10.500/8.375 = _____
7. 6.875/12.0625 = _____
8. .0875/0.345 = _____

Exercise 4.3: Proportions

A. Determine whether or not each of the following is a proportional statement. Circle the ones that are proportional statements.

1. 1/4 = 4/16
2. 1/2 = 5/10
3. 3/5 = 12/25
4. 5/8 = 15/32
5. 7/8 = 28/36
6. 9/16 = 32/64
7. 5/32 = 12/64
8. 9/16 = 18/32
9. 3.5/11.38 = 10.5/32.14

B. Solve for the term that makes the following proportions true. Round off to three decimal places if necessary.

1. _____ /16 = 48/64

2. 3/ _____ = 12/32

3. 7/8 = 56/ _____

4. 3/4 = _____ /22

5. 19.3/2 = 8.5/ _____

6. 11.5/ _____ = 18/7.2

7. 0.875/1.5 = 3.25/ _____

8. _____ /0.375 = 18/0.375

9. 1.35/17.5 = 5.2/ _____

10. 1/17.3 = 0.75/_____

Exercise 4.4: Percents

A. Calculate the percent, percentage, or base in the following problems.

1. What is 50% of $96?   1. _____

2. What is 12.5% of $382?   2. _____

3. 30 is what percent of 150?   3. _____

4. $16.50 is 6.25% of what amount?   4. _____

5. 195 is 15% of what amount?   5. _____

6. What percent of 68 is 17?   6. _____

7. What is 16% of 58?   7. _____

8. $8.82 is 90% of what amount?   8. _____

9. What percent of 300 is 360?   9. _____

10. What is 2% of $180?   10. _____

11. 7.35 is 6.5% of what amount?   11. _____

12. What is 100% of $17.20?   12. _____

13. $9.75 is what percent of $5.50?   13. _____

14. 725 is 250% of what amount?   14. _____

15. $0.75 is what percent of $3.75?   15. _____

B. Solve the following word problems.

1. On an estimate, 132 hours were given as required time to produce a control device. The estimate stated that 35% of the production time would be required for milling and 8% of the production time would be required for polishing. (a) How many hours should be scheduled for milling? (b) How many hours should be scheduled for polishing?

1a. _____

1b. _____

2. In a shop employing six people, a time study revealed that of the 240 hours of a normal week, (a) 50 hours were spent on milling machines, (b) 85 hours were spent on lathes, (c) 25 hours were spent in the grinding room, (d) 45 hours were spent on other machines, and (e) 35 hours were spent on layout and inspection. What percent of the total time was spent in each of the five areas?

2a. _____

2b. _____

2c. _____

2d. _____

2e. _____

3. Common brass is made up of 70% copper and 30% zinc. How many pounds of each are required to make 400 pounds of this common brass?

3. _____

4. A job requires 1.2 hours for grinding during production, which is 30% of the total production time required. What is the total time required to do the job?

4. _____

5. A shop uses an average of $42,000 of raw material yearly, which is 14% of its total annual operating expense. What is the total operating expense?

5. _____

6. You make $1,416 monthly, and $496 is taken out for taxes and other deductions. What percent of your wage is deducted?

6. _____

7. A set of micrometers listed at $395 is on sale at a 12% discount. What is the sale price?

7. _____

8. Manganese steel contains up to 12% manganese. Manganese is added to steel to make it ductile. How many pounds of manganese are contained in 5,000 pounds of manganese steel of a 12% manganese content?

8. _____

9. Vanadium steel contains up to 0.25% vanadium. Vanadium is added to steel to increase its tensile strength. How many pounds of vanadium are contained in 5,000 pounds of vanadium steel of 0.25% vanadium content?

9. _____

Exercise 4.5: Tapers

A. Find the missing measurements in the following diagrams.

1. taper = _____

2. taper = _____

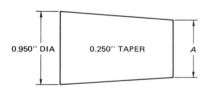

3. A = _____

4. A = _____

5. A = _____

6. A = _____

Exercise 4.6: TPF and TPI Specifications

A. Solve the following problems. Give answers in five decimal places.

1. The specified TPF for a number 4 Brown & Sharpe taper shank is 0.50240″. What is the TPI?

1. _____

2. A twist drill shank having a Morse 2 taper has a TPF of 0.59941″. If the length is 3-1/8″, what is the actual taper of the shank?

2. _____

3. The inside taper for a sleeve has a number 3 Morse taper having a TPI of 0.05019″. What is the diameter of the small end (*A*)?

3. _____

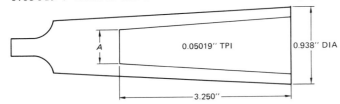

4. A piece with a number 5 Jarno taper that has a TPF of 0.600″ has a large-end diameter of 0.625″. How far from the large end is the diameter of the piece 0.615″ (what is the measurement of *A*)?

4. _____

5. A piece 5.125″ long has a TPF of 1.250″. The large-end diameter is 2.375″. What is the small-end diameter (*A*)?

5. _____

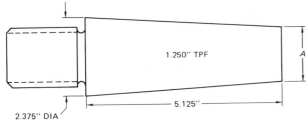

B. Solve the following taper problems.

1. Find the TPI and TPF.

1a. TPI = _____

1b. TPF = _____

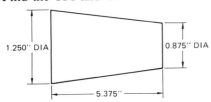

2. Find the TPI and length *A*.

2a. TPI = _____

2b. *A* = _____

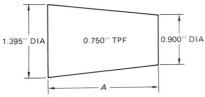

3. Find length *A* of the taper.

3. *A* = _____

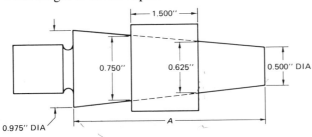

4. Find the small-end diameter (*A*).

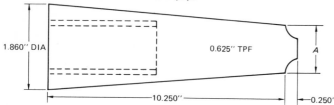

4. *A* = _____

5. Find the length (*A*).

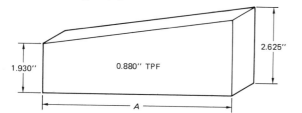

5. *A* = _____

6. Find lengths *A* and *B*.

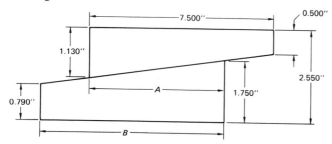

6a. *A* = _____

6b. *B* = _____

Exercise 4.7: Simple Gear and Pulley Systems

A. Determine the size ratios for the following simple systems. Reduce all ratios to lowest terms. Round off to two decimal places if necessary.

1. For the gears *A*, *B*, *C*, and *D*, state the following ratios.

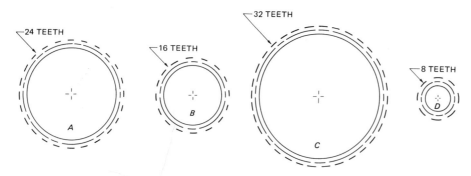

a. *A* to *B* = _____   **b.** *B* to *C* = _____   **c.** *D* to *A* = _____

d. *B* to *D* = _____   **e.** *A* to *C* = _____   **f.** *B* to *A* = _____

g. *D* to *C* = _____   **h.** *A* to *D* = _____

2. Gears *A*, *B*, *C*, *D*, *E*, and *F* have the following pitch diameters:

$A = 1.25''$ $C = 2.5''$ $E = 7.5''$

$B = 4''$ $D = 8''$ $F = 10''$

State the following ratios.

a.   *A* to *C* = _____   b.   *A* to *B* = _____   c.   *E* to *A* = _____

d.   *C* to *F* = _____   e.   *B* to *E* = _____   f.   *D* to *B* = _____

g.   *E* to *C* = _____   h.   *F* to *E* = _____

3. Pulleys *A*, *B*, *C*, *D*, *E*, and *F* have the following outside diameters:

$A = 2''$ $C = 7''$ $E = 8''$

$B = 3.5''$ $D = 10.5''$ $F = 15''$

State which two pulleys give the following ratios.

a.   3 to 1 _____   b.   2.14 to 1 _____   c.   1 to 2.29 _____

d.   1 to 7.5 _____   e.   1.88 to 1 _____   f.   2 to 1 _____

Exercise 4.8: Size and RPM Ratios

A. State the size ratio and RPM ratios for the gears and pulleys of the following simple systems. Express all ratios from driver to driven and in lowest terms. Round off to two decimal places if necessary.

1.

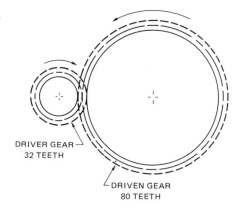

DRIVER GEAR
32 TEETH

DRIVEN GEAR
80 TEETH

1a.   teeth ratio = _____

1b.   RPM ratio = _____

2.

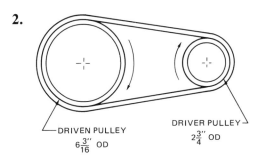

DRIVEN PULLEY
$6\frac{3}{16}''$ OD

DRIVER PULLEY
$2\frac{3}{4}''$ OD

2a.   OD ratio = _____

2b.   RPM ratio = _____

3.

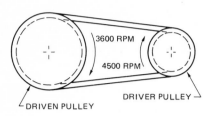

DRIVEN PULLEY   DRIVER PULLEY

3a. OD ratio _____

3b. RPM ratio _____

4.

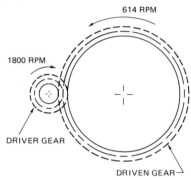

614 RPM
1800 RPM
DRIVER GEAR
DRIVEN GEAR

4a. P. Dia. ratio _____

4b. RPM ratio _____

5.

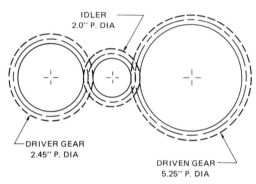

IDLER 2.0" P. DIA
DRIVER GEAR 2.45" P. DIA
DRIVEN GEAR 5.25" P. DIA

5a. P. Dia. ratio _____

5b. RPM ratio _____

6.

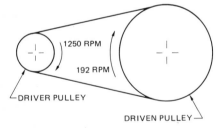

1250 RPM
192 RPM
DRIVER PULLEY
DRIVEN PULLEY

6a. OD ratio _____

6b. RPM ratio _____

B. Solve the following shop-related problems.

1. A motor running at 1250 RPM is fitted with a 4.5″ V-pulley to run a fan having an 8.25″ pulley. To the nearest RPM, how fast will the fan rotate?

1. _____

2. Complete the following table and give the answers to the nearest whole number.

Driver Gear		Driven Gear	
Pitch Dia.	RPM	Pitch Dia.	RPM
5″	600		150
	72	4″	96
1.25″	1425	3.5″	
1.75″		2.85″	150

3. A large gear with 180 teeth turning at 600 RPM powers a small gear turning at 900 RPM. How many teeth must the small gear have?

4. A system requiring a 3.5 to 1 RPM ratio has a driver gear with a 2.35 pitch diameter. What size gear should be meshed with it?

5. In the following system, the driver gear has 32 teeth and turns at 1500 RPM in a clockwise direction. It powers an idler gear having 20 teeth, which in turn powers the driven gear having 46 teeth.

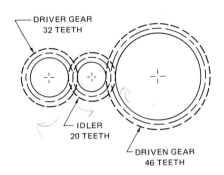

DRIVER GEAR
32 TEETH

IDLER
20 TEETH

DRIVEN GEAR
46 TEETH

a. What is the RPM of the driven gear?

b. What is the RPM ratio of this system (2 decimal places)?

c. What is the direction of rotation of the driven gear?

The idler is removed from the system.

d. What is the RPM of the driven gear?

e. What is the RPM ratio of the system?

f. What is the direction of rotation of the driven gear?

6. The following diagram shows a simple system.

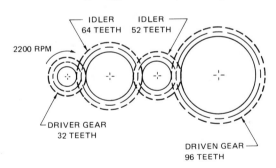

IDLER
64 TEETH

IDLER
52 TEETH

2200 RPM

DRIVER GEAR
32 TEETH

DRIVEN GEAR
96 TEETH

a. What is the RPM of the driven gear?

b. What is its direction of rotation?

c. What is the RPM of the idler having 52 teeth?

d. If the speed of the driven gear is to be doubled, how fast should the driver turn?

7. On a pulley system requiring a 4.5 to 1 RPM reduction, how large should the driven pulley be if the driving pulley is 2.25"?

8. On a gear system requiring a 1 to 4.5 RPM increase, how large should the driven gear be if the driving gear has a 6" P. Dia.?

3. _____

4. _____

5a. _____
5b. _____
5c. _____
5d. _____
5e. _____
5f. _____

6a. _____
6b. _____
6c. _____
6d. _____

7. _____

8. _____

9. On a system requiring an RPM increase, power on the driving shaft is 1500 RPM. The desired RPM on the driven shaft is 2400 RPM. A selection of gears is available with the following number of teeth: 16, 18, 20, 24, 32, 40, 44, 50, 54, 60, 64, 72, 80, and 96. Give four possible combinations that would give the desired ratio.

9a. _____

9b. _____

9c. _____

9d. _____

10. A common pulley system used to vary RPM's on shop equipment is shown below. State the four different RPM ratios of this system.

DRIVER GEAR   6.5″ | 8″ | 10″ | 12″

DRIVEN GEAR   11″ | 8″ | 6″ | 5″

10a. _____

10b. _____

10c. _____

10d. _____

Exercise 4.9: Compound Gear and Pulley Systems

A. For the following compound systems, state the gear and pulley RPM and the number of teeth on gears to the nearest whole number unless specified differently. State the pitch diameters of gears, the outside diameters of pulleys, and all ratios in decimals rounded off to two places.

1. The following diagram shows a compound system.

1a. _____

1b. _____

1c. _____

1d. _____

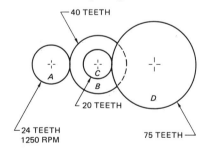

40 TEETH

A

C

B

D

24 TEETH
1250 RPM

20 TEETH

75 TEETH

a. What is the RPM of gear *D?*

b. What is the RPM ratio between gears *A* and *B?*

c. What is the RPM ratio between gears *C* and *D?*

d. What is the RPM ratio of the system?

2. Refer to the diagram shown with problem 1. The RPM of gear *A* is 1500. (a) What is the RPM of gear *D*? (b) What is the RPM ratio of the system?

2a. _____

2b. _____

3. The following diagram shows a compound pulley system.

3a. _____

3b. _____

3c. _____

3d. _____

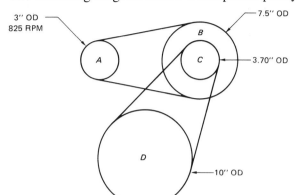

3″ OD
825 RPM

7.5″ OD

B

C

3.70″ OD

A

D

10″ OD

a. What is the RPM of pulley *D*?

b. What is the RPM ratio between pulleys *A* and *B*?

c. What is the RPM ratio between pulleys *C* and *D*?

d. What is the RPM ratio of the system?

4. Refer to the diagram shown with problem 3. Pulley *C* is replaced with a 4″ OD pulley. (a) What is the RPM of pulley *D*? (b) What is the RPM ratio between pulleys *A* and *B*? (c) What is the RPM ratio between pulleys *C* and *D*? (d) What is the RPM ratio of the system?

4a. _____

4b. _____

4c. _____

4d. _____

5. The diagram below illustrates a drive train.

5a. _____

5b. _____

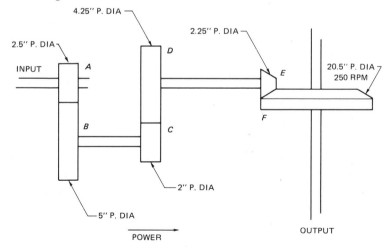

4.25″ P. DIA

2.25″ P. DIA

2.5″ P. DIA

INPUT

A

D

E

20.5″ P. DIA
250 RPM

B

C

F

2″ P. DIA

5″ P. DIA

POWER

OUTPUT

a. What is the RPM of gear *A*?

b. What is the RPM ratio of the system?

6. The following diagram shows a drive train on a lathe for supplying power to the lead screw for cutting a thread.

6a. _____

6b. _____

6c. _____

24 TEETH

24 TEETH
32 TEETH
48 TEETH

54 TEETH
18 TEETH
72 TEETH

18 TEETH

80 TEETH

LEAD SCREW

a. What is the RPM of the gear with 80 teeth on the lead screw if the gear with 24 teeth on the headstock turns at 80 RPM?

b. What is the RPM ratio of this system?

c. How many teeth does the idler gear have?

7. The following diagram shows a compound system. Gear *A* rotates at 720 RPM in a clockwise direction.

7a. _____

7b. _____

7c. _____

7d. _____

7e. _____

7f. _____

7g. _____

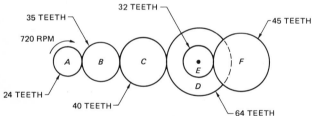
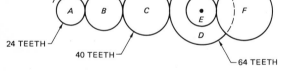

35 TEETH

32 TEETH

45 TEETH

720 RPM

A   B   C   E   F
D

24 TEETH

40 TEETH

64 TEETH

a. What is the RPM of gear *F*?

b. What is the direction of rotation of gear *F*?

c. What is the RPM ratio of the system?

Gear *B* is removed from the system.

d. What is the RPM ratio of the system?

e. What is the direction of rotation of gear *F*?

Gears *B* and *C* are removed from the system.

f. What is the RPM ratio of the system?

g. What is the direction of rotation of gear *F*?

8. The following diagram shows a compound system. The RPM ratio between pulleys *A* and *B* is 3.5 to 1. The RPM ratio between pulleys *C* and *D* is 1 to 2.

POWER

    a. What is the RPM ratio of the system?

    b. If pulley *A* rotates at 250 RPM, at what RPM does pulley *D* rotate?

    c. If pulley *A* is 2.5″ and pulley *C* is 6.5″, what size is pulley *B*?

    d. What size is pulley *D*?

8a. _____

8b. _____

8c. _____

8d. _____

CHAPTER 5

FORMULA CALCULATIONS

Learning Objectives

After studying this chapter, you should be able to:
— State the operations indicated by a formula
— Calculate the squares of numbers
— Calculate the square roots of numbers
— State the correct sequence of operations specified by a formula
— State three steps to follow when solving problems with formulas
— Apply cutting speeds and feeds formulas to solve problems
— Apply thread formulas to solve problems
— Apply gear formulas to solve problems

Machinists often need to make simple arithmetic calculations. These calculations involve the addition, subtraction, multiplication, or division of known measurements in order to find unknown measurements.

For example, consider the problem of determining the length of the taper on the arbor shown in Figure 5.1. In this case, we need only to subtract 1.250″ and 1.500″ from 8.375″ to find the unknown measurement. This calculation is simple arithmetic and is the obvious calculation for solving the problem. The relationship between the unknown measurement (length of the taper) and the known measurements (1.250″, 1.500″, and 8.375″) is easy to recognize.

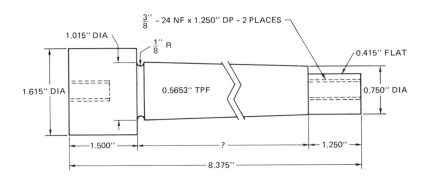

Figure 5.1

A machinist is also often required to make formula calculations. A *formula* is a statement that expresses the relationship between one value and one or more other values. *Formula calculations* are calculations made with formulas. We have used formulas in earlier chapters to find, for example, the size and RPM ratios of gears and pulleys.

INTERPRETATION OF FORMULAS

A formula is like a recipe. A recipe tells you what ingredients are needed, the procedure for combining those ingredients, and the order in which they are to be combined. A formula tells you the same thing. It tells you what values are needed (by using symbols), what computations are necessary to combine those values (by using operation signs), and in what order to combine them (by using grouping signs).

For example, to find the depth of cut necessary to make the 0.415″ flat of the arbor illustrated in Figure 5.1, we need to make a formula calculation. The flat is further illustrated in Figure 5.2.

The formula used to calculate the depth of cut is:

$$H = \frac{1}{2}\left(D - \sqrt{D^2 - W^2}\right)$$

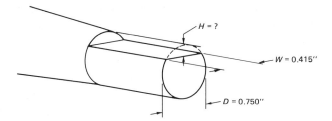

Figure 5.2

The formula tells us what ingredients (values) are needed to calculate H, the depth of cut, where D is the diameter of the round shaft, and W is the width of the flat. H is not an ingredient. It is the desired product, just as the desired product of a recipe is, for example, a pie. From Figure 5.2, we know that:

$$D = 0.750''$$
$$W = 0.415''$$

We need to find the value of H, the depth of cut. Therefore, D and W are the known values in the formula, and H is the unknown value.

> **NOTE:** We can find only one unknown value in a formula in one set of calculations. The other value or values must be stated in the figure or problem, or we must make other calculations to find one of the unknown values.

When we substitute the values given in Figure 5.2, the formula becomes:

$$H = \frac{1}{2} \left(0.750 - \sqrt{0.750^2 - 0.415^2} \right)$$

By performing the calculations indicated, we can determine the depth of cut needed to make the flat. The procedures for these calculations are explained later in the chapter.

An understanding of algebra is helpful when working with formulas. However, a machinist does not need a complete knowledge of algebra. Machinists do not need to develop the formulas they use. The formulas already exist. But we do need to be able to recognize the correct formula to use and know how to use it. At first, using formulas may seem to be difficult, but it is not. Again, formulas are like recipes, and just as we follow a soup recipe to make soup or a hot-dish recipe to make a hot dish, we can use circle formulas to work circle problems (finding the depth of cut is a circle problem), triangle formulas to work triangle problems, taper formulas to work taper problems, and so on. We will learn how to solve triangle and circle problems in later chapters.

In general, formula calculations are more involved than simple arithmetic calculations. Solving a formula usually requires a series (more than one) of computations in a sequential (step-by-step) manner. Moreover, the required sequence of calculations is not obvious, as it is in simple arithmetic calculations. Again, formula calculations may at first seem to be difficult, but they are not. In this respect, too, formulas are like recipes. When we make soup, we may not know why this should be cooked first, then that added, and the mixture cooked again

—but if we follow instructions, we get the desired soup. Similarly, formulas will give us the desired results—if we follow instructions. This chapter covers what machinists need to know about formulas in order to follow their instructions properly.

FORMULA NOTATIONS

Remember, a formula tells us what values are needed (by using symbols) and the computation(s) necessary to combine those values (by indicating operations). *Symbols* are letters used to represent quantities. *Operations* are the computations we make to combine the quantities. Addition, subtraction, multiplication, and division are the four fundamental operations.

Symbols

Formulas are actually statements. They are statements that are expressed by the use of symbols. These symbols are also referred to as *variables* because the values assigned to them are variable to every problem situation for which the formula is used. However, before we can assign values to the symbols of a formula, we must know what each symbol represents. For example, in Chapter 4 we learned that the length of a tapered piece can be found by dividing the taper of the piece by its taper per inch (TPI). This statement, expressed as a formula using symbols, becomes:

$$L = T \div \text{TPI} \quad \text{or} \quad L = \frac{T}{\text{TPI}}$$

where
$$L = \text{length of the tapered piece}$$
$$T = \text{taper of the tapered piece}$$
$$\text{TPI} = \text{taper per inch of the tapered piece}$$

When we know what the symbols of this formula represent, we can assign values to them. The following example shows how to calculate the length of the tapered part of a plug.

EXAMPLE

Problem

Find the length (L) of the taper (T) of the plug shown in Figure 5.3, where D is the large-end diameter, d is the small-end diameter, and the taper (T) is $D - d$.

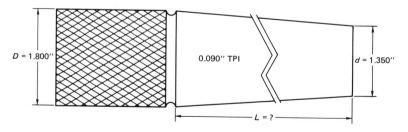

Figure 5.3

Analysis

Use the formula

$$L = \frac{T}{\text{TPI}}$$

where
L = length
$T = D - d$ (large-end diameter minus small-end diameter)
TPI = 0.090″

Solution

Step 1:   Follow the rule for finding the taper

$$T = D - d$$
$$= 1.800 - 1.350$$
$$= 0.450″$$

Step 2:   Substitute the known values into the formula

$$L = \frac{0.450}{0.090}$$

Step 3:   Divide to find L

Answer

$$L = 5″$$

Operation Notations

To understand formulas as statements, we must properly interpret the operations indicated in the formulas.

Addition and Subtraction

In formulas, the operations of addition and subtraction are indicated by the conventional signs + (plus) and − (minus). Thus, just as we indicate when to add and subtract whole numbers—such as 8 + 9 − 13—we indicate when to add and subtract values of formulas.

RULES

To indicate that the values of a *and* b *in a formula are to be added, write:*

$a + b$

To indicate that the value of c *is to be subtracted from the value of* d, *write:*

$$d - c$$

The following example shows how the operation notation for addition is used in solving a formula.

EXAMPLE

Problem

Find the measurement (M) of the external dovetail shown in Figure 5.4, where C is the center-to-center distance of two 0.250″ cylindrical plugs and D is the diameter of the cylindrical plugs.

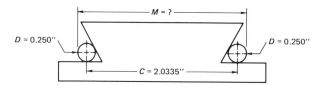

Figure 5.4

Analysis

Use the formula

$$M = C + D$$

where $C = 2.0335″$
          $D = 0.250″$

Solution

Step 1: Substitute the known values into the formula

$$M = 2.0335 + 0.250$$

Step 2: Add to find M

Answer

$$M = 2.2835″$$

Multiplication and Division

In formulas, the operations of multiplication and division are not indicated by the conventional signs ($\times$ and $\div$). Instead, they are indicated by the way the symbols are placed in relation to each other.

RULES

To indicate that the values of the symbols a *and* b *(or a symbol and a number) in a formula are to be multiplied, write the symbols and numbers next to each other or enclose them in parentheses:*

$5a$ is understood to mean $5 \times a$

$5ab$ is understood to mean $5 \times a \times b$

$5(a + b)$ is understood to mean $5 \times$ the sum of a and b

To indicate that the values of the symbols a *and* b *(or a symbol and a number) are to be divided, write them in fractional form to show that the value of the top (or first) symbol is to be divided by the value of the second (or bottom) symbol:*

$\dfrac{a}{5}$ (or $a/5$) is understood to mean $a \div 5$

$\dfrac{a}{b}$ (or a/b) is understood to mean $a \div b$

$\dfrac{5}{ab}$ (or $5/ab$) is understood to mean $5 \div (a \times b)$

The following example shows how the operation notations for multiplication and division are used in solving a formula. Note that the definitions and rules for working with spur gear formulas are discussed in the next section of this chapter.

EXAMPLE

Problem

Find the circular pitch (P_C) of the spur gear shown in Figure 5.5, where D is the pitch diameter and N is the number of teeth.

Analysis

Use the formula:

$$P_C = \frac{3.1416(D)}{N}$$

where $D = 2.125''$
$\quad N = 17$ teeth

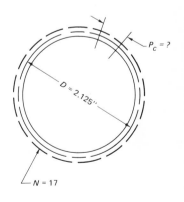

Solution

Step 1: Substitute the known values into the formula

$$P_C = \frac{3.1416(2.125)}{17}$$

Figure 5.5

Step 2:   Perform the multiplication operation indicated by the parentheses

$$P_C = \frac{6.6759}{17}$$

Step 3:   Divide to solve the formula

Answer

$$P_C = 0.393''$$

NOTE: The number 3.1416 was given as part of the formula in the problem above. A formula often includes a number as well as symbols. The number may represent engineering requirements or mathematical properties to which the formula applies. When we find such a number, we treat it as we treat the other known values, according to the instructions of the formula. Here, 3.1416 is the accepted value of π (the Greek letter pi), a constant that is mathematically related to a circle.

Squares and Square Roots

Square and square root operations are opposite operations, just as addition and subtraction are opposite operations. Generally, machinists perform square root operations only when they are required in formulas.

The *square* of a number is the product of that number multiplied by itself:

The square of 5 is 25 (5 $\times$ 5 = 25)

The square of 9 is 81 (9 $\times$ 9 = 81)

The *square root* of a number is a number that, when multiplied by itself, has the original number as the product:

The square root of 25 is 5 (5 $\times$ 5 = 25)

The square root of 64 is 8 (8 $\times$ 8 = 64)

RULES

To indicate that a number is to be squared, indicate the operation in the following manner:

5^2 means to square the value of 5: $5^2 = 25$

9^2 means to square the value of 9: $9^2 = 81$

To indicate that the square root of a number is to be found, indicate the operation by using the radical sign ($\sqrt{}$):

$\sqrt{25}$ means to find the square root of 25: 25 = 5

$\sqrt{64}$ means to find the square root of 64: 64 = 8

NOTE: In formulas, these operations are indicated in the same manner:

a^2 means to square the value of a: $a^2 = a \times a$

b^2 means to square the value of b: $b^2 = b \times b$

$\sqrt{a}$ means to find the square root of the value of a

$\sqrt{b}$ means to find the square root of the value of b

Finding the square roots of numbers like 25 and 64 is simple because they are whole numbers and they are *perfect squares* (the square roots of perfect squares are also whole numbers). Finding the square roots of numbers like 23 and 9.875 by a longhand method is not so simple because their square roots are continuous decimals:

$$\sqrt{23} = 4.795831523 \ldots$$
$$\sqrt{9.875} = 3.142451272 \ldots$$

An electronic calculator should be used to calculate square roots. The square-root key on the calculator generally has a radical sign ($\sqrt{}$) printed on it. Always consult the handbook supplied with a calculator to ensure correct use of its square-root key.

The following examples show how to use operation notations for square and square root to find unknown values in formulas.

EXAMPLE 1

Problem

Find the unknown measurement (a) of the V-slot inspection shown in Figure 5.6, where b is the radius of the cylindrical plug.

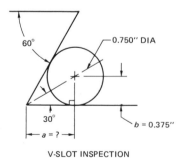

V-SLOT INSPECTION

Figure 5.6

Analysis

Use the formula

$$a = b\sqrt{3}$$

where $b = 0.375''$

Solution

Step 1:   Substitute the known value into the formula

$$a = 0.375\sqrt{3}$$

Step 2:   Substitute the value of the square root of 3

$$a = 0.375 \times 1.732$$

Note: $1.732 = \sqrt{3}$, rounded off.

Step 3:   Multiply to find a

Answer

$$a = 0.650''$$

EXAMPLE 2

Problem

Find the unknown measurement in the center-to-center inspection shown in Figure 5.7, where a is the vertical dimension and b is the horizontal dimension.

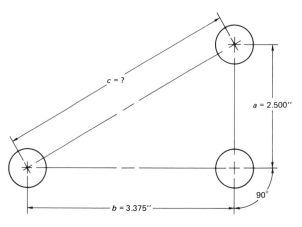

CENTER-TO-CENTER INSPECTION

Figure 5.7

Analysis

Use the formula

$$c = \sqrt{a^2 + b^2}$$

where $a = 2.500''$
$b = 3.375''$

Solution

Step 1:   Substitute the known values into the formula

$$c = \sqrt{2.500^2 + 3.375^2}$$

Step 2:   Perform the operations within the radical sign

$$c = \sqrt{11.391 + 625}$$
$$= \sqrt{17.641}$$

Step 3:   Find the square root of 17.641

Answer

$$c = 4.200''$$

Sequence of Operations

Knowing how to recognize the operations indicated by formulas is not enough. To solve formulas, we must perform the indicated operations in the proper sequence (order). If the instructions given in a formula are not followed, the correct answer will not be obtained. The instructions given by formulas for the order of performing operations are governed by general rules.

RULES

To perform operations in formulas in the proper sequence, first carry out all operations contained within a grouping sign, such as parentheses (   ) *and* brackets [   ]. *This procedure is called* clearing the parentheses:

$a(3 + 7)$ means that the sum of $3 + 7$ must be found before multiplying by a

$3[a + b]$ means that the sum of $a + b$ must be found before multiplying by 3

To perform operations in formulas in the proper sequence, perform all operations contained within square-root (radical) signs before the square root is calculated:

$\sqrt{6 - b}$ means that the result of $6 - b$ must be found before the square root is calculated.

$\sqrt{x + 2 - 4}$ means that the result of the addition and subtraction indicated must be found before the square root is calculated.

To perform operations in formulas in the proper sequence, perform square and square-root operations before the operation of multiplication:

$b\sqrt{3}$ indicates that the square root of 3 must be found before multiplying by b

πr^2 indicates that the value of r^2 must be found before multiplying by the value of π

To perform operations in formulas in the proper sequence, calculate all operations within numerators and denominators independently of each other before division.

$\dfrac{b\sqrt{3}}{2+a}$ indicates that (1) the product of $b \times \sqrt{3}$ is to be found in the numerator, (2) the sum of $2 + a$ is to be found in the denominator, and (3) the product $b \times \sqrt{3}$ of the numerator is to be divided by the sum $2 + a$ of the denominator.

The following examples show how the rules for the proper sequence of operations are followed in solving formula problems.

EXAMPLE 1

Problem

Solve the formula:

$$w = 2\sqrt{h(2r - h)}$$

where $h = 0.375$
               $r = 0.750$

Analysis

After substituting the known values into the formula, perform the indicated operations according to the rules for sequence of operations.

Solution

Step 1:   Substitute the known values for the symbols h and r:

$$w = 2\sqrt{0.375 \times (2 \times 0.750 - 0.375)}$$

Step 2:   Perform the operations under the radical rule
Step 2a: First perform the indicated multiplication

$$w = 2\sqrt{0.375 \times (1.500 - 0.375)}$$

Step 2b: Perform the subtraction indicated to clear the parentheses

$$w = 2\sqrt{0.375 \times 1.125}$$

Step 2c: Perform the remaining multiplication operation under the radical rule

$$w = 2\sqrt{0.422}$$

Step 3: Substitute the value of the square root of 0.422

$$w = 2 \times 0.650$$

Step 4: Multiply to solve the formula

Answer

$$w = 1.300$$

EXAMPLE 2

Problem

Solve the formula:

$$A = \pi r^2$$

where $r = 2.5$

Analysis

After substituting the known values into the formula, perform the square operation before multiplying.

Solution

Step 1: Substitute the known values into the formula (remember that $\pi = 3.1416$)

$$A = 3.1416(2.5)^2$$

Step 2: Square 2.5 and place the result in the formula

$$A = 3.1416(6.25)$$

Step 3: Multiply to solve the formula

Answer

$$A = 19.635$$

EXAMPLE 3

Problem

Solve the formula:

$$D = \frac{2bh}{b + 2c}$$

where
$$b = 1.75$$
$$h = 0.85$$
$$c = 0.375$$

Analysis

After substituting the known values into the formula, carry out the operations indicated in the numerator and the denominator (follow the rules for sequence of operations) before dividing.

Solution

Step 1: Substitute the known values into the formula:

$$D = \frac{2 \times 1.75 \times 0.85}{1.75 + (2 \times 0.375)}$$

Step 2: Carry out the multiplication indicated in the numerator:

$$D = \frac{2.975}{1.75 + (2 \times 0.375)}$$

Step 3: Perform the operations indicated in the denominator
Step 3a: Multiply to clear the parentheses

$$D = \frac{2.975}{1.75 + 0.75}$$

Step 3b: Perform the indicated addition

$$D = \frac{2.975}{2.5}$$

Step 4: Divide to solve for D

Answer

$$D = 1.19$$

The two examples that follow further illustrate the proper sequence for performing the specified operations of formulas.

We are given the formula:

$$e = \frac{a^2 + b^2 - c^2}{2b}$$

where $a = 3.5$
$b = 7.5$
$c = 5.5$

We perform the operations used to solve this formula in the following sequence.

1. Substitute the known values into the formula:

$$e = \frac{3.5^2 + 7.5^2 - 5.5^2}{2 \times 7.5}$$

2. Perform the operations indicated in the numerator by first squaring 3.5, 7.5, and 5.5:

$$e = \frac{12.25 + 56.25 - 30.25}{2 \times 7.5}$$

Then perform the addition and subtraction operations in the numerator:

$$e = \frac{38.25}{2 \times 7.5}$$

3. Perform the multiplication indicated in the denominator:

$$e = \frac{38.25}{15}$$

4. Divide to find e:

$$e = 2.55$$

We are given the formula:

$$h = r - \sqrt{r^2 - (\tfrac{1}{2}w)^2}$$

where $r = 4.5$
$w = 2.5$

We perform the operations used to solve this formula in the following sequence.

1. Substitute the known values into the formula:

$$h = 4.5 - \sqrt{4.5^2 - (\tfrac{1}{2} \times 2.5)^2}$$

2. Perform the operations indicated within the radical by first multiplying 1/2 by 2.5:

$$h = 4.5 - \sqrt{4.5^2 - 1.25^2}$$

Square 4.5 and 1.25:

$$h = 4.5 - \sqrt{20.25 - 1.5625}$$

Complete the operations within the radical by subtracting 1.5625 from 20.25:

$$h = 4.5 - \sqrt{18.6875}$$

3. Substitute the value of the square root of 18.6875:

$$h = 4.5 - 4.323$$

4. Subtract to find h:

$$h = 0.177$$

PROBLEM SOLVING

Formulas are designed to solve specific types of problems. When we properly apply the right formula to a problem, we find the desired unknown value. However, many times the choice of the formula necessary for the solution of a problem is not obvious. We must be able to analyze a problem thoroughly in order to choose the correct formula. We need to inspect the problem in a step-by-step manner until we recognize a formula situation. We can follow three steps to analyze a problem.

Step 1: Inspect the problem to find out how the desired unknown value is related to the known values in the problem.

Step 2: Identify the values that are given directly and indirectly in the problem. Values that are given directly are those that are stated (or shown in a diagram or print). Values that are given indirectly are those that exist because of the nature of the problem. For example, some measurements can be found easily by adding or subtracting stated values. Others, which we will study in the following chapters, are implied by geometric relationships.

Step 3: Check for familiar ways of applying formulas. In some cases, two or more formula calculations are needed to obtain a desired value.

Cutting speeds and feeds, threads, and gears are three areas of the machine shop that require formula calculations. In the following sections, we apply formula-solving procedures to problems in these areas. In later chapters, we will use these procedures to solve geometric relationships that are important to the machine shop.

Cutting Speeds and Feeds

A machinist's job is basically to remove metal from stock material, thereby shaping the stock to a desired form. We can remove metal in many different ways, and our objective is to remove it as fast as possible. However, the rate at which metal can be removed to shape a part depends on many factors:

1. Type of metal to be worked (brass, stainless steel, tool steel, and so on)
2. Material of tool (tool, steel, carbide, ceramic, and so on)
3. Type of cut being taken (roughing or finishing)
4. Feed rates at which the machine is set (inches per revolution)
5. Cutting speed or FPM (the distance in feet that a point on the outer surface of rotating tools or work travels in one minute)

In most cases, the machinist has no control over the type of metal to be used in making a part. The metal is generally specified on the print. We do, however, often have a choice as to the type of tool to use. When roughing, our objective is to remove as much metal as we can as quickly as we can. When finishing, our concern is to maintain tolerances.

The last two factors on the list depend on the first two factors. Since most of the machines used in the machine shop use rotating power to remove metal, we can control the *cutting speed* and the *feed* by controlling the RPM of the machines.

RULES

To express the relationship between cutting speed and RPM, use the formula:

$$CS = \frac{3.14(D)(RPM)}{12}$$

where
- CS = cutting speed rate in feet per minute (FPM)
- D = diameter in inches of the rotating cutting tool or of the round workpiece
- RPM = revolutions per minute, the spindle speed of the machines

Note that in milling and drilling, the endmills and twist drills rotate. In lathe work, the work material rotates.

To express the relationship between feed and RPM, use the formula:

$$F = \frac{L}{T(RPM)}$$

where
- F = feed rate in inches per revolution
- L = length of cut in inches
- T = time of cut in minutes

For example, suppose that a 1.25"-diameter piece of cast iron is being turned in a lathe at 200 RPM. A 5"-long cut is made in 2.5 minutes. Thus, we know that:

$$D = 1.25''$$
$$\text{RPM} = 200$$
$$L = 5''$$
$$T = 2.5 \text{ minutes}$$

To find the cutting speed, we use the formula:

$$CS = \frac{3.14(D)(\text{RPM})}{12}$$

First, we substitute the known values into the formula:

$$CS = \frac{(3.14)(1.25)(200)}{12}$$

Next, we perform the multiplication in the numerator:

$$CS = \frac{785}{12}$$

Finally, we divide to find the cutting speed:

$$CS = 65.4 \text{ FPM}$$

To find the feed rate, we use the formula:

$$F = \frac{L}{T(\text{RPM})}$$

We substitute the known values into the formula:

$$F = \frac{5}{2.5(200)}$$

We perform the multiplication in the denominator:

$$F = \frac{5}{500}$$

We divide to find the feed rate:

$$F = 0.010''/\text{revolution}$$

The most common shop problem involving these relationships is the need to determine *machine speed* (RPM) in terms of proper cutting speed and feed. Proper cutting speeds for metals can be obtained from *Machinery's Handbook*. The cutting speeds are based on the type of cutting tool, specified rate of feed, and depth of cut. In our example, if the cast iron is ASTM class 45, and a 0.125″ depth of cut with a HSS cutting tool is made, then a rate of feed of 0.010″/revolution at a cutting speed of 65.4 RPM would be proper machine settings.

RULE

To determine the machine speed (RPM) in terms of proper cutting speed, use the formula:

$$RPM = \frac{12\,(CS)}{3.14(D)}$$

For example, suppose we have a 4.75″-diameter piece of stainless steel (Ferritic type 405). We need to turn it down to 4.375″ and to drill 4 holes, 0.75″ each, 2″ on centers. For lathe work, this metal requires a cutting speed of 300 FPM when a carbide cutter is used; the feed rate is 0.012″ per revolution, and the depth of cut is 0.125″.

To determine the spindle speed of the lathe, we use the formula:

$$RPM = \frac{12\,(CS)}{3.14(D)}$$

This formula uses the diameter of the piece because the metal is being rotated. We substitute the known values into the formula:

$$RPM = \frac{12(300)}{3.14(4.75)}$$

We next perform the multiplication in the numerator and denominator:

$$RPM = \frac{3600}{14.915}$$

We then divide to find the machine speed:

$$RPM = 241$$

For drilling, the proper cutting speed is 65 FPM when an HHS twist drill is used. Note that we use the diameter of the twist drill because it is being rotated. To determine the spindle speed for drilling, we again substitute the known values into the formula:

$$RPM = \frac{12(65)}{3.14(0.75)}$$

We perform the multiplication in the numerator and the denominator:

$$\text{RPM} = \frac{780}{2.355}$$

We then divide to find the machine speed for drilling:

$$\text{RPM} = 331$$

RULE

To find the time of cut (T) in terms of feed rate and machine speeds (RPM), use the formula:

$$T = \frac{L}{F(\text{RPM})}$$

For example, to determine the amount of time needed to drill a hole 1.75″ deep when the drill rotates at 150 RPM and has a feed rate of 0.005″ per revolution, we use the formula:

$$T = \frac{L}{F(\text{RPM})}$$

We substitute the known values into the formula:

$$T = \frac{1.75}{0.005(150)}$$

We next perform the multiplication in the denominator:

$$T = \frac{1.75}{0.750}$$

We then divide to find the time needed to drill the hole:

$$T = 2.33 \text{ minutes}$$

With experience in the machining of metals, machinists are able to judge proper cutting speeds and feed rates just by the way the cutting tools are removing the metal.

Threads

Threads are used to hold parts together, to transmit power, and to make adjustments. Cutting and measuring threads are important machining skills, and both are common procedures in the shop. In this section, we cover only the basic concepts of threads and the formulas that apply to them. When more technical information is necessary, we can obtain it from *Machinery's Handbook*.

Definition of Terms

— An *external thread*, shown in Figure 5.8a, is a thread on the outside of a piece

— An *internal thread*, shown in Figure 5.8b, is a thread on the inside of a piece

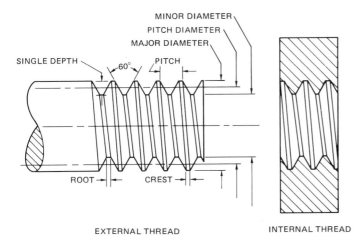

EXTERNAL THREAD   INTERNAL THREAD

Figure 5.8a   **Figure 5.8b**

— *Major diameter* (*D*) is the largest diameter of a thread. Major diameter was formerly called "outside diameter" on an external thread and "full diameter" on an internal thread

— *Minor diameter* (*d*) is the smallest diameter of a thread. Minor diameter was formerly called "root diameter" on an external thread and "inside diameter" on an internal thread

— *Pitch diameter* (D_P) is the diameter of an imaginary cylindrical surface that would pass through the threads and make the widths and spaces of the threads equal

— *Pitch* (*P*) is the distance from a point on one thread to a corresponding point on the next thread

— *Crest* (*C*) is the top surface of a thread. It is the surface of major-diameter measurement

— *Root* (*R*) is the bottom surface of a thread. It is the surface of minor-diameter measurement

— *Single depth* (*SD*) is the vertical distance between the crest and root of a thread

— *Double depth* (*DD*) is twice the single depth

— *Lead* is the distance a screw thread advances in one complete turn

On a single thread, shown in Figure 5.9a, the lead equals the pitch of the thread. On a double thread (two threads), shown in Figure 5.9b, the lead is twice the pitch of the thread.

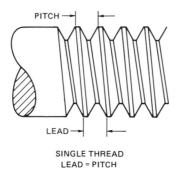

Figure 5.9a   Figure 5.9b

American National Screw Thread

The *American National screw thread* was adopted as a replacement for the V-thread and has itself been superseded by the Unified thread. The American National screw thread is, however, still widely used in the United States.

The two most important facts we need to know about a thread, other than its major diameter, are the number of threads per inch (N) and the pitch of the thread (P), shown in Figure 5.10. The following rules provide the formulas for finding these and other dimensions of American National threads.

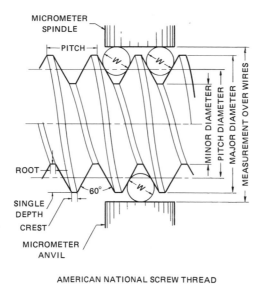

AMERICAN NATIONAL SCREW THREAD

Figure 5.10

RULES FOR AMERICAN NATIONAL THREADS

To find	Use the formula:
number of threads per inch (N)	$N = \dfrac{1.000}{P}$
pitch (P)	$P = \dfrac{1.000}{N}$
crest (C)	$C = \dfrac{P}{8}$
root measurements (R)	$R = \dfrac{P}{8}$
single depth (SD)	$SD = \dfrac{0.6495}{N}$
double depth (DD)	$DD = \dfrac{1.299}{N}$
pitch diameter (D_P)	$D_P = D - SD$
minor diameter (d)	$d = D - DD$
size of hole (S)	$S = D - \dfrac{1.299(\% \text{ full thread})^*}{N}$
best wire diameter (W_1)	$W_1 = \dfrac{0.57735}{N}$
maximum wire diameter (W_2)	$W_2 = \dfrac{0.90}{N}$
minimum wire diameter (W_3)	$W_3 = \dfrac{0.56}{N}$
measurement over three wires (M)	$M = D + 3W - \dfrac{1.5155}{N}$

For example, the American National screw thread 1/2″–20 NF has a basic major diameter of 1/2″ and has 20 threads per inch. It is an American National fine thread.

To find the pitch of the screw thread:

$$P = \frac{1.000}{N}$$

$$= \frac{1}{20} = 0.050''$$

*The % full thread refers to the % of the total thread making contact between the internal and external thread. See the Appendix for a table giving drill sizes for the common 75% full thread fit.

To find the crest measurement:

$$C = \frac{P}{8}$$

$$= \frac{0.050}{8} = 0.0063''$$

To find the root measurement:

$$R = \frac{P}{8}$$

$$= \frac{0.050}{8} = 0.0063''$$

To find the single-depth measurement:

$$SD = \frac{0.6495}{N}$$

$$= \frac{0.6495}{20} = 0.0325''$$

To find the double-depth measurement:

$$DD = \frac{1.299}{N}$$

$$= \frac{1.299}{20} = 0.0650''$$

To find the pitch diameter:

$$(D_P) = \text{major diameter} - SD$$
$$= 0.500 - 0.0325 = 0.4675''$$

To find the minor diameter:

$$d = \text{major diameter} - DD$$
$$= 0.500 - 0.0650 = 0.4350''$$

To determine the size of the hole to be bored or drilled for a 75% full-thread fit, we use the formula:

$$S = D - \frac{1.299(\% \text{ full thread})}{N}$$

$$= 0.500 - \frac{1.299(0.75)}{20} = 0.500 - \frac{0.974}{20} = 0.4513''$$

Notice that we change the percent to a decimal for use in the formula.

For a thread measurement over three wires (best wire measurement, W_1):

$$W_1 = \frac{0.57735}{N} = \frac{0.57735}{20} = 0.0289''$$

To find the measurement over three wires (M):

$$M = D + 3W - \frac{1.5155}{N}$$

$$= 0.500 + 3(0.0289) - \frac{1.5155}{20} = 0.500 + 0.0867 - 0.0758$$

$$= 0.5108''$$

Unified Threads

Unified threads, shown in Figure 5.11, have basically the same thread form as American National threads. Thus, they are interchangeable with American National threads of the same diameter and pitch. The differences between the two threads are in their thread designation and their allowances and tolerances.

On a Unified thread, the root on the external thread is twice the width of the root on an American National thread, and it can be either flat or rounded (internal threads are always rounded). The crest is the same width on both threads and may be rounded on Unified threads. The dimensions of the Unified thread are expressed

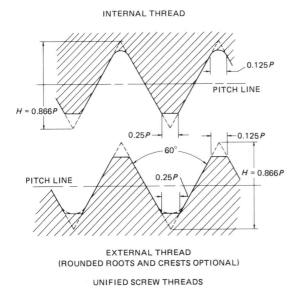

Figure 5.11

in terms of the thread depth (H) on a standard V-thread and the pitch (P) of the thread. $H = 0.8666P$, and the following rules provide the formulas for finding other dimensions of Unified external threads.

RULES FOR UNIFIED THREADS

To find	Use the formula:
crest (C)	$C = 0.125P$
root (R)	$R = 0.250P$
single depth (SD)	$SD = \dfrac{0.6138}{N}$
double depth (DD)	$DD = \dfrac{1.2276}{N}$
pitch diameter (D_P)	$D_P = D - \dfrac{0.650}{N}$
minor diameter (d)	$d = D - DD$
size of hole* (S)	$S = D - \dfrac{1.0825(\% \text{ full thread})}{N}$
measurement over three wires	$M = D + 3W - \dfrac{1.5155}{N}$

The Unified thread 1/2″–20 UNF has a basic major diameter of 1/2″ and has 20 threads per inch. It is a fine thread. In the following examples, we apply the formulas for finding the measurements of a Unified thread.

To find the pitch of a Unified thread:

$$P = \frac{1}{N}$$

$$= \frac{1}{20} = 0.050''$$

To find the crest of a Unified thread:

$$C = 0.125P$$

$$= 0.125(0.050) = 0.0063''$$

*The Unified thread series has a maximum and minimum hole size, depending on class of thread and length of engagement of the thread. Refer to *Machinery's Handbook* for this specific information.

To find the root of a Unified thread:

$$R = 0.250P$$
$$= 0.250(0.050) = 0.0125''$$

To find the single diameter of a Unified thread:

$$SD = \frac{0.6138}{N}$$
$$= \frac{0.6138}{20} = 0.307''$$

To find the double diameter of a Unified thread:

$$DD = \frac{1.2276}{N}$$
$$= \frac{1.2276}{20} = 0.0614''$$

To find the pitch diameter of a Unified thread:

$$D_P = D - \frac{0.650}{N}$$
$$= 0.500 - \frac{0.650}{20} = 0.500 - 0.033 = 0.465''$$

To find the minor diameter of a Unified thread:

$$d = D - DD$$
$$= 0.500 - 0.0614 = 0.4386''$$

To find the hole size for a 75% full-thread fit:

$$S = D - \frac{1.0825(\% \text{ full thread})}{N}$$
$$= 0.500 - \frac{0.8119}{20} = 0.500 - 0.0406 = 0.4594''$$

The measurement over three wires for a Unified thread is the same as that for an American National thread 1/2''–20 NF. We calculated this measurement earlier and found that the three-wire measurement is 0.5108'' if wires of 0.0289'' (W_1 = best wire measurement) diameter are used.

Translation Threads

Thread forms commonly used where repeated movement of machine parts is needed under heavy loads are commonly referred to as *translation threads*. The square, Acme, and buttress thread forms are commonly used for this purpose.

The *square thread*, shown in Figure 5.12, is the most efficient but the most difficult to make. The following rules provide the formulas that apply to square threads.

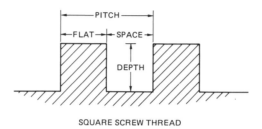

SQUARE SCREW THREAD

Figure 5.12

RULES FOR SQUARE THREADS

To find	Use the formula:
flat (*F*)	$F = \dfrac{0.500}{N}$
depth (*De*)	$De = \dfrac{0.500}{N}$
space (*Sp*)	$Sp = \dfrac{0.500}{N}$
minor diameter (*d*)	$d = D - P$

The *Acme thread*, shown in Figure 5.13, is not as efficient as the square thread, but is stronger and easier to make. The following rules provide the formulas that apply to Acme threads.

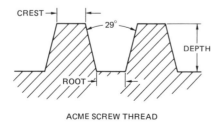

ACME SCREW THREAD

Figure 5.13

RULES FOR ACME THREADS

To find	Use the formula:
crest (C)	$C = \dfrac{0.3707}{N}$
minor diameter (d)	$d = D - P$
root (R)	$R = \dfrac{0.3707}{N}$
depth (De)	$De = \dfrac{0.500}{N} + 0.010''$

The *buttress thread,* shown in Figure 5.14, is used in the translation of loads in one direction. It has the efficiency of a square thread, but the ease of manufacturing of an Acme thread. The following formulas apply to the buttress thread.

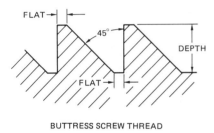

BUTTRESS SCREW THREAD

Figure 5.14

RULES FOR BUTTRESS THREADS

To find	Use the formula:
flat (F)	$F = \dfrac{P}{8}$
depth (De)	$De = 0.750P$
minor diameter (d)	$d = D - 1.5P$

Gears

In Chapter 4, we discussed the use of gears in power trains. Here, we focus on the dimensioning of gears and the formulas on which these dimensions are based. Like threads, gears are very technical and a great deal of information about them is available. Again, *Machinery's Handbook* is recommended for additional reference. There are different types of gears, but our attention will be on the *spur gear*.

Definition of Terms

The following basic terms apply to spur gears. The parts referred to are labeled in Figure 5.15.

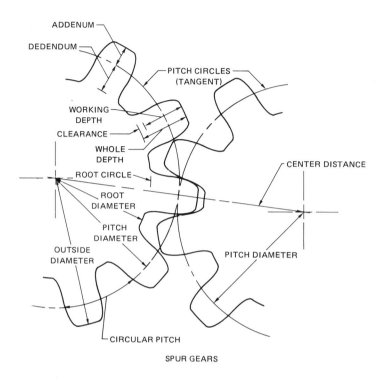

SPUR GEARS

Figure 5.15

— *Pitch circle* is an imaginary circle located about halfway down the teeth of a gear. This circle serves as the basis of gear dimensioning. When two gears are meshed, their pitch circles are tangential (touching each other)

— *Pitch diameter* (D) is the diameter of the pitch circle. In the figure, D_G stands for the diameter of the first gear and D_M stands for the diameter of the mating gear

— *Diametral pitch* (P_D) is the number of teeth per inch of the pitch diameter of a gear. Diametral pitch is one means we use to specify the size of teeth on a gear. Only gears with the same diametral pitch can mesh together properly

— *Circular pitch* (P_C) is the distance, measured on the pitch circle, from a point on one tooth to the same point on an adjacent tooth. Circular pitch is the second means we use to specify the size of the teeth on a gear

— *Root diameter* (D_R) is the diameter of the circle (root circle) formed by the bottoms of the teeth of a gear

— *Outside diameter* (D_O) is the diameter of the circle formed by the tops of the teeth of a gear

— *Addendum (S)* is the height of the teeth above the pitch circle

— *Dedendum (U)* is the depth of the teeth below the pitch circle

— *Whole depth (H)* is the total depth of the teeth

— *Working depth (W)* is the designed depth of engagement of the gear when meshed with another gear

— *Clearance (C)* is the measurement between the end of a tooth and the bottom of a mating tooth

— *Backlash* is the amount by which the width of a tooth exceeds the space of a mating tooth along the pitch circle

— *Center distance (c)* is the proper distance between the centers of two properly meshed gears

Spur Gear Formulas

The spur gear is an excellent example of the application of formulas, since the spur gear's dimensions are governed by a multitude of formulas. The general formulas applied to the spur gear are shown in the rules below. The following notations are used in the formulas:

N = number of teeth
P_D = diametral pitch
P_C = circular pitch
D = pitch diameter
D_G = pitch diameter of gear
D_M = pitch diameter of mating gear
N_G = number of teeth of gear
N_M = number of teeth of mating gear
D_O = outside diameter
D_R = root diameter
S = addendum
U = dedendum
C = clearance
H = whole depth
W = working depth
c = center distance

RULES FOR SPUR GEARS

To find	Use the formula:
diametral pitch (P_D)	$P_D = \dfrac{N}{D}$
	$P_D = \dfrac{(N + 2)}{D_O}$
	$P_D = \dfrac{3.1416}{P_C}$

To find	Use the formula:
pitch diameter (D)	$D = \dfrac{N}{P_D}$
	$D = \dfrac{(N \times P_C)}{3.1416}$
	$D = D_O - 2S$
number of teeth (N)	$N = P_D \times D$
	$N = \dfrac{3.1416D}{P_C}$
circular pitch (P_C)	$P_C = \dfrac{3.1416D}{P_D}$
	$P_C = \dfrac{3.1416D}{N}$
outside diameter (D_O)	$D_O = \dfrac{(N + 2)}{P_D}$
	$D_O = D + 25$
root diameter (D_R)	$D_R = D - 2U$
	$D_R = \dfrac{(N - 2.5)}{P_D}$
addendum (S)	$S = \dfrac{1.000}{P_D}$
	$S = \dfrac{P_C}{3.1416}$
clearance (C)	$C = 0.250P_C$
	$C = 0.0796P_C$
whole depth (H)	$H = \dfrac{2.250}{P_D}$
	$H = 0.7162P_C$
center distance $(C\text{-to-}C)$	$C\text{-to-}C = \dfrac{N_G + N_M}{2P_D}$
	$C\text{-to-}C = \dfrac{D_G + D_M}{2}$
dedendum (U)	$U = S + C$
	$U = \dfrac{1.250}{P_D}$
	$U = 0.3979P_C$

working depth (W)

$$W = \frac{2.000}{P_D}$$

$$W = 0.6366 \, P_C$$

Suppose that a gear with 45 teeth and a 3.750″ pitch diameter is required on a transfer unit. We can use the formulas shown in the table to find diametral pitch, circular pitch, outside diameter, whole depth, addendum, dedendum, and root diameter. Notice that in some cases, we can apply more than one formula. The calculations of these measurements are shown below.

To find the diametral pitch:

$$P_D = \frac{N}{D}$$

$$= \frac{45}{3.750} = 12$$

To find the circular pitch:

$$P_C = \frac{3.1416D}{N}$$

$$= \frac{3.1416(3.750)}{45} = \frac{11.781}{45} = 0.2618''$$

To find the outside diameter:

$$D_O = \frac{(N + 2)}{P_D}$$

$$= \frac{45 + 2}{12} = \frac{47}{12} = 3.9167''$$

To find the whole depth:

$$H = \frac{2.250}{P_D}$$

$$= \frac{2.250}{12} = 0.1875''$$

To find the addendum:

$$S = \frac{1.000}{P_D}$$

$$= \frac{1.000}{12} = 0.0833''$$

To find the dedendum:

$$U = \frac{1.250}{P_D}$$

$$= \frac{1.250}{12} = 0.1042''$$

To find the root diameter:

$$D_R = \frac{(N - 2.5)}{P_D}$$

$$= \frac{45 - 2.5}{12} = \frac{42.5}{12} = 3.542''$$

Remember, formulas give us three instructions. They tell us: (1) in terms of symbols, what values are needed for the calculation; (2) in terms of operation notations, what operations to perform to combine those values; and (3) in terms of grouping signs, in what order the operations are to be performed.

In this chapter, we learned how to use formulas properly. In the following chapters, we will continue to look at formulas, especially those that are geometrically based.

TERMS FOR REVIEW

— formula
— formula calculations
— symbols
— operations
— variables
— square
— square root
— radical sign
— perfect squares
— parentheses
— brackets
— clearing the parentheses
— cutting speeds
— feed
— machine speed
— time of cut
— external thread
— internal thread
— major diameter
— minor diameter
— pitch diameter
— pitch
— crest
— root

— single depth
— double depth
— lead
— American National screw thread
— Unified thread
— translation threads
  – square thread
  – Acme thread
  – buttress thread
— spur gear
— pitch circle
— pitch diameter
— diametral pitch
— circular pitch
— root diameter
— outside diameter
— addendum
— dedendum
— whole depth
— working depth
— clearance
— backlash
— center distance

EXERCISES

Exercise 5.1: Interpretation of Formulas

A. Answer the following questions.

1. What are formulas? _____

2. What are the three instructions of every formula? _____

Exercise 5.2: Formula Notations

A. Use an electronic calculator to find the square of each of the following numbers. Round off the answer to three decimal places if necessary.

1. $3^2 =$ _____

2. $10^2 =$ _____

3. $8.5^2 =$ _____

4. $7.62^2 =$ _____

5. $10.789^2 =$ _____

6. $16.9^2 =$ _____

7. $0.875^2 =$ _____

8. $0.375^2 =$ _____

9. $5.451^2 =$ _____

B. Use an electronic calculator to find the square root of each of the following numbers. Round off the answer to three decimal places if necessary.

1. $\sqrt{64} =$ _____

2. $\sqrt{36} =$ _____

3. $\sqrt{169} =$ _____

4. $\sqrt{7.869} =$ _____

5. $\sqrt{32.733} =$ _____

6. $\sqrt{152.768} =$ _____

7. $\sqrt{205.973} =$ _____

8. $\sqrt{0.875} =$ _____

9. $\sqrt{0.591} =$ _____

C. In the following formula notations, specify all the operations indicated.

(Example: $\dfrac{2r}{3}$ — multiplication and division)

1. $\dfrac{h^2}{F}$ _____

2. $\sqrt{ef}$ _____

3. $\dfrac{c\sqrt{2}}{2}$ _____

4. $\sqrt{c^2 - a^2}$ _____

5. $\dfrac{a^2 + b^2 - c^2}{2b}$ _____

6. $r - \sqrt{r^2 - (\frac{1}{2}w)^2}$ _____

Exercise 5.3: Sequence of Operations

A. Indicate the sequence in which the operation of the following formula notations should be performed.

(Example: $\dfrac{2r}{3}$ — first multiply, then divide)

1. $\dfrac{2a}{3}$ _____

2. $\sqrt{a^2 + b^2}$ _____

3. $\sqrt{ef}$ _____

4. $\dfrac{(\frac{1}{2}w)^2 - h^2}{2h}$ _____

5. $\dfrac{2bh}{a + b + c}$ _____

Exercise 5.4: Problem Solving

A. Answer the following question.

1. What are the three steps to be followed when problem-solving situations require the use of formulas?

Exercise 5.5: Cutting Speeds and Feeds

A. Use the following four formulas to solve for the indicated values. Round off answers to one decimal place.

$$CS = \frac{3.14(D)(RPM)}{12} \qquad F = \frac{L}{T(RPM)}$$

$$RPM = \frac{12(CS)}{3.14(D)} \qquad T = \frac{L}{F(RPM)}$$

1. Find the cutting speed of a 7/8″ twist drill rotating at 125 RPM.

1. _____

2. At what speed should we operate a milling machine for a 1.25″ drill to run at 65 FPM?

2. _____

3. How long would it take to make fifteen 3″ cuts on a lathe using a feed of 0.012″/revolution and a speed of 300 RPM?

3. _____

4. If a cutting speed of 450 FPM is used on a 3-1/2″ piece of stock, what is the required RPM of the spindle?

4. _____

5. What is the time needed to make one pass with a mill on a surface 24″ long if the cutter is turning at 80 RPM and the feed rate is 0.020″/revolution?

5. _____

6. At a speed of 500 RPM and a feed rate of 0.003″/revolution, how long will it take a 9/16″ drill to go through brass 5.75″ thick?

6. _____

7. On aluminum castings, the finishing light cuts can be safely made at 950 FPM. If a 3″ cutter is used, at what RPM should it be run?

7. _____

8. The recommended cutting speed for carbon steel 1006 is 450 FPM when a carbide tool is used, the feed rate is 0.012″/revolution, and the depth of cut is 0.125″. A piece of 5″ rough stock 4.5″ long is to be machined down to 4.375″. (a) At what RPM should the machine be set? (b) How long will it take to complete the job? (c) If the machine speed is not changed, what is the cutting speed on the last cut?

8a. _____

8b. _____

8c. _____

9. The recommended cutting speed for cutting 16 to 24 threads/inch on AISI-1010 steel is 40 FPM. What machine speed is required to get this cutting speed on a 9/16″ arbor?

10. The recommended cutting speed for milling stainless steel is 75 FPM on an HSS cutter and 275 FPM on a carbide cutter. What is the machine speed for (a) the HSS cutter and (b) the carbide cutter if each is 3″ in diameter?

11. (a) What is the cutting speed of a cutting tool when the first cut is made on a 7″ piece of stock rotating at 250 RPM? (b) What is the cutting speed if the cut is made on a 5.5″ piece of stock rotating at 250 RPM?

12. How fast is a 3/4″ drill being fed through a piece of cast iron 3.5″ thick if it rotates at 200 RPM and takes 2-1/2 minutes to drill through?

Exercise 5.6: Threads

A. Solve the following thread problems. Use the following notation:

UN = Unified National thread
UNC = Unified National Coarse thread
UNF = Unified National Fine thread
NC = American National Coarse thread
NF = American National Fine thread

1. Determine the pitch of the following threads.

a. 1/4″–20 NC = _____   b. 3/8″–16 NC = _____

c. 1/2″–20 NF = _____   d. 9/16″–20 UN = _____

e. 5/8″–11 UNC = _____   f. 7/8″–12 UN = _____

g. 5/8″–18 NF = _____   h. 10–32 NF = _____

i. 4–40 NC = _____   j. 10–24 UNC = _____

2. What is the pitch of an Acme thread that has 8 threads/inch?

2. _____

3. Determine the lead of the following screws: (a) a single-thread screw that has 16 threads/inch and (b) a double-thread screw that has 16 threads/inch.

3a. _____
3b. _____

4. Determine the following measurements of a 7/16″–20 NF (American National) thread.

a. crest = _____   b. root = _____

c. single depth = _____   d. double depth = _____

e. pitch diameter = _____   f. minor diameter = _____

5. Determine the following measurements of a 7/8″–9 NC (American National) thread.

a. crest = _____   b. root = _____

c. single depth = _____   d. double depth = _____

e. pitch diameter = _____   f. minor diameter = _____

6. What size hole should be drilled to tap a 3/4″–16 NF thread if 60% full thread fit is required?

6. _____

7. Find the single depth of the following American National threads.

a. 1/2"–13 NC = _____

b. 5/8"–11 NC = _____

c. 3/4"–16 NF = _____

d. 3/8"–24 NF = _____

e. 1/4"–20 NC = _____

f. 1/4"–28 NF = _____

g. 9/16"–12 NC = _____

h. 1-3/4"–5 NC = _____

8. Determine the following measurements of a 3/4"–16 UNF (Unified) thread.

a. crest = _____

b. root = _____

c. single depth = _____

d. double depth = _____

e. pitch diameter = _____

f. minor diameter = _____

9. Find the single depth of the following Unified National threads.

a. 5/16"–18 UNC = _____

b. 1/4"–28 UNF = _____

c. 7/8"–9 UNC = _____

d. 1-1/2"–5 UNC = _____

e. 3"–4 UNC = _____

f. 1/2"–20 UNF = _____

10. Determine the required drill to drill the holes to tap the following threads. State the exact or nearest smallest fractional-, letter-, or wire-gage-size drill. A 60% full thread fit is desired.

a. 1/2"–13 NC = _____

b. 1/4"–28 NF = _____

c. 3/8"–16 NC = _____

d. 3/8"–24 NF = _____

e. 5/8"–11 NC = _____

f. 1/4"–20 UNC = _____

g. 5/8"–18 UNF = _____

h. 7/8"–9 UNC = _____

i. 9/16"–12 UNC = _____

j. 7/16"–20 UNF = _____

11. Determine the best wire size and the three-wire measurements for the following threads.

a. 1/2"–13 NC = _____ and _____

b. 5/8"–16 NC = _____ and _____

c. 3/4"–16 NC = _____ and _____

d. 7/8"–14 UNF = _____ and _____

e. 5/8"–11 UNC = _____ and _____

f. 1/2"–20 UNF = _____ and _____

12. The cross-feed screw on a lathe is a 3/4"–6 square thread. (a) What is the depth of the thread? (b) What is its minor diameter?

12a. _____

12b. _____

13. A heavy floor jack uses a 2"–4 square double thread. (a) What is the depth of the thread? (b) What is its minor diameter? (c) What is its lead?

13a. _____

13b. _____

13c. _____

14. The adjusting screw on a machine uses a 1-1/2"–5 Acme thread. (a) What is the depth of the thread? (b) What is its minor diameter?

14a. _____

14b. _____

15. A compression screw on a machine uses a 1"–6 buttress thread. (a) What is the depth of the thread? (b) What is its minor diameter?

15a. _____

15b. _____

Exercise 5.7: Gears

A. Solve the following spur gear problems.

1. Find the circular pitch for spur gears with the following diametral pitch.

a. 14 pitch = _____

b. 8-1/2 pitch = _____

c. 18 pitch = _____

d. 5-1/2 pitch = _____

e. 9 pitch = _____

f. 24 pitch = _____

g. 32 pitch = _____

h. 4.1888 pitch = _____

2. Find the diametral pitch for spur gears with the following circular pitch.

a. 0.500″ = _____

b. 0.625″ = _____

c. 0.720″ = _____

d. 1.250″ = _____

e. 1.375″ = _____

f. 0.250″ = _____

3. Find the pitch and outside diameters of the following spur gears.

a. Gear with 48 teeth and a diametral pitch of 8 = _____ and _____

b. Gear with 35 teeth and a circular pitch of 0.8″ = _____ and _____

c. Gear with 20 teeth and a circular pitch of 1.25″ = _____ and _____

d. Gear with 32 teeth and diametral pitch of 18 = _____ and _____

4. Find the whole depth of the following gears.

a. 16 diametral pitch = _____

b. 8.5 diametral pitch = _____

c. 0.875″ circular pitch = _____

d. 5 diametral pitch = _____

e. 0.250″ circular pitch = _____

f. 22 diametral pitch = _____

g. 7.5 diametral pitch = _____

h. 1.25″ circular pitch = _____

5. What is the outside diameter of a gear having 68 teeth and a 12 diametral pitch?

5. _____

6. A gear with 38 teeth and a circular pitch of 0.750″ is to be machined. Determine the following measurements:

a. diametral pitch = _____

b. outside diameter = _____

c. pitch diameter = _____

d. root diameter = _____

e. whole depth = _____

f. working depth = _____

g. addendum = _____

h. dedendum = _____

i. clearance = _____

7. The speed ratio desired between two gears, A and B, is 2 to 3. The diametral pitch of the gears is 12, and the center distance between them is 15″. Determine the following measurements.

a. pitch diameter A = _____

b. pitch diameter B = _____

c. outside diameter A = _____

d. outside diameter B = _____

e. number of teeth A = _____

f. number of teeth B = _____

8. If a gear has 80 teeth and an outside diameter of 10″, what is its diametral pitch?

8. _____

9. Find the center distance between the following gears.

   a. 16 and 28 teeth gears with a diametral pitch of 4

   b. 23 and 54 teeth gears with a diametral pitch of 12

   c. 15 and 35 teeth gears with a circular pitch of 1.250″

   d. 50 and 120 teeth gears with a circular pitch of 0.125″

9a. _____

9b. _____

9c. _____

9d. _____

10. What is the outside diameter of a blank for a gear with 120 teeth and 0.750″ circular pitch?

10. _____

11. What is the outside diameter of a blank for a gear with 27 teeth and a diametral pitch of 8?

11. _____

12. The driven gear on a 3-to-1 reduction unit was badly damaged. The outside diameter of the driving gear is 2.833″, and it has 32 teeth. Determine the following measurements of the damaged gear.

a. diametral pitch = _____   **b.** outside diameter = _____

c. number of teeth = _____   **d.** whole depth = _____

e. root diameter = _____

CHAPTER 6

METRIC SYSTEM

Learning Objectives

After studying this chapter, you should be able to:

— State the meaning of the prefixes kilo-, centi-, and milli-

— Understand the structure of the SI metric system

— Read a standard metric rule in millimeters

— Be familiar with the amounts represented by a centimeter, millimeter, gram, kilogram, liter, and milliliter

— Understand what soft and hard conversions are

— Recognize dual dimensions

— Recognize the use of commas to indicate place value

During the past few years, we have been witnessing the increasing use of new units of measurement—meter, liter, degree Celsius, and others—in the United States. These units belong to the SI metric system, which is becoming the universal language of measurement throughout the world.

In the United States, scientists and educators had long called for the introduction of the metric system. But industry in the United States did not begin to make the change on its own until the 1970s. Since then, many major corporations have established metrication programs and are now well along the way to full conversion.

The *SI metric system* (from the French, *système international d'unites*) is the modern version of the original metric system. It is the version that is being used today. The system is built from seven base units of measure and two supplementary units, combined with prefixes based on the decimal system. It is very simple to use. This chapter does not present a thorough study of the metric system. For detailed study, two pamphlets are recommended:

— *Metric Practice Guide and Style Manual* (AMJ Publishing Company)
— *Metric Guide for Educational Materials* (American National Metric Council)

METRICATION

In this section, we look at aspects of the metric system that the machinist needs to know. We also look at the changes we can expect to occur in the shop.

Prefixes

The metric system is often referred to as the decimalized system of weights and measures because the system is decimally based. That is, the units are formed by multiples of 10. This characteristic makes working with the system very easy. The multiple or submultiple units are represented by the *prefixes* listed below. Machinists should know thoroughly the prefixes that are starred (*). The proper symbol for each prefix is shown in parentheses:

kilo (k)	1000
hecto (h)	100
deka (da)	10
deci (d)	0.1
*centi (c)	0.01
*milli (m)	0.001

Units of Measurement
Linear Measurement

Machinists work with measurements of length more than any other type of measurement. Thus, an ability to work with measurements of length is of primary importance. In the *U.S. Customary system*, the inch is the unit of length used in the machine shop. Because we have worked with inch measurements, we have developed mental pictures of inches. We know what an inch measurement is; we know what a half-inch measurement is; and we even know that a 0.002″ measurement is about the thickness of a hair.

With the coming of the SI metric system, we must now develop a similar sense of measurement in metric units. In the SI metric system, the base unit of length is the *meter,* which is approximately 39.37″. The unit of length used in the shop, however, is a submultiple of the meter—the *millimeter* (mm). The millimeter is a small unit in comparison with an inch. The millimeter is about the thickness of a dime. The *milli-* prefix of the unit millimeter tells us that a millimeter is 1 one-thousandth (0.001) of a meter. Therefore, 1000 millimeters equals 1 meter. Figure 6.1 shows some of the relationships between the millimeter and other units of measurement.

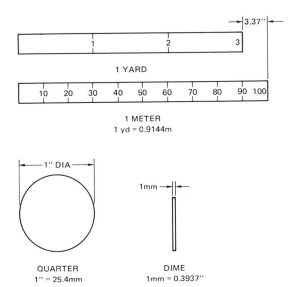

Figure 6.1

A typical metric rule is illustrated in Figure 6.2. The numbers on the rule indicate the centimeter marks. The prefix *centi-* tells us that the *centimeter* (cm) is 1 one-hundredth (0.01) of a meter. Therefore, 100 centimeters equals 1 meter.

Figure 6.2

The intermediate marks on the rule are millimeter marks. Note that 10 millimeters equals 1 centimeter. Even though the rule reads in centimeters, we do not indicate measurements in centimeters. We indicate measurements only in millimeters. To read the rule in millimeters, multiply the number of centimeters by 10, as Figure 6.3 illustrates.

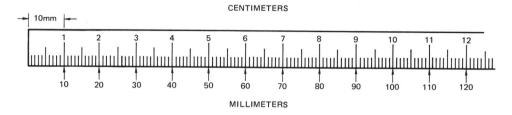

Figure 6.3

Since the millimeter is a very small unit, the degree of accuracy represented by thousandths of an inch can be stated easily as hundredths of a millimeter. The following are some common millimeter measurements:

4.85mm,   21.26mm,   12.00mm,   0.02mm

In summary, machinists use only millimeters for length measurements. Centimeters should never be used, even though rules are usually marked in centimeters. Knowing the following equivalents is important:

1000 millimeters (mm) = 1 meter (m)

100 centimeters (cm) = 1 meter

10 millimeters = 1 centimeter

Volume Measurement

Machinists occasionally deal with volumes. The most familiar units of volume in the U.S. Customary system are the gallon and quart. In the SI metric system, machinists most often use the liter (l) and, on occasion, the milliliter (ml).

The *liter* is slightly larger than the quart. The difference is 1.8 fluid ounces, or a little less than 1/4 cup. The milliliter is 1 one-thousandth (0.001) of a liter. Figure 6.4 shows the relationships of the liter and milliliter to other volume measurements.

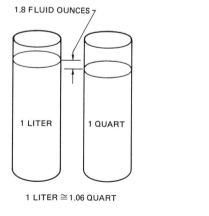

Figure 6.4

Mass Measurement

Metals in bulk are often referred to in terms of the U.S. Customary unit, the pound. In the SI metric system, the *kilogram* (kg) and, occasionally, the gram (g) are used. A dime has a mass close to 2 grams. A kilogram, therefore, is 1000 grams, about 2.2 pounds. Some relationships of some of the units used in the measurement of mass are shown in Figure 6.5.

1 KILOGRAM   1 POUND

1 KILOGRAM ≅ 2.2 POUNDS

5 QUARTERS   1 DIME
(1 OUNCE)   (2 GRAMS)

1 OUNCE ≅ 28.4 GRAMS

Figure 6.5

CONVERSIONS

During the metrication process, we will see our world of measurement change. We will encounter both soft and hard conversions. We will also encounter dual dimensioning, which will aid in these conversions.

Soft Conversion

Soft conversion is the process by which a metric unit of measurement equal (or almost equal) to a U.S. Customary unit is determined. Changing the indicated measurement of a 0.500″ hole to 12.70mm is a good example of soft conversion. Because eventually the millimeter will be used for measurements in the machine shop, it might seem that we will have to make a lot of soft conversions. However, we will not. Machinists will be required to make very few of these calculations.

Soft conversions should always be made before a machinist receives the blueprints because what may seem like a simple conversion actually is not. A machinist works with many different types of dimensions. Each of these dimensions cannot be converted in the same way if the original tolerance (degree of accuracy) is to be maintained. Use of the standard rounding-off procedure (see Chapter 2, Rounding Off Decimals) may result in converted dimensions that are smaller than the original minimum specifications or larger than the original maximum specifications. Therefore, different rounding-off procedures must be applied. The following are a few examples of the problem:

— A converted minimum value of 24.75493mm rounded off to the nearest hundredth of a millimeter is 24.75mm, a smaller value
— A converted maximum value of 24.75512mm rounded off to the nearest hundredth of a millimeter is 24.76mm, a larger value

Hard Conversion

Hard conversion is the process by which a physical structure is changed so that the measurements conform to metric units. Replacing the present fractional twist drills with a new series of metric drills is a good example of a hard conversion. Use of 1-liter and 2-liter containers for commercial bottling of soft drinks and other liquids is another example.

Hard conversions are the major, and more difficult, conversions encountered in the machine shop. If the measurements of a finished piece are to be changed to metric units, there must be changes, for example, in the dials, feed gears, and the lead screw of the lathe used in machining the piece. New metric taps, drills, end mills, dies, and other machinery tools are needed. New metric micrometers, calipers, gage blocks, and other precision measuring and testing equipment are also needed in order to "go metric."

Dual Dimensioning

Dual dimensioning means specifying both U.S. Customary and SI metric units for each measurement. The metric unit is usually stated first. The following are examples of dual dimensioning:

57.15mm / 2.250″

544 g / 1.2 lb

946 ml / 1 qt

12.70 ±0.05mm / 0.500 ±0.002″

Dual dimensioning is used to aid in the conversion process by making us familiar with equivalent metric units. Dual dimensioning is used for soft conversions to educate the machinist in the new language of metric measurement. Dual dimensioning is used for hard conversions to accommodate our inability to use metric measurements, since all traditional machines, tools, and scales in the machine shop are still inch dimensioned.

The Comma

In the United States, we use the decimal point to indicate place value, but many other countries use the comma. Thus, we can expect to see commas used to indicate place value. Knowing the meaning of the comma in metric measurements is important. The following are a few examples:

0,48mm	is the same as	0.48mm
2,68mm	is the same as	2.68mm
75,05mm	is the same as	75.05mm

TERMS FOR REVIEW

— SI metric system
— prefixes
  – kilo
  – hecto
  – deka
  – deci
  – centi
  – milli
— U.S. Customary system

— meter
— millimeter
— centimeter
— liter
— kilogram
— soft conversion
— hard conversion
— dual dimensioning

EXERCISES

Exercise 6.1: Units of Measurement

A. Indicate the measurements of the points *A* through *L* in millimeters on the following scale.

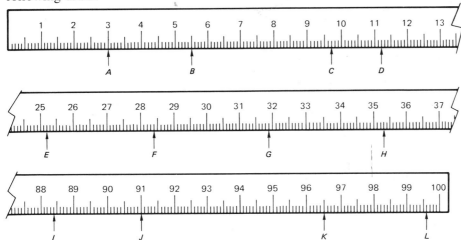

1. *A* = _____   **2.** *B* = _____   **3.** *C* = _____   **4.** *D* = _____

5. *E* = _____   **6.** *F* = _____   **7.** *G* = _____   **8.** *H* = _____

9. *I* = _____   **10.** *J* = _____   **11.** *K* = _____   **12.** *L* = _____

B. Calculate the following equivalents.

1. 2km = _____m   **2.** 3m = _____cm   **3.** 8000mm = _____m

4. 17cm = _____mm   **5.** 5.81mm = _____cm   **6.** 3.78m = _____cm

7. 1752m = _____km   **8.** 83mm = _____m   **9.** 3.5m = _____mm

C. Circle the closest millimeter measurement for the dimensions indicated on the following figures. Do not use a ruler.

1.

a. 1mm   **b.** 12mm   **c.** 6mm

2.

a. 10mm   **b.** 25mm   **c.** 40mm

3.

a. 10mm   **b.** 35mm   **c.** 18mm

4.

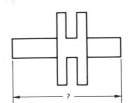

a. 20mm   **b.** 55mm   **c.** 40mm

5.

a. 50mm   **b.** 95mm   **c.** 60mm

Exercise 6.2: Shop-Related Problems

A. Find the indicated unknown dimensions. Only simple arithmetic calculations—addition, subtraction, multiplication, and division—are required.

1. Determine dimensions A and B of the following twist drill.

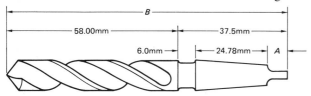

1a. A = _____

1b. B = _____

2. Determine the wall thickness (A) of the following bushing.

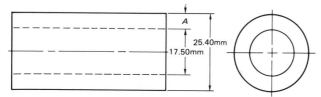

2. A = _____

3. Determine dimensions A, B, C, and D of the following pin.

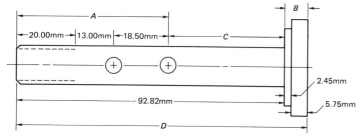

3a. A = _____

3b. B = _____

3c. C = _____

3d. D = _____

4. Determine dimensions A, B, C, D, E, F, and G of the V-block illustrated.

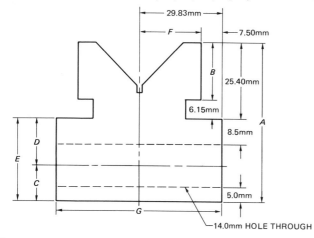

4a. A = _____

4b. B = _____

4c. C = _____

4d. D = _____

4e. E = _____

4f. F = _____

4g. G = _____

5. Determine dimensions *A*, *B*, *C*, *D*, *E*, *F*, *G*, and *H* of the following arbor.

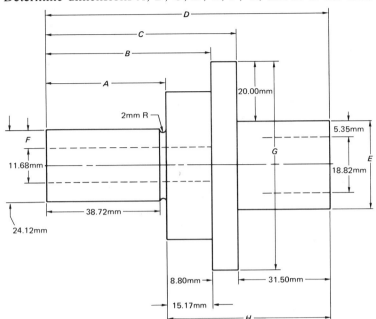

5a. *A* = _____

5b. *B* = _____

5c. *C* = _____

5d. *D* = _____

5e. *E* = _____

5f. *F* = _____

5g. *G* = _____

5h. *H* = _____

6. Determine dimensions *A*, *B*, and *C* of the angle plate illustrated.

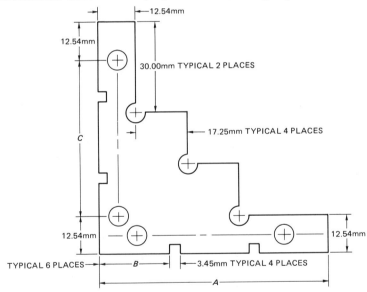

6a. *A* = _____

6b. *B* = _____

6c. *C* = _____

7. Determine dimensions *A*, *B*, *C*, and *D* of the following vise.

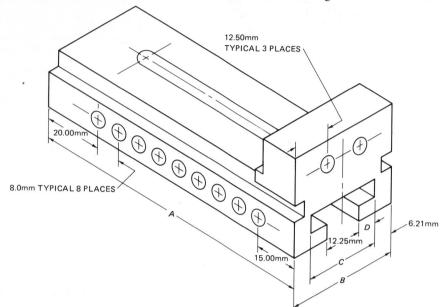

7a. *A* = _____

7b. *B* = _____

7c. *C* = _____

7d. *D* = _____

CHAPTER 7

MEASUREMENT OF ANGLES

Learning Objectives

After studying this chapter, you should be able to:

— Visualize angles of given measurement
— Add, subtract, multiply, and divide angular measurements
— Convert angular measurements of minutes and seconds to decimal degrees and vice versa
— Apply terms relating to angles
— Interpret relationships of angles to solve problems

Other than linear measurement, the most common measurement with which machinists work is measurement of angles. Basically, angular measurement is finding the size of angles. Many tools have been developed to help the machinist measure angles. Dividing heads, rotary tables, and level protractors are just a few.

INTERPRETATION OF ANGLES

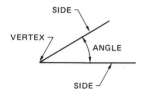

Figure 7.1

An *angle* is a measure of the size of the opening between two straight lines that intersect. An angle has three parts—two sides (the lines that form the angle) and the *vertex* (the point at which the two lines intersect). These three parts are identified in Figure 7.1. The symbol $\angle$ is used to represent an angle.

Measurement of Angles

The size of an angle does not depend on the length of its sides. The three angles shown in Figure 7.2 are all equal. The lengths of the sides of the angles in the figure are different, but the openings between the sides of each angle are the same.

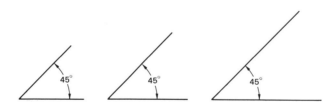

Figure 7.2

Units of Measurement

The basic unit used to measure angles is the degree. There are 360 degrees in a circle. Therefore, a *degree* is 1/360 of a circle. The symbol for degrees is °. An angle of 90° is the measurement of 90 × 1/360 of a circle. An angle of 55° is 55 × 1/360 of a circle, and an angle of 300° is 300 × 1/360 of a circle. These angles are illustrated in Figure 7.3.

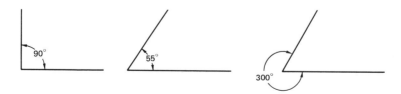

Figure 7.3

The degree is divided into a smaller unit called the *minute*. There are 60 minutes (noted as 60′) in one degree:

$$1° = 60′$$

The minute is further divided into a smaller unit called the *second*. There are 60 seconds (noted as 60″) in one minute:

$$1′ = 60″$$

We read an angular measurement by combining these units. For example, the measurement of the angle shown in Figure 7.4a is read as "21 degrees, 30 minutes." The measurement of the angle shown in Figure 7.4b is read as "47 degrees, 20 minutes, 45 seconds."

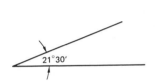

Figure 7.4a   Figure 7.4b

ARITHMETIC OPERATIONS

Calculating angular measurements involves the operations of addition, subtraction, multiplication, and division. The rules that follow are used for these operations when calculating angular measurements.

NOTE: When calculating angular measurements, we must sometimes simplify the values for minutes and seconds that are more than 59 (60′ = 1° and 60″ = 1′). Minutes are divided by 60 to simplify them to degrees. The quotient is the number of degrees; and the remainder is the remaining minutes:

63′ = 63 ÷ 60 = 1, with 3 remainder   so 63′ = 1°3′

87′ = 87 ÷ 60 = 1, with 27 remainder   so 87′ = 1°27′

132′ = 132 ÷ 60 = 2, with 12 remainder   so 132′ = 2°12′

Seconds are simplified to minutes in the same way, with the quotient being the minutes and the remainder, the remaining seconds:

70″ = 70 ÷ 60 = 1, with 10 remainder   so 70″ = 1′10″

182″ = 182 ÷ 60 = 3, with 2 remainder   so 182″ = 3′2″

Therefore:

31°62′72″   is simplified to   32°3′12″

119°59′64″   is simplified to   120°0′4″

Addition

RULE

To add angular measurements, add degrees to degrees, minutes to minutes, and seconds to seconds. Simplify the minutes and seconds in the answer if necessary.

For example, to add 25°25′ and 46°48′, we add the degrees and then add the minutes:

$$\begin{array}{r} 25°25' \\ +\ \ 46°48' \\ \hline 71°73' \end{array}$$

However, we must simplify 73′ because 73′ is more than 1°—it is 1° (= 60′) plus 13′:

$$\begin{array}{r} 71°00' \\ +\ \ \ \ 1°13' \\ \hline 72°13' \end{array}$$

In the problem of adding 10°31′45″ and 40°18′30″, we add the seconds, minutes, and degrees:

$$\begin{array}{r} 10°31'45'' \\ +\ \ 40°18'30'' \\ \hline 50°49'75'' \end{array}$$

Here, 75″ must be simplified to 1′15″ because 75″ is 15″ more than 1′ (= 60″):

$$\begin{array}{r} 50°49'00'' \\ +\ \ \ \ \ \ \ \ 1'15'' \\ \hline 50°50'15'' \end{array}$$

Subtraction

RULE

To subtract angular measurements, subtract degrees from degrees, minutes from minutes, and seconds from seconds. Convert degrees to minutes or minutes to seconds if necessary to gain digits in the minutes or seconds place.

For example, to subtract 42°16′ from 90°, first convert 90° to 89°60′ to gain digits in the minutes place and then subtract:

$$\begin{array}{r} 89°60' \\ -\ \ 42°16' \\ \hline 47°44' \end{array}$$

Similarly, to subtract 89°15′42″ from 142°, first convert 142° to 141°59′60″ to gain digits in the minutes and seconds places, then subtract:

$$
\begin{array}{r}
141°59′60″ \\
-89°15′42″ \\
\hline
52°44′18″
\end{array}
$$

Multiplication

RULE

To multiply angular measurements, multiply the degrees, seconds, and minutes separately. Simplify the minutes and seconds in the answer if necessary.

For example, suppose we want to multiply the angular measurement 14°48′ by 4. We first multiply 14° by 4:

$$14° \times 4 = 56°$$

We then multiply 48′ by 4:

$$48′ \times 4 = 192′$$

We now have:

$$14°48′ \times 4 = 56°192′$$

However, 192′ must be simplified:

$$192 \div 60 = 3, \text{ with 12 remainder}$$

We can now add 3°12′ to 56° to obtain the simplified answer:

$$
\begin{array}{r}
56°00′ \\
+3°12′ \\
\hline
59°12′
\end{array}
$$

Therefore, 14°48′ × 4 = 59°12′.

In the problem of multiplying the angular measurement 17°25′33″ by 3, we first multiply 17° by 3:

$$17° \times 3 = 51°$$

We then multiply 25′ by 3:

$$25′ \times 3 = 75′$$

We next multiply 33″ by 3:

$$33'' \times 3 = 99''$$

We now have:

$$17°25'33'' \times 3 = 51°75'99''$$

However, 75′ as well as 99″ must be simplified:

$$75 \div 60 = 1, \text{ with 15 remainder}$$
$$99 \div 60 = 1, \text{ with 39 remainder}$$

We can now add to obtain the simplified answer:

$$
\begin{array}{r}
51°00'00'' \\
1°15'00'' \\
+ \ 00° \ \ 1'39'' \\
\hline
52°16'39''
\end{array}
$$

Therefore, $17°25'33'' \times 3 = 52°16'39''$.

Division

RULE

To divide angular measurements, first divide the degrees. Then convert any remainder degrees to minutes and add them to the minutes in the original problem before dividing the minutes. Convert any remainder minutes to seconds and add them to the seconds in the original problem before dividing the seconds. Round off the answer to the nearest second.

For example, if we want to divide 45°6′ in half, we first divide 45° by 2:

$$45° \div 2 = 22°, \text{ with 1° remainder}$$

We next convert the 1° remainder to minutes by multiplying by 60:

$$1° \times 60 = 60'$$

We next add the 60′ to the original 6′ to find a new total number of seconds:

$$60' + 6' = 66'$$

We now divide the total minutes by 2:

$66' \div 2 = 33'$, with 0 remainder

We now add the degrees and minutes together:

$22° + 33' = 22°33'$

Thus, $45°6' \div 2 = 22°33'$.

A more complicated problem is to divide $75°30'17''$ by 4. We first divide $75°$ by 4:

$75° \div 4 = 18°$, with $3°$ remainder

Convert the $3°$ remainder to minutes by multiplying by 60:

$3° \times 60 = 180'$

Add the $180'$ to the original $30'$ to obtain a new total number of minutes:

$180' + 30' = 210'$

Then divide $210'$ by 4:

$210' \div 4 = 52'$, with $2'$ remainder

Convert the $2'$ remainder to seconds by multiplying by 60:

$2' \times 60 = 120''$

Add the $120''$ to the original $17''$ to find a new total number of seconds:

$120'' + 17'' = 137''$

Divide $137''$ by 4:

$137'' \div 4 = 34''$, with $1''$ remainder

Round off the answer to the nearest second:

$137'' \div 4 = 34''$

Add the degrees, minutes, and seconds to get the answer:

$18° + 52' + 34'' = 18°52'34''$

Thus $75°30'17'' \div 4 = 18°52'34''$. The problem is shown below in long-division form:

$$
\begin{array}{r}
\;\; 18° \qquad\qquad 52' \qquad\qquad 34'' \\
\hline
4)\;\; 75° \qquad\qquad .\,30' \qquad\qquad 17'' \\
-\;72° \\
\hline
3° \;(\times\; 60 \;=\; +\;180') \\
\hline
210' \\
-\;208' \\
\hline
2' \;(\times\; 60 \;=\; +\;120'') \\
\hline
137'' \\
-\;136'' \\
\hline
1'' \text{ remainder}
\end{array}
$$

Decimal Conversions

Many of the electronic calculators most of us use can deal with angular measurements only in decimal form. We must, therefore, know how to convert minutes and seconds to equivalent decimal degrees and vice versa.

Converting Minutes and Seconds to Decimal Degrees

RULE

To convert an angular measurement given in minutes to the decimal form of a degree, divide the minutes by 60 because $60' = 1°$.

For example, if we want to convert $45°30'$ to the decimal form, we divide $30'$ by 60 to find the decimal because $30' = 30/60$ of a degree:

$$30' \div 60 = 0.5°$$

We then add the $0.5°$ to the original $45°$ to find the total degree value in decimal terms:

$$45° + 0.5° = 45.5°$$

Thus, $45°30' = 45.5°$.

Or, to convert $20°25'$ to the decimal form, we divide $25'$ by 60 to find the decimal because $25' = 25/60$ of a degree:

$$25' \div 60 = 0.4166° \text{ (rounded to the fourth decimal place)}$$

We then add the 0.4166° to the original 20° to find the total degree value in decimal terms:

$$20° + 0.4166° = 20.4166°$$

Thus, 20°25′ = 20.4166°.

RULE

To convert an angular measurement given in minutes and seconds to decimal degrees, convert all minute values into seconds and divide the combined total seconds by 3600 because 3600″ = 1°.

For example, if we want to convert 20°45′30″ to an equal decimal expression, we first convert 45′ to seconds:

$$45′ \times 60 = 2700″$$

We then add the 2700″ to the original 30″ to find the total number of seconds:

$$2700″ + 30″ = 2730″$$

We now divide by 3600 to find the decimal because 2730″ = 2730/3600 of a degree:

$$2730 \div 3600 = 0.7583° \text{ (rounded off to the fourth decimal place)}$$

Thus, 45′30″ = 0.7583°.
To find the total degree value, add the 0.7583° to the original 20°:

$$20° + 0.7583° = 20.7583°$$

Thus, 20°45′30″ = 20.7583°.
   To convert 85°15′46″ to an equal value in decimal terms, first multiply 15′ by 60 to convert the minutes to seconds:

$$15′ \times 60 = 900″$$

Add the 900″ to the original 46″ to find the total number of seconds:

$$46″ + 900″ = 946″$$

Then divide by 3600 to find the decimal because 946″ = 946/3600 of a degree:

$$946 \div 3600 = 0.2628° \text{ (rounded off to the fourth decimal place)}$$

Thus, 15′46″ = 0.2628°.

Add the 0.2628° to the original 85° to find the total degree value in decimal terms:

$$85° + 0.2628° = 85.2628°$$

Thus, $85°15'46'' = 85.2628°$.

Converting Decimal Degrees to Minutes and Seconds

RULE

To convert a decimal degree to minutes, multiply the decimal by 60 and round off the answer to the nearest minute.

For example, to convert the decimal of 30.463° to minutes, we first multiply 0.463° by 60:

$$0.463° \times 60 = 27.78'$$

Thus, $0.463° = 27.78'$, or 28' rounded off to the nearest minute. To find the total number of degrees and minutes, we add the 28' to the original 30°:

$$30° + 28' = 30°28'$$

Thus, $30.463° = 30°28'$.

RULE

To convert a decimal degree to minutes and seconds, multiply the decimal degree by 60 to find the minutes, then multiply the decimal minute by 60 to find the seconds and round off the answer to the nearest second.

For example, to convert the decimal 17.856° to minutes and seconds, we first multiply 0.856° by 60 to find the number of minutes:

$$0.856° \times 60 = 51.36' \quad (51' + 0.36')$$

Then, we multiply 0.36' by 60 to find the number of seconds:

$$0.36' \times 60 = 21.6'', \text{ or } 22'' \text{ rounded off to the nearest second}$$

We now add the 51' and the 22'' to the original 17° to find the total value:

$$17° + 51' + 22'' = 17°51'22''$$

Thus, $17.856° = 17°51'22''$.

Metric Angular Measurement

The metric unit of angular measurement is the *radian*. The radian is the angle between two radii of a circle that cut off, on the circumference, an arc that is equal in length to the radius. The radian will probably not be used with the adoption of the metric system; we will continue to use the degree. However, minutes and seconds may be eliminated. Decimals of a degree will be used instead. In this book, we will use decimal degrees for all metric-related problems.

TYPES OF ANGLES

A *right angle,* shown in Figure 7.5, is an angle that has a measurement of 90°. The right angle is by far the most important angle that machinists have to work with. When two straight lines or surfaces meet at a right angle, we call these lines or surfaces *perpendicular*. The symbol used is ⊥. Surfaces that form right angles are often also referred to as being "square." Notice that in Figure 7.5, a small square at the vertex of the angle is used to indicate that the angle measures 90° and that the sides are perpendicular.

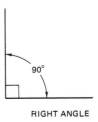

RIGHT ANGLE

Figure 7.5

The names of some types of angles refer to the number of degrees in the angle:

— *Acute angles,* shown in Figure 7.6, are angles that have a measurement of less than 90°

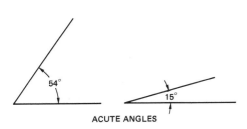

ACUTE ANGLES

Figure 7.6

— *Obtuse angles,* shown in Figure 7.7, are angles that have a measurement greater than 90° but less than 180°

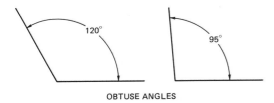

OBTUSE ANGLES

Figure 7.7

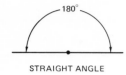

STRAIGHT ANGLE

Figure 7.8

— *Straight angles* are angles of 180°; a straight line, shown in Figure 7.8, is a straight angle

The names of other types of angles refer to the relationship of the angles to each other. *Complementary angles* are any two angles whose sum is 90°. For example, the sum of the complementary angles shown in Figure 7.9a is:

$$30° + 60° = 90°$$

The angles shown in Figure 7.9b are also complementary:

$$18° + 72° = 90°$$

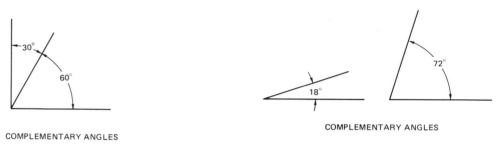

COMPLEMENTARY ANGLES

Figure 7.9a

COMPLEMENTARY ANGLES

Figure 7.9b

Supplementary angles are any two angles whose sum is 180°. For example, the sum of the supplementary angles shown in Figure 7.10a is:

$$120° + 60° = 180°$$

The angles shown in Figure 7.10b are also supplementary:

$$145° + 35° = 180°$$

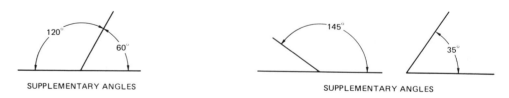

SUPPLEMENTARY ANGLES

Figure 7.10a

SUPPLEMENTARY ANGLES

Figure 7.10b

Included angle generally means total angle. For example, the total angle of a taper is referred to as the included angle. The included angle is equally divided by the center line of the workpiece. The Morse 3 taper shown in Figure 7.11a has an included angle of 2°52′30″.

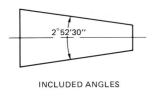

INCLUDED ANGLES

Figure 7.11a

INCLUDED ANGLES

Figure 7.11b

NOTE: If we draw a line parallel to the center line to form $\angle A$, as shown in Figure 7.11b, this angle is also one-half the included angle:

$$\angle A = \frac{2°52'30''}{2} = 1°26'15''$$

Vertical angles are the opposite angles formed when two lines cross. As shown in Figure 7.12, vertical angles are always equal:

$$\angle A = \angle B \quad \text{and} \quad \angle C = \angle D$$

Alternate angles are the corresponding vertical angles formed when two parallel lines are intersected by another line, as in Figure 7.13a, or by pairs of parallel lines, as in Figure 7.13b. Since alternate angles are corresponding vertical angles, they are always equal. As shown in Figure 7.13:

$$\angle A = \angle B = \angle C = \angle D \quad \text{and} \quad \angle E = \angle F = \angle G = \angle H$$

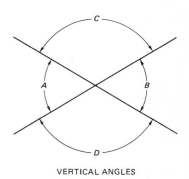

VERTICAL ANGLES

Figure 7.12

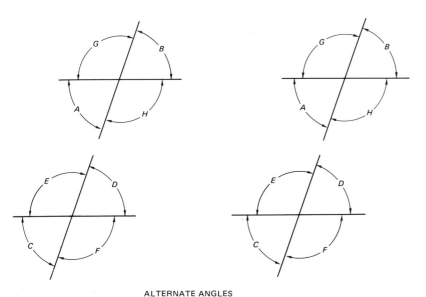

ALTERNATE ANGLES

Figure 7.13a   **Figure 7.13b**

Interior angles, shown in Figure 7.14, are the inside angles of polygons. (*Polygons* are closed plane figures formed by three or more straight lines.) The sum

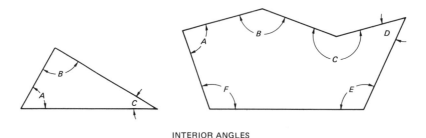

INTERIOR ANGLES

Figure 7.14a   **Figure 7.14b**

of the interior angles of all polygons having the same number of sides is the same and can be found by using the formula:

$$180 (N - 2)$$

where N is the number of sides.

For example, the triangle shown in Figure 7.14a is a three-sided figure, so $N = 3$. To find the sum of the interior angles, we use the formula:

$$\text{sum of angles} = 180(N - 2)$$
$$= 180(3 - 2) = 180(1) = 180$$

Thus, $\angle A + \angle B + \angle C = 180°$.

The polygon shown in Figure 7.14b has six sides, so $N = 6$. To find the sum of the interior angles, we use the formula:

$$\text{sum of angles} = 180(6 - 2) = 180(4) = 720$$

Thus, $\angle A + \angle B + \angle C + \angle D + \angle E + \angle F = 720°$.

Central angles are the angles of a circle that have their vertex at the center of the circle, as shown in Figure 7.15. Since the total number of degrees in a circle is 360, the sum of a circle's central angles is 360°. In the circle shown in Figure 7.15:

$$\angle A + \angle B + \angle C + \angle D + \angle E + \angle F = 360°$$

ANGULAR CALCULATIONS

The definitions of the various types of angles can be applied to solve typical angular calculation problems in the machine shop. The following example shows how to use our knowledge of the properties of angles to solve a shop-related problem.

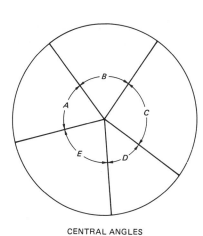

CENTRAL ANGLES

Figure 7.15

EXAMPLE

Problem

Find the measurements of ∠A, ∠B, ∠C, ∠D, ∠E, and ∠F in the angle step block illustrated in Figure 7.16.

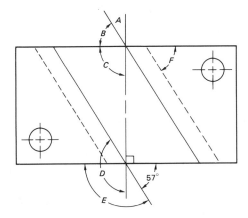

Figure 7.16

Analysis

We know from Figure 7.16 that the parallel horizontal lines are intersected by the parallel diagonal lines to form alternate angles. We also know that one of the angles shown is a right angle and that the center line is perpendicular to the horizontal lines.

Solution

Step 1: Find the value of ∠B. Since we are given one 57° angle, and ∠B is an alternate angle, we know that ∠B also = 57°.

Step 2: Find the value of ∠C. Since we know that the center line is perpendicular to the horizontal lines, we know that ∠C = 90°. ∠C is also opposite a 90° angle, so it is a vertical angle equal to the 90° angle.

Step 3: Find the value of $\angle A$. We know that $\angle A + \angle B = 90°$, so $\angle A$ and $\angle B$ are complementary. To find the value of $\angle A$, subtract the found value of $\angle B$ from 90°:

$$\angle A = 90° - 57° = 33°$$

Step 4: Find the value of $\angle F$. We know that the vertical angle opposite $\angle B$ is also equal to 57°. $\angle F$ is an alternate angle formed by the pairs of parallel lines. Therefore, $\angle F = 57°$.

Step 5: Find the value of $\angle D$. We know that one part of $\angle D$ is a right angle because it is a vertical angle equal to a 90° angle. The other part of $\angle D$ is a vertical angle equal to the 57° angle. Therefore:

$$\angle D = 90° + 57° = 147°$$

Step 6: Find the value of $\angle E$. We know that one part of $\angle E$ is a right angle. We know that the other part of $\angle E$ is an alternate angle equal to $\angle A$. Therefore:

$$\angle E = 90° + 33° = 123°$$

Note: We can find the value of $\angle E$ another way. We know from the figure that $\angle E + 57° = 180°$, a straight angle. Therefore:

$$\angle E = 180° - 57° = 123°$$

Answer

$$\angle A = 33°, \ \angle B = 57°, \ \angle C = 90°, \ \angle D = 147°,$$
$$\angle E = 123°, \ \angle F = 57°$$

In the following example, we use our knowledge of central angles to find the missing measurement in a shop-related problem.

EXAMPLE

Problem

Find the measurement of $\angle A$ of the insulating cover shown in Figure 7.17.

Analysis

Figure 7.17 shows a center line. Since the total number of degrees in a circle is 360, the center line leaves half of that, or 180°. Alternately, we know that the center line is a straight angle equal to 180°. Therefore, we must subtract the total number of degrees given in the figure from 180°.

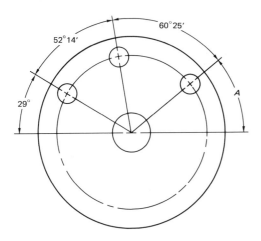

Figure 7.17

Solution

Step 1: Find the total number of degrees and minutes given in Figure 7.17

$$29° + 52°14' + 60°25' = 141°39'$$

Step 2: Subtract 141°39' from 180°

$$180° - 141°39' = 179°60' - 141°39' = 38°21'$$

Answer

$$\angle A = 38°21'$$

TERMS FOR REVIEW

— angle
— vertex
— degree
— minute
— second
— radian
— right angle
— perpendicular
— acute angle
— obtuse angle

— straight angle
— complementary angles
— supplementary angles
— included angle
— vertical angles
— alternate angles
— interior angles
— polygons
— central angles

EXERCISES

Exercise 7.1: Interpretation of Angles

A. Draw the following angles by estimation.

1. 90° _____   **2.** 30° _____   **3.** 60° _____   **4.** 45° _____

5. 15° _____   **6.** 135° _____   **7.** 120° _____   **8.** 80° _____

9. 20° _____   **10.** 270° _____   **11.** 330° _____   **12.** 180° _____

Exercise 7.2: Angular Calculations

A. Add the following angles.

1. 48°15′ + 15°50′ = _____

2. 21°53′ + 41°21′ = _____

3. 32°18′36″ + 48°30′41″ = _____

4. 27°43′44″ + 10°54′25″ = _____

5. 72°51′30″ + 21°53′40″ + 15°45′45″ = _____

6. 36°12′55″ + 18°20′20″ + 54°18′26″ = _____

7. 40°50′30″ + 22°40′28″ + 16°18′32″ = _____

8. 8°30′20″ + 35°42′45″ + 5°42′15″ = _____

B. Subtract the following angles from 90°.

1. 45° = _____   **2.** 30° = _____   **3.** 52° = _____

4. 43°20′ = _____   **5.** 18°25′ = _____   **6.** 43°45′ = _____

7. 75°18′ = _____   **8.** 13°25′30″ = _____   **9.** 55°20′45″ = _____

10. 42°25′52″ = _____   **11.** 12°30′30″ = _____   **12.** 30°30′30″ = _____

C. Multiply the following angles.

1. 2 × 45° = _____   **2.** 2 × 30°45′ = _____

3. 2 × 18°20′15″ = _____   **4.** 4 × 45°18′30″ = _____

5. 6 × 42°20′42″ = _____   **6.** 8 × 19°30′30″ = _____

7. 2 × 20°53′48″ = _____   **8.** 3 × 11°32′35″ = _____

D. Divide the following angles.

1. 90° ÷ 5 = _____   **2.** 90° ÷ 3 = _____   **3.** 90° ÷ 4 = _____

4. 180° ÷ 12 = _____   **5.** 360° ÷ 4 = _____   **6.** 360° ÷ 5 = _____

7. 360° ÷ 6 = _____   **8.** 360° ÷ 8 = _____   **9.** 42°30′ ÷ 3 = _____

10. 320°40′ ÷ 5 = _____   **11.** 55°20′16″ ÷ 3 = _____   **12.** 89°43′20″ ÷ 6 = _____

E. Convert the following angles to degree decimals. Round off to three decimal places. (Example: 45°30′ = 45.5°)

1. 45°30′ = _____   **2.** 14°22′ = _____   **3.** 33°47′ = _____

4. 95°35′ = _____   **5.** 16°40′35″ = _____   **6.** 53°18′21″ = _____

7. 68°23′43″ = _____   **8.** 75°20′29″ = _____

F. Convert the following decimal degrees to degrees, minutes, and seconds.

1. 42.75° = _____   **2.** 18.166° = _____   **3.** 89.333° = _____

4. 63.452° = _____   **5.** 39.253° = _____   **6.** 28.896° = _____

7. 73.780° = _____   **8.** 51.655° = _____

Exercise 7.3: Metric Angular Measurements

A. Answer the following questions. Give all answers only in degrees.

1. Add the following angular measurements.

    a. 38° + 46° = _____   **b.** 16.5° + 24.38° + 25° = _____

    c. 93.45° + 54.25° = _____   **d.** 15.75° + 90.127° = _____

    e. 180° + 46.35° = _____

2. Subtract the following angular measurements.

    a. 54° − 22.5° = _____   **b.** 89.127° − 19.25° = _____

    c. 180° − 42.78° = _____   **d.** 89.35° − 37.70° = _____

    e. 90° − 15.83° = _____

3. Multiply the following angular measurements.

    a. 3 × 15.5° = _____   **b.** 2 × 52.76° = _____

    c. 5 × 25.138° = _____   **d.** 3 × 5.28° = _____

    e. 6 × 2.93° = _____

4. Divide the following angular measurements.

    a. 1/2 of 38.69° = _____   **b.** 1/4 of 129.76° = _____

    c. 1/3 of 76.25° = _____   **d.** 1/5 of 240.70° = _____

    e. 1/2 of 45° = _____

5. Find the complement of each of the following angular measurements.

    a. 26.45° = _____   **b.** 58.125° = _____

    c. 8.36° = _____   **d.** 79.50° = _____

    e. 29.72° = _____

Exercise 7.4: Types of Angles

A. Answer the following questions.

1. Illustrate the following: (a) right angle, (b) acute angle, and (c) obtuse angle.

    a. _____   b. _____   c. _____

2. (a) What do we call angles A and B in the following illustration? (b) What relationship do they have to each other?

2a. _____

2b. _____

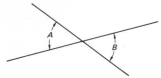

3. In the following illustration, $\angle A$ is complementary to $\angle B$. (a) What is the measurement of $\angle A$? (b) Why?

3a. _____

3b. _____

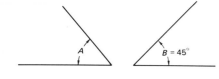

4. In the following illustration, $\angle A$ is supplementary to $\angle B$. (a) What is the measurement of $\angle A$? (b) Why?

4a. _____

4b. _____

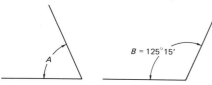

5. In the following illustration, line 1 is parallel to line 2 and line 3 is parallel to line 4. Which angles are equal in measurement?

5a. _____

5b. _____

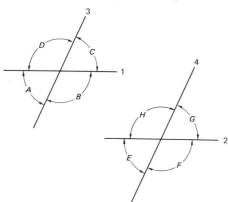

6. In the following illustration, what is the measurement of $\angle A$?

6. $\angle A =$ _____

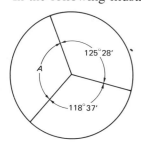

7. (a) What is the sum of the interior angles illustrated in the following diagram?

    (b) What is the measurement of ∠A if the sum of the other interior angles is 488°36′?

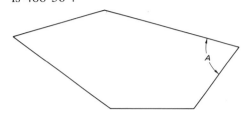

Exercise 7.5: Shop-Related Problems

A. The following diagrams represent situations that could be found in the machine shop. Solve for the indicated unknown angles.

1. Determine ∠A on the following tapered plug.

1. ∠A = _____

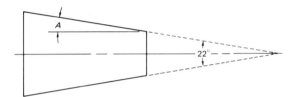

2. Determine ∠A, ∠B, ∠C, ∠D, and ∠E of the following gig.

2a. ∠A = _____

2b. ∠B = _____

2c. ∠C = _____

2d. ∠D = _____

2e. ∠E = _____

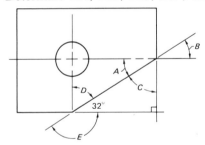

3. Determine ∠A in the following illustration.

3. ∠A = _____

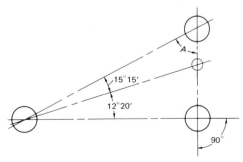

4. Determine $\angle A$ in the following illustration.

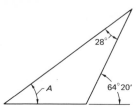

4. $\angle A =$ _____

5. Determine $\angle A$, $\angle B$, and $\angle C$ in the following illustration. The included angle of the tapered cut is 50°.

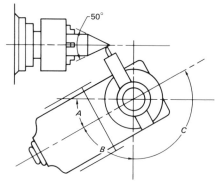

5a. $\angle A =$ _____

5b. $\angle B =$ _____

5c. $\angle C =$ _____

6. Determine $\angle A$, $\angle B$, $\angle C$, $\angle D$, $\angle E$, and $\angle F$ in the following illustration.

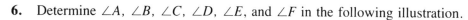
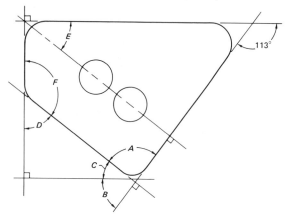

6a. $\angle A =$ _____

6b. $\angle B =$ _____

6c. $\angle C =$ _____

6d. $\angle D =$ _____

6e. $\angle E =$ _____

6f. $\angle F =$ _____

7. Determine $\angle A$, $\angle B$, and $\angle C$ in the following illustration.

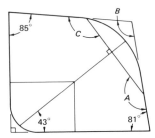

7a. $\angle A =$ _____

7b. $\angle B =$ _____

7c. $\angle C =$ _____

8. Determine ∠A, ∠B, and ∠C of the following transfer bushing.

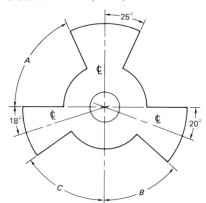

9. Determine ∠A and ∠B in the following illustration.

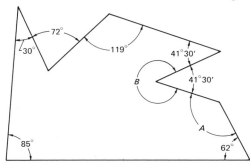

10. Determine ∠A, ∠B, and ∠C in the following illustration.

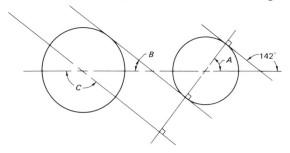

CHAPTER 8

TRIANGLES

Learning Objectives

After studying this chapter, you should be able to:

— Recognize the different types of triangles
— Apply the properties of special triangles in problem solving
— Apply triangle formulas in problem solving
— Recognize squares, rectangles, parallelograms, regular pentagons, and regular hexagons
— Apply right-triangle formulas to squares, rectangles, parallelograms, regular pentagons, and regular hexagons

An understanding of the properties of triangles is another useful tool for machinists. In the shop, we use our knowledge of the properties of triangles in activities ranging from initial machine setup to final part inspection. Right-triangle properties are used in many of the formulas that determine linear and angular measurements. They are applied to sine bars, table movements of milling machines, determination of depth and angle of cut, and inspection measurements that cannot be measured directly. Although these properties of triangles are very useful, we should keep in mind that, like any other tool, they are only as useful as our skill in using them.

INTERPRETATION OF TRIANGLES

A *plane figure* is a flat, two dimensional figure. A *triangle* is a closed plane figure that has three straight sides, as Figure 8.1 shows. In Chapter 7 we saw that triangles have three sides and that the sum of the interior angles of any triangle is 180°. For both triangles shown in Figure 8.1:

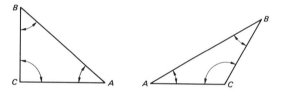

Figure 8.1

$$\angle A + \angle B + \angle C = 180°$$

Triangles are divided into two categories—right triangles and oblique triangles. A *right triangle,* shown in Figure 8.2, has a right angle as an interior angle. An

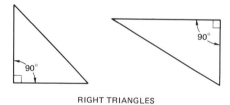

RIGHT TRIANGLES

Figure 8.2

oblique triangle, shown in Figure 8.3, does not have a right angle as an interior angle.

Right triangles are the more useful and important for machinists because they have mathematical relationships that are applied in making formula calculations. In fact, these relationships are the basis for most of the formulas a machinist uses. Oblique triangles also have some special relationships that are important to know.

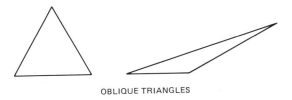

OBLIQUE TRIANGLES

Figure 8.3

RIGHT TRIANGLES

Remember that a right triangle is a triangle that has a right angle as an interior angle. When working with right triangles, we use special terms for the various parts of the triangle, as illustrated in Figure 8.4:

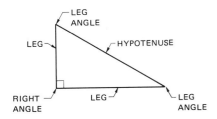

Figure 8.4

— A *right angle* is a 90° angle.

— *Leg angles* are the other two interior angles of a right triangle. The sum of the two leg angles is always 90°.

— The *hypotenuse* is the side opposite the right angle. The hypotenuse is always the longest side.

— The *legs* are the other two sides of a right triangle. These two sides form the right angle, and they are always perpendicular to each other.

NOTE: The legs of a right triangle are also called the *altitude* and the *base*, as shown in Figure 8.5. Either leg can be the altitude or the base, depending on how the triangle is positioned.

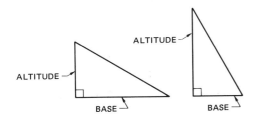

Figure 8.5

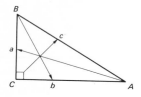

Figure 8.6

When working with formulas that apply to right triangles, we use the letters of the alphabet to represent the dimensions of the different parts of the triangle. The most common system of lettering is illustrated in Figure 8.6; however, there are other systems. Knowing what side and angle each letter stands for is important because formulas use these letters. The most common system of lettering is:

C = right angle
c = hypotenuse, the side opposite the right angle
b = base
B = leg angle opposite the base
a = altitude
A = leg angle opposite the altitude

Pythagorean Theorem

The *Pythagorean (pa- tha- ga-' re-an) theorem* is the basic mathematical relationship that exists between the lengths of the legs and the length of the hypotenuse of a right triangle. The theorem states that the square of the hypotenuse equals the sum of the squares of the legs. Using the terms *altitude* and *base* for the legs, the Pythagorean theorem states:

$$(\text{hypotenuse})^2 = (\text{altitude})^2 + (\text{base})^2$$

In equation form, as shown in Figure 8.7, we write:

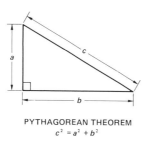

PYTHAGOREAN THEOREM
$c^2 = a^2 + b^2$

Figure 8.7

$$c^2 = a^2 + b^2$$

We can use this relationship to state basic formulas that apply to all right triangle problems. Many other formulas are derived from these basic formulas. We now look at the basic formulas and some examples of how they are used.

NOTE: We always need to know the measurements of two sides of a triangle in order to use the basic formulas.

RULE

To find the length of the hypotenuse when the lengths of the altitude and base are known, use the formula:

$$c = \sqrt{a^2 + b^2}$$

For example, to find the length of the hypotenuse of the right triangle shown in Figure 8.8, we first note the length of the legs:

$$a = 5''$$
$$b = 7''$$

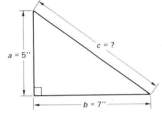

Figure 8.8

We then follow the rule for finding the length of the hypotenuse (c) when the lengths of the legs are known:

$$c = \sqrt{a^2 + b^2}$$

We next substitute the known values into the formula:

$$c = \sqrt{5^2 + 7^2}$$

We perform the operations within the radical by squaring 5 and 7:

$$c = \sqrt{25 + 49}$$

We add the squared values within the radical:

$$c = \sqrt{74}$$

Finally, we find the square root of the sum:

$$c = 8.602$$

Thus, the length of the hypotenuse of the triangle shown in Figure 8.8 is 8.602″, with the answer rounded off to the nearest thousandth.

RULE

To find the length of one of the legs (altitude or base) of a right triangle when the lengths of the hypotenuse and the other leg are known, use one of the following formulas:

$$b = \sqrt{c^2 - a^2} \quad \text{or} \quad a = \sqrt{c^2 - b^2}$$

The following example shows how to find the length of the base of a right triangle when the lengths of the hypotenuse and the altitude are known.

EXAMPLE

Problem

Find the length of the base (b) of the triangle shown in Figure 8.9.

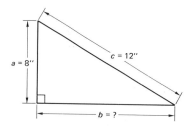

Figure 8.9

Analysis

First note the length of the hypotenuse (c) and of the altitude (a):

$$c = 12''$$
$$a = 8''$$

Then follow the rule for finding the length of the base when the lengths of the hypotenuse and the altitude are known:

$$b = \sqrt{c^2 - a^2}$$

Solution

Step 1:   Substitute the known values into the formula

$$b = \sqrt{12^2 - 8^2}$$

Step 2:   Perform the operations within the radical by squaring 12 and 8:

$$b = \sqrt{144 - 64}$$

Step 3:   Subtract the squared values and find the square root of the difference

$$b = \sqrt{80} = 8.944$$

Answer

$$b = 8.944'', \text{ rounded off to the nearest thousandth}$$

Special Right Triangles

There are three special right triangles—the 45°–45° (isosceles) right triangle, the 30°–60° right triangle, and the 3–4–5 right triangle. These triangles are called special right triangles because they have special properties.

45°– 45° Right Triangles

A *45°–45° (isosceles) right triangle* is a right triangle with leg angles of 45° and legs of equal length, as shown in Figure 8.10a. Any right triangle that has leg angles of 45° ($\angle A = \angle B = 45°$) is certain to have legs that are also equal. Likewise, any right triangle with equal legs ($a = b$) is certain to have 45° leg angles ($\angle A = \angle B = 45°$). One property cannot exist without the other.

Since the legs of a 45°–45° right triangle are equal, we usually use s rather than a or b to represent the leg measurement, as shown in Figure 8.10b. The three formulas derived earlier can then be simplified into two other formulas by replacing both a and b with s:

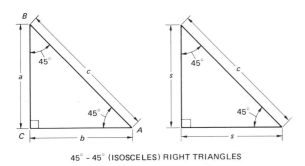

45° – 45° (ISOSCELES) RIGHT TRIANGLES

Figure 8.10a   **Figure 8.10b**

$$c = \sqrt{a^2 + b^2} \quad \text{is simplified to} \quad c = s\sqrt{2}$$

$$b = \sqrt{c^2 - a^2} \quad \text{is simplified to} \quad s = \frac{c}{\sqrt{2}}$$

$$a = \sqrt{c^2 - b^2} \quad \text{is simplified to} \quad s = \frac{c}{\sqrt{2}}$$

We must keep in mind that these formulas apply only to 45°–45° right triangles.

RULE

To find the length of the hypotenuse of a 45°–45° right triangle when the length of the legs is known, use the simplified formula:

$$c = s\sqrt{2}$$

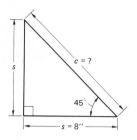

Figure 8.11

For example, Figure 8.11 tells us three things about the illustrated triangle: (1) it is a right triangle; (2) one leg measures 8″; (3) one leg angle is 45°. We want to know the dimensions that are not given.

We know the triangle is a 45°–45° right triangle because (1) the right angle is given, and (2) since one leg angle is 45°, the other leg angle must also be 45°. Since one leg measures 8″, the other leg must also measure 8″. The only dimension we need to find is the length of the hypotenuse (c). To find c, we follow the rule for finding the length of the hypotenuse of a 45°–45° right triangle when the length of the legs is known:

$$c = s\sqrt{2}$$

We substitute the known value of s into the formula:

$$c = 8\sqrt{2}$$

We next substitute the value of the square root of 2:

$$c = 8 \times 1.4142$$

We now multiply to solve the problem:

$$c = 11.314$$

Thus, the length of the hypotenuse of the 45°–45° right triangle shown in Figure 8.11 is 11.314″, with the answer rounded off to the nearest thousandth.

RULE

To find the length of the legs of a 45°–45° right triangle when the length of the hypotenuse is known, use the formula:

$$s = \frac{c}{\sqrt{2}}$$

The following example shows how to find the length of the legs of a 45°–45° right triangle when the length of the hypotenuse is known.

EXAMPLE

Problem

Find the length of the legs of the triangle shown in Figure 8.12.

Analysis

We know from Figure 8.12 that the triangle is a 45°–45° right triangle; since one leg angle is 45°, the other leg angle is also 45°. Since both legs of a 45°–45° right triangle are the same length, we need to find the length (s) of only one leg. Follow the rule for finding the length of the leg of a 45°–45° right triangle when the length of the hypotenuse is known:

$$s = \frac{c}{\sqrt{2}}$$

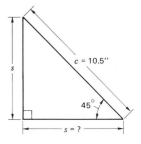

Figure 8.12

Solution

Step 1: Substitute the known value of c into the formula

$$s = \frac{10.5}{\sqrt{2}}$$

Step 2: Find the square root of 2 and divide to find the answer

$$s = \frac{10.5}{1.4142} = 7.425$$

Answer

$s = 7.425''$, rounded off to the nearest thousandth

30°– 60° Right Triangles

A *30°–60° right triangle* is a right triangle with leg angles of 30° and 60°. What makes this triangle special is that the length of the leg opposite the 30° angle is always one-half the length of the hypotenuse, as shown in Figure 8.13:

$$b = \frac{1}{2}c$$

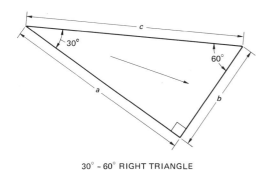

30° – 60° RIGHT TRIANGLE

Figure 8.13

The three basic right-triangle formulas can be simplified into formulas that apply only to 30°–60° right triangles because of the special relationship between the length of the hypotenuse and the length of the leg opposite the 30° angle. We need to keep in mind that these formulas do not apply to other right triangles.

NOTE: In the following rules and formulas, the short leg (opposite the 30° angle) is called *b,* and the long leg (opposite the 60° angle) is called *a,* as shown in Figure 8.13.

RULES

To find the length of the long leg (a) of a 30°–60° right triangle, use the formula:

$a = b\sqrt{3}$ (when the length of leg *b* is known)

$a = \dfrac{c\sqrt{3}}{2}$ (when the length of the hypotenuse is known)

To find the length of leg b of a 30°–60° right triangle, use the formulas:

$b = \dfrac{a}{\sqrt{3}}$ (when the length of leg *a* is known)

$b = \dfrac{1}{2}c$ (when the length of the hypotenuse is known)

To find the length of the hypotenuse of a 30°–60° right triangle, use the formula:

$c = \dfrac{2a}{\sqrt{3}}$ (when the length of the long leg, *a,* is known)

$c = 2b$ (when the length of the short leg, *b,* is known)

The following examples show how to use these formulas to find the length of the legs and the hypotenuse of 30°–60° right triangles.

EXAMPLE

Problem

Find the length of leg *b* of the 30°–60° right triangle shown in Figure 8.14.

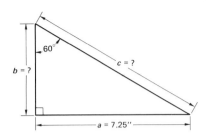

Figure 8.14

Analysis

We know that leg a of the right triangle shown in Figure 8.14 is 7.25″ and that it is opposite a 60° angle. Since the right angle and a leg angle of 60° are known, the other leg angle must be 30°. Therefore, the triangle is a 30°–60° right triangle. Since we know the length of leg a, we can follow the rule for finding the length of leg b of a 30°–60° right triangle when the length of leg a is known:

$$b = \frac{a}{\sqrt{3}}$$

Solution

Step 1: Substitute the known value of a into the formula

$$b = \frac{7.250}{\sqrt{3}}$$

Step 2: Substitute the value of the square root of 3

$$b = \frac{7.250}{1.732}$$

Step 3: Divide to find the length of leg b

Answer

$b = 4.186″$, rounded off to the nearest thousandth

Let us look again at the right triangle shown in Figure 8.14. We know that it is a 30°–60° right triangle. We know that $a = 7.250″$. We have already found that $b = 4.186″$. Now let us find the length of the hypotenuse.

We can follow either of the rules for finding the length of the hypotenuse when the length of one of the legs is known. In this case, one of the formulas is preferred because it uses a value (a) given in the problem statement. The other formula uses a calculated value, the length of side b. If a mistake is made in calculating the length of b, then the second calculation will also be wrong.

> **NOTE:** The preferred formula uses a value given in the problem statement rather than a calculated value.

Consider both ways of finding the length of the hypotenuse. First, we follow the preferred rule for finding the length of the hypotenuse when the length of leg a (opposite the 60° angle) is known:

$$c = \frac{2a}{\sqrt{3}}$$

We substitute the known value of a into the formula:

$$c = \frac{2 \times 7.25}{\sqrt{3}}$$

We then find the square root of 3:

$$c = \frac{2 \times 7.25}{1.732}$$

We next carry out the operations in the numerator:

$$c = \frac{14.50}{1.732}$$

Finally, we divide to find the length of c:

$$c = 8.372'', \text{ rounded off to the nearest thousandth}$$

We can also calculate the length of the hypotenuse by following the rule for finding the length of the hypotenuse when the length of leg b (opposite the 30° angle) is known:

$$c = 2b$$

Substitute the found value of b into the formula:

$$c = 2 \times 4.186$$

Finally, multiply to find the length of the hypotenuse:

$$c = 8.372''$$

EXAMPLE

Problem

Find the length of leg a and the hypotenuse (c) of the 30°–60° right triangle shown in Figure 8.15.

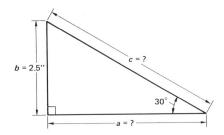

Figure 8.15

Analysis

We know that leg b of the right triangle in Figure 8.15 is 2.5″ and that it is opposite a 30° angle. We also know the triangle is a right triangle. From this information we recognize the triangle as a 30°–60° right triangle. Since the right angle and a leg angle of 30° are known, the other leg angle must be 60°.

Step 1a: Find the length of the hypotenuse by following the rule:

$$c = 2b$$

Step 1b: Substitute the known value of b into the formula:

$$c = 2 \times 2.5$$

Step 1c: Multiply to find the length of the hypotenuse

$$c = 5$$

Step 2a: Find the length of leg a by following the rule:

$$a = b\sqrt{3}$$

Step 2b: Substitute the known value of b into the formula

$$a = 2.5\sqrt{3}$$

Step 2c: Find the square root of 3

$$a = 2.5 \times 1.732$$

Step 2d: Multiply to find a

Answer

$$a = 4.330″, \text{ rounded off to the nearest thousandth}$$

3–4–5 Right Triangles

A *3–4–5 right triangle* is a right triangle whose sides measure 3–4–5 or multiples of these lengths, such as 6–8–10, as shown in Figure 8.16. We use basic right-triangle formulas to solve 3–4–5 right triangles.

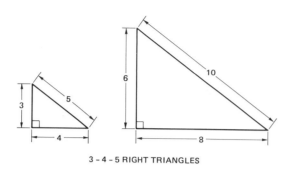

3 – 4 – 5 RIGHT TRIANGLES

Figure 8.16

Of the three special right triangles, the 3–4–5 right triangles have the least importance for machinists. They are used primarily when making up right triangles because 3–4–5 are easy numbers to remember.

OBLIQUE TRIANGLES

Recall that oblique triangles are triangles that do not have an interior right angle. However, all oblique-triangle formulas are derived from the relationships of right triangles. Thus, oblique triangles have their own special properties and right-triangle properties as well.

Special Oblique Triangles

There are two special oblique triangles—the equilateral triangle and the isosceles triangle.

Equilateral Triangles

An *equilateral triangle* is a triangle in which all three of the sides are the same length, as shown in Figure 8.17a:

$$a = b = c$$

All the interior angles of an equilateral triangle are always 60°:

$$\angle A = \angle B = \angle C$$

One property cannot exist without the other. When we see a triangle with three equal sides, we know that all the angles of that triangle are 60° and vice versa.

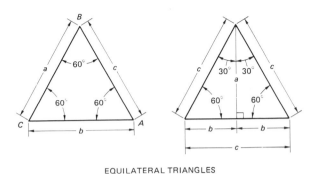

EQUILATERAL TRIANGLES

Figure 8.17a   **Figure 8.17b**

If we draw a line (a) from any vertex of an equilateral triangle perpendicular to the opposite side, the result is two equal 30°–60° right triangles, as illustrated in Figure 8.17b. Notice that line a divides side c into two equal parts. Therefore, all the formulas for 30°–60° right triangles can be used for equilateral triangles.

Isosceles Triangles

An *isosceles triangle,* shown in Figure 8.18a, is a triangle in which two of the sides are the same length:

$$a = c$$

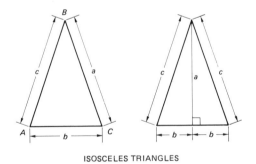

ISOSCELES TRIANGLES

Figure 8.18a   **Figure 8.18b**

The two angles opposite the equal sides of an isosceles triangle are also always equal:

$$\angle A = \angle C$$

Recall that a 45°–45° right triangle is an isosceles triangle.

If we draw a line (a) from the unequal angle perpendicular to the opposite side of an isosceles triangle, the result is two equal triangles, as shown in Figure 8.18b. Again, line a divides the base into two equal parts. Here, too, we can apply the basic formulas for right triangles.

RULE

To find the measurements of an isosceles triangle, first draw a line from the unequal angle perpendicular to the opposite side to form two equal right triangles, and then apply the necessary right-triangle formula.

The following example shows how to solve a shop-related problem involving an isosceles triangle.

EXAMPLE

Problem

Determine the center-to-center distance x of the insulating ring shown in Figure 8.19a. The three holes are equally spaced.

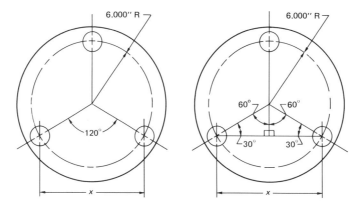

Figure 8.19a   Figure 8.19b

Analysis

Draw a center line between any two holes to form the third side (x) of a triangle with a 120° angle, as shown in Figure 8.19b. Since each of the other two sides of the triangle is a radius of the circle and each equals 6″, we know that we have an isosceles triangle. We now draw a line from the vertex of the isosceles triangle perpendicular to the third side to form two 30°–60° right triangles. From the figure, we see that the hypotenuse of each 30°–60° right triangle = 6″. We also know that the perpendicular line we have drawn = 3″ because the side opposite the 30° angle = one-half the hypotenuse. Thus, in terms of a 30°–60° right triangle, we know that:

$$c = 6''$$
$$b = 3''$$

We can use either of two formulas to find the measurement of the third side:

$$a = b\sqrt{3} \quad \text{or} \quad a = \frac{c\sqrt{3}}{2}$$

Solution

Step 1: Choose one of the formulas for finding the side of a 30°–60° right triangle opposite the 60° angle:

$$a = b\sqrt{3}$$

Step 2: Substitute the known value of b and the value of the square root of 3 into the formula:

$$a = 3 \times 1.732$$

Step 3: Multiply to find a

$$a = 5.196$$

Step 4: Multiply a by 2 to find x

Note: Since the perpendicular line creates two equal 30°–60° right triangles, the sides opposite the 60° angles are the same. In other words, the perpendicular line divides x into two equal parts.

Answer

$$x = 10.392''$$

Scalene Triangles

A *scalene triangle* is a triangle in which none of the sides are the same length and none of the angles are equal. A scalene triangle is the most difficult type of triangle to work with. However, we can apply a formula to scalene triangles if the lengths of its three sides are known. This formula is called the *projection formula*.

As Figure 8.20 shows, we must first draw an altitude to apply the projection

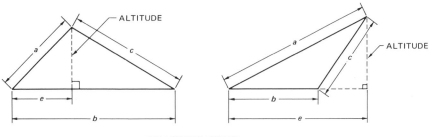

SCALENE TRIANGLES

Figure 8.20a   **Figure 8.20b**

formula to a scalene triangle. An *altitude* is a line drawn from the vertex of one of the angles perpendicular to the opposite side, as in Figure 8.20a, or to an extension of the opposite side, as in Figure 8.20b. The altitude creates two right triangles. We then use the projection formula to calculate dimension *e*. When the value of *e* is known, we can use right-triangle formulas, in which $b = e$, for any further calculations.

RULE

To apply right-triangle formulas to scalene triangles, first draw in an altitude and use the projection formulas to calculate an additional length, e:

$$e = \frac{a^2 + b^2 - c^2}{2b}$$

Then apply the basic right-triangle formulas, substituting e for b in the formulas.

OTHER GEOMETRIC FIGURES

Geometric figures other than triangles are also important to the work of machinists. We already understand some of these figures fairly well—squares and rectangles, for example. Each has its own special properties, but we will again find that the formulas for right triangles can be usefully applied.

Squares

A *square* is a four-sided plane figure in which all four sides are equal and all interior angles are 90°. Figure 8.21a illustrates a square. A line (*c*) drawn to connect two opposite angles of a square creates two equal 45°–45° right triangles, as shown in Figure 8.21b. A *diagonal* is a line connecting two nonconsecutive (not next to each other) vertexes. Thus, the formulas for 45°–45° right triangles can be applied to squares.

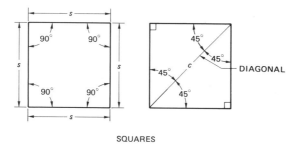

SQUARES

Figure 8.21a   Figure 8.21b

RULE

To find the measurements of a square, first draw a diagonal to form two equal 45°–45° right triangles and then apply the formulas for 45°–45° right triangles.

Rectangles

A *rectangle*, shown in Figure 8.22a, is a four-sided plane figure in which the opposite sides are equal and each interior angle is 90°. Figure 8.22b shows that a diagonal (*c*) drawn to connect the opposite angles of a rectangle will create two equal right triangles. The angular measurements of the leg angles will depend on the length of the legs. In this case, the general formulas for right triangles will apply. Squares are special rectangles.

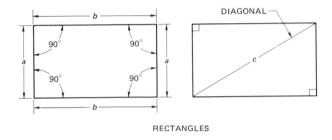

RECTANGLES

Figure 8.22a   Figure 8.22b

RULE

To find the measurements of a rectangle, first draw a diagonal to connect the opposite angles to create two equal right triangles. Then apply the basic right-triangle formulas.

Parallelograms

A *parallelogram*, shown in Figure 8.23a, is a four-sided plane figure in which the opposite sides are equal and parallel and the opposite interior angles are equal. *Parallel lines* are straight lines that are always the same distance apart and never

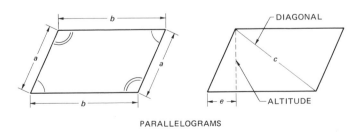

PARALLELOGRAMS

Figure 8.23a   Figure 8.23b

meet. Drawing a diagonal (*c*) in a parallelogram, as shown in Figure 8.23b, creates two equal (but not right) triangles. Since no right triangles are formed by the diagonals, the projection formula for scalene triangles is used with parallelograms. Squares and rectangles are special parallelograms.

RULE

To find the measurements of a parallelogram, first draw a diagonal to create two equal triangles and then use the projection formula for scalene triangles.

The following example shows how to find the measurements of a parallelogram in a shop-related problem.

EXAMPLE

Problem

Determine the thickness (*x*) of the parallelogram-shaped spacer needed between the male and female dovetails shown in Figure 8.24. The spacer is needed to maintain proper slippage between the dovetails.

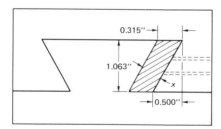

Figure 8.24

Analysis

First find the measurements of the sides of the parallelogram by using the basic right-triangle formulas. Then draw a diagonal to create two equal triangles and use the projection formula for scalene triangles to find the measurement of *x*.

Solution

Step 1: Use the basic right-triangle formula to find the measurement of the hypotenuse of the right triangle whose sides are 0.500″ and 1.063″

$$c = \sqrt{a^2 + b^2}$$
$$= \sqrt{1.063^2 + 0.500^2} = \sqrt{1.130 + 0.25} = \sqrt{1.38}$$
$$= 1.175$$

STEP 1

Step 2: Draw a diagonal in the parallelogram and use the basic right-triangle formula to find the measurement of the hypotenuse (diagonal)

$$c = \sqrt{a^2 + b^2}$$
$$= \sqrt{1.063^2 + 0.815^2} = \sqrt{1.130 + 0.664} = \sqrt{1.794}$$
$$= 1.339$$

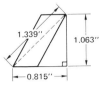

STEP 2

Step 3: Draw an altitude to create a right triangle and use the projection formula to find e

$$e = \frac{a^2 + b^2 - c^2}{2b}$$
$$= \frac{1.339^2 + 1.175^2 - 0.315^2}{2 \times 1.175} = \frac{1.793 + 1.381 - 0.099}{2.35} = \frac{3.075}{2.35}$$
$$= 1.308$$

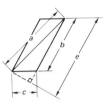

STEP 3

Step 4: Subtract 1.175 from 1.308 to find the side of the right triangle whose hypotenuse is $0.315''$ and use the basic right-triangle formula to find the measurement of x

STEP 4

$$a = \sqrt{c^2 - b^2}$$
$$= \sqrt{0.315^2 - 0.133^2} = \sqrt{0.099 - 0.018} = \sqrt{0.081}$$
$$= 0.285$$

Answer

$$x = 0.285''$$

Regular Pentagons

A *regular pentagon* is a five-sided plane figure in which all the sides are the same length and each interior angle is equal to 108°, as shown in Figure 8.25a. Two different isosceles triangles can be constructed in a regular pentagon, as shown in Figure 8.25b. One can be constructed by drawing a diagonal connecting the vertexes

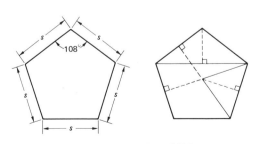

REGULAR PENTAGONS

Figure 8.25a   Figure 8.25b

of opposite angles. The other can be constructed by drawing lines from the vertexes of any two neighboring angles perpendicular to their opposite sides. The triangles formed in these two ways are shown in Figure 8.25b. Since both triangles formed within a regular pentagon are isosceles triangles, right triangles can also be constructed, as discussed earlier.

RULE

To find the measurements of a regular pentagon, first construct isosceles triangles within the pentagon and then follow the rule for finding the measurements of isosceles triangles.

Regular Hexagons

A *regular hexagon* is a six-sided plane figure in which all the sides are the same length and each interior angle is 120°, as shown in Figure 8.26a. Diagonals drawn through the center of a regular hexagon to connect the vertexes of opposite angles will create equilateral triangles. Then, 30°–60° right triangles can be constructed, as shown in Figure 8.26b.

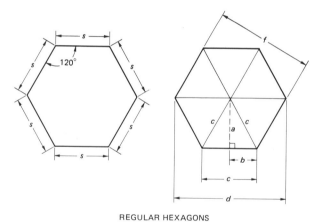

REGULAR HEXAGONS

Figure 8.26a   Figure 8.26b

RULE

To find the dimensions of equilateral triangles constructed within a regular hexagon, draw diagonals through the center to create equilateral triangles. Then construct 30°–60° right triangles and use the formulas for 30°–60° right triangles to find the measurements.

Since the regular hexagon is often encountered in the machine trades, additional formulas are used to find the diagonal length (*d*) and the distance across the flats (*f*) directly. These dimensions are illustrated in Figure 8.26b.

RULE

To find the diagonal length (d) and the distance across the flats (f) directly, use the formulas:

$$d = 2c$$

$$d = \frac{2f}{\sqrt{3}}$$

$$e = \frac{d\sqrt{3}}{2}$$

Metric Applications

All the concepts and formulas presented in this chapter also apply when metric units are used. The only change is that the distances are measured in millimeters instead of in inches.

TERMS FOR REVIEW

— plane figure
— triangle
— right triangle
— oblique triangle
— right angle
— leg angles
— hypotenuse
— legs
— altitude
— base
— Pythagorean theorem
— 45°–45° (isosceles) right triangle
— 30°–60° right triangle

— 3–4–5 right triangle
— equilateral triangle
— isosceles triangle
— scalene triangle
— projection formula
— altitude
— square
— diagonal
— rectangle
— parallelogram
— parallel lines
— regular pentagon

Exercises

Exercise 8.1: Right Triangles

A. Solve the following problems for the altitude, base, or hypotenuse as indicated. Round off answers to the nearest thousandth.

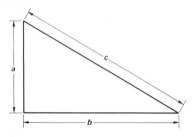

1. Find c when $a = 6$ and $b = 8$.
2. Find c when $b = 9$ and $a = 10$.
3. Find b when $c = 13$ and $a = 7$.
4. Find a when $c = 25$ and $b = 18$.
5. Find b when $c = 10$ and $a = 5.5$.
6. Find c when $b = 8.485$ and $a = 5.348$.
7. Find b when $c = 18.555$ and $a = 9.492$.
8. Find a when $c = 7.250$ and $b = 3.375$.

1. $c =$ _____
2. $c =$ _____
3. $b =$ _____
4. $a =$ _____
5. $b =$ _____
6. $c =$ _____
7. $b =$ _____
8. $a =$ _____

B. Calculate the unknown dimensions in the following illustrations. Round off answers to the nearest thousandth.

1. Determine the diameter (x) in the following illustration.

1. $x =$ _____

2. Determine dimension x in the following illustration.

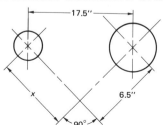

2. $x =$ _____

3. Determine the center-to-center dimension (*x*) of the following plate.

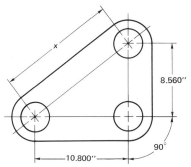

3. *x* = _____

4. Determine dimension *x* in the following illustration.

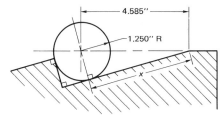

4. *x* = _____

5. Determine dimension R in the following illustration.

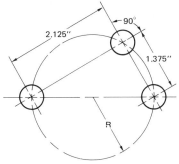

5. R = _____

6. Determine dimensions *x* and *y* in the following illustration.

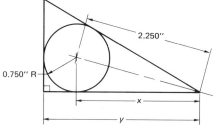

6a. *x* = _____

6b. *y* = _____

7. Determine dimensions *x* and *y* of the following tapered arbor.

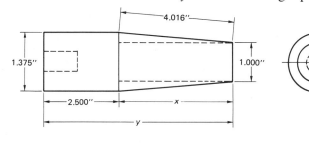

7a. *x* = _____

7b. *y* = _____

8. Determine dimensions x and y in the following illustration.

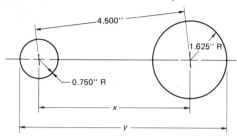

8a. x = _____

8b. y = _____

9. Determine the overall length x of the following tube section.

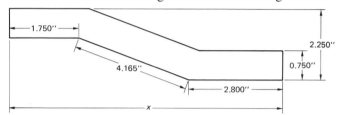

9. x = _____

Exercise 8.2: Special Right Triangles

A. Determine the unknown dimensions indicated on the following triangles 1, 2, 3, 4, 5, and 6. Round off the answers to the nearest thousandth.

1.

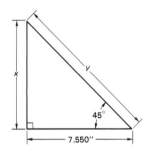

x = _____

y = _____

2.

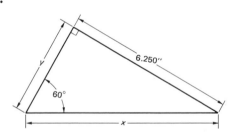

x = _____

y = _____

3

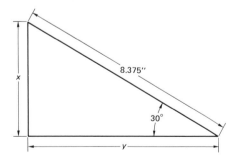

x = _____

y = _____

4.

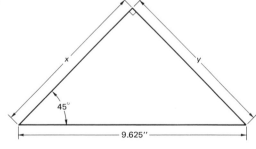

x = _____

y = _____

5.

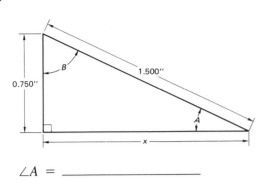

$\angle A =$ _____

$\angle B =$ _____

$x =$ _____

6.

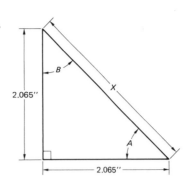

$\angle A =$ _____

$\angle B =$ _____

$x =$ _____

B. The following are possible problem situations in the shop. Round off all answers to the nearest thousandth.

1. Determine the diameter (D) of the round stock needed to cut a 1.750″ square form.

1. $D =$

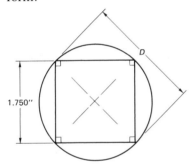

2. Determine dimension x of the following piece.

2. $x =$

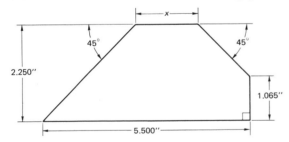

3. Determine dimensions x and y of the following dovetail.

3a. $x =$

3b. $y =$ _____

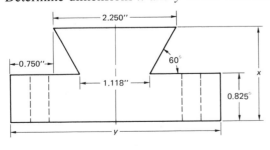

4. Determine dimensions x and y of the following plate.

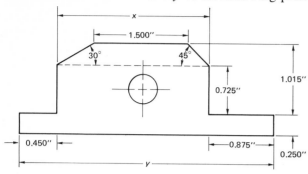

4a. x = _____

4b. y = _____

5. Determine dimension x of the following heating point.

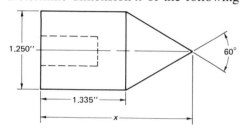

5. x = _____

6. Determine dimensions x and y of the following piece.

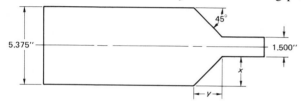

6a. x = _____

6b. y = _____

7. Determine the x and y coordinate dimensions of the following illustration.

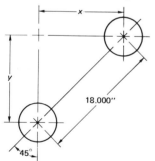

7a. x = _____

7b. y = _____

8. Determine the x and y dimensions of the following coupling.

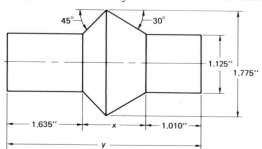

8a. x = _____

8b. y = _____

Exercise 8.3: Oblique Triangles

A. Calculate the unknown dimensions indicated on the following diagrams. Round off answers to the nearest thousandth.

1.

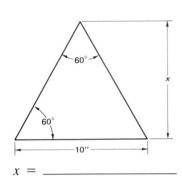

$x =$ _____

2.

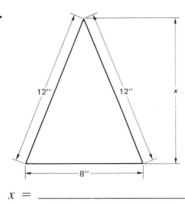

$x =$ _____

3.

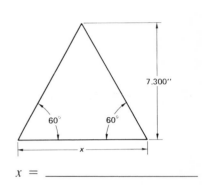

$x =$ _____

4.

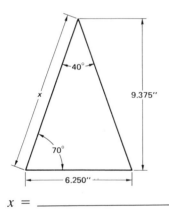

$x =$ _____

5.

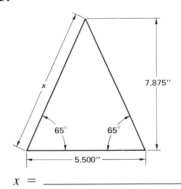

$x =$ _____

6.

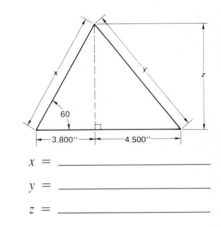

$x =$ _____

$y =$ _____

$z =$ _____

7.

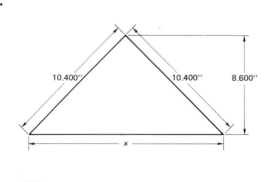

$x =$ _____

8.

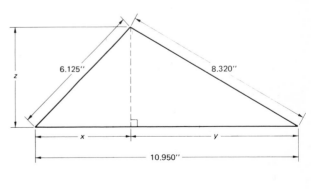

$x =$ _____

$y =$ _____

$z =$ _____

9.

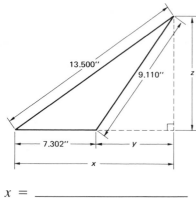

$x =$ _____

$y =$ _____

$z =$ _____

B. The following are possible problem situations in the shop. Round off answers to the nearest thousandth.

1. Determine the depth (x) of the V-thread illustrated.

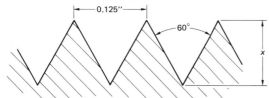

1. $x =$ _____

2. Determine the outside diameter (x) of the following gear.

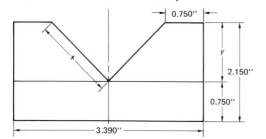

2. $x =$ _____

3. Determine dimensions x and y of the block illustrated.

3a. $x =$ _____

3b. $y =$ _____

4. Determine the center-to-center distance (*x*) of the plate illustrated.

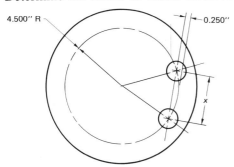

4. *x* = _____

5. Determine dimensions *x* and *y* of the following piece.

5a. *x* = _____

5b. *y* = _____

Exercise 8.4: Other Geometric Figures

A. Solve the following problems. Round off all answers to the nearest thousandth.

1. What is the diagonal measurement of a 8.000″ square?

1. _____

2. What is the length of the longest side of a rectangular piece having a width of 4.500″ and a diagonal measurement of 15″?

2. _____

3. What is the diagonal measurement of a 7.5″ × 19″ rectangle?

3. _____

4. What is the length of the sides of a square if the diagonal measurement of the square is 12.550″?

4. _____

5. If the distance across the flats on a regular hexagon is 4.350″, what are the lengths of its sides?

5. _____

6. If the distance across the corners of a regular hexagon is 1.375″, what is the distance across the flats?

6. _____

B. Solve for the unknown dimensions in the following problem situations in the shop. Round off answers to the nearest thousandth.

1. Determine dimensions x and y of the following 0.875″ square cut from a piece of round stock

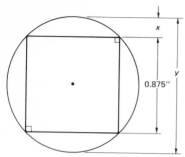

1a. x = _____

1b. y = _____

2. Determine dimensions x, y, and z of the following regular hexagon cut from a 1.500″ piece of round stock.

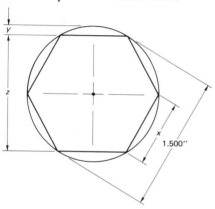

2a x = _____

2b. y = _____

2c. z = _____

3. Determine angles A, B, and C of the following parallelogram.

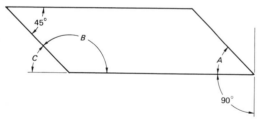

3a. $\angle A$ = _____

3b. $\angle B$ = _____

3c. $\angle C$ = _____

4. Determine dimensions x and y of the following regular pentagon.

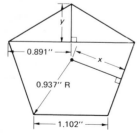

4a. x = _____

4b. y = _____

Exercise 8.5: Metric Applications

A. Solve the following problems. Round off all answers to the nearest hundredth.

1. What is the length of the hypotenuse of a right triangle if the legs measure 58.30mm and 75.15mm?

1. _____

2. If the leg opposite the 30° angle of a right triangle is 38.02mm, what is the length of (a) the hypotenuse and (b) the other leg?

2a. _____

2b. _____

3. What is the diagonal measurement of a 95.8mm × 165.5mm rectangle?

3. _____

4. If the length of the side of a regular hexagon is 59.15mm, what is the distance across the flats?

4. _____

5. What is the length of the legs of a 45°–45° right triangle if the hypotenuse is 44.75mm?

5. _____

6. Determine dimensions *x* and *y* of the following square.

6a. *x* = _____

6b. *y* = _____

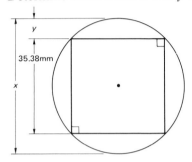

7. Determine dimensions *x* and *y* of the following illustration.

7a. *x* = _____

7b. *y* = _____

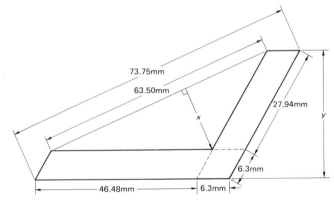

8. Determine dimensions *u*, *v*, *w*, *x*, *y*, and *z* of the following hole layout pattern.

8a. *u* = _____

8b. *v* = _____

8c. *w* = _____

8d. *x* = _____

8e. *y* = _____

8f. *z* = _____

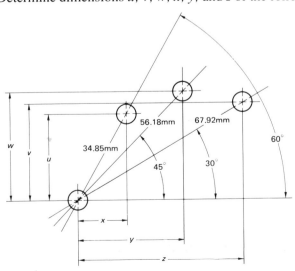

CHAPTER 9

CIRCLES

Learning Objectives

After studying this chapter, you should be able to:

— Calculate radius, diameter, chord, circumference, and arc measurements of circles
— Apply tangent relationships to make linear- and angular-measurement calculations
— Apply angle-circle relationships to make angular-measurement calculations
— Make inscribed circle and triangle calculations
— Apply circle concepts, relationships, and formulas to solve shop-related problems
— Index circles through direct-, simple-, and angular-indexing methods

Circles and their geometric properties are important to us as machinists. These properties are applied to shop work that involves circular shapes and curves as well as rotational operations.

INTERPRETATION OF CIRCLES

A *circle*, shown in Figure 9.1, is a figure formed by a closed curved line. Every point on the curved line is equally distant from a center point.

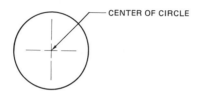

Figure 9.1

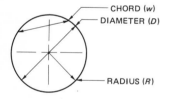

Figure 9.2

Circular shapes and curves are defined by one of two measurements—the radius or the diameter. The *radius* (plural *radii*) of a circle is the measurement from the center of a circle to a point on the circle. Any circle has only one radius measurement. However, we can make that measurement from the center to any point on the circle. In Figure 9.2, R is the radius.

The *diameter* of a circle is the measurement from one point to another point on the circle across the center. There is only one diameter measurement for any circle. However, the measurement can be made through the center from any point on the circle. In Figure 9.2, D is the diameter. The diameter is always two times the radius:

$$D = 2R$$

We also work with other measurements of circles—chords, the circumference, and arcs. A *chord* is a measurement across a circle between any two points on the circle. In Figure 9.2, w is a chord. Unlike the radius or diameter, there are many possible chords of a circle. Notice that the diameter is one of the chords.

The *circumference, c,* is the measurement around a circle, as shown in Figure 9.3a. Fractional parts of the circumference, shown in Figure 9.3b, are called arcs. An *arc*, then, is the measurement along the curve between two points on a circle. The points that define an arc can be marked by a chord or by two radii, or an arc can be a curved part of a workpiece. Notice from Figure 9.3 that there are always two arc measurements between any two points on a circle—the major (larger) arc and the minor (smaller) arc.

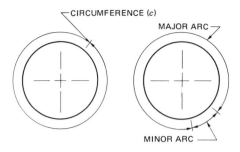

Figure 9.3a   Figure 9.3b

When working with circular shapes or curves, we must always be concerned with the center. The center is the most important point of any circular shape. *Concentric circles,* shown in Figure 9.4, are circles that have the same center. The symbol used is ⊙.

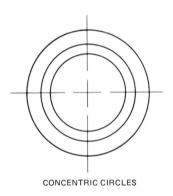

CONCENTRIC CIRCLES

Figure 9.4

Chords

We have already stated that the measurement of one particular chord, the diameter of a circle, is two times the radius, or $D = 2R$. Other chord measurements are calculated by using formulas. These formulas are quite useful in the shop, especially in problems concerned with keyway or flat measurements on round shafts. The chord formulas most often used are given in the following rules, where Figure 9.5 is used for reference. In the figure, h is the height of the arc, w is the chord, R is the radius, and D is the diameter.

Figure 9.5

RULES

To find the chord measurement (w) from the diameter of the circle and the height of the arc, use the formula:

$$w = 2\sqrt{Dh - h^2}$$

To find the diameter (D) of a circle from the chord measurements, use the formula:

$$D = \frac{(1/2\ w)^2 + h^2}{h}$$

To find the height of the arc (h) from the chord measurement and the diameter, use the formula:

$$h = \frac{D - \sqrt{D^2 - w^2}}{2}$$

The following example shows how to use these formulas in a shop situation.

EXAMPLE

Problem

Calculate the depth of a (h) cut necessary to produce a 0.375″ flat on a 0.875″ shaft, as shown in Figure 9.6.

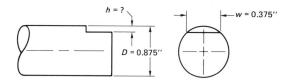

Figure 9.6

Analysis

Use the formula for finding the height of the arc from the chord measurement and the diameter:

$$h = \frac{D - \sqrt{D^2 - w^2}}{2}$$

We know that:

$$D = 0.875″$$
$$w = 0.375″$$

Solution

Step 1:　Substitute the known values into the formula:

$$h = \frac{0.875 - \sqrt{0.875^2 - 0.375^2}}{2}$$

Step 2: Perform the operations within the radical

$$h = \frac{0.875 - \sqrt{0.766 - 0.141}}{2}$$

$$= \frac{0.875 - \sqrt{0.625}}{2}$$

Step 3: Substitute the value of the square root of 0.625

$$h = \frac{0.875 - 0.791}{2}$$

Step 4: Perform the subtraction operation indicated in the numerator

$$h = \frac{0.084}{2}$$

Step 5: Divide to find h

Answer

$$h = 0.042''$$

Circumference

When working with circumference measurements of circular shapes, we use the formulas given in the following rules. These formulas are stated in reference to Figure 9.7.

> **NOTE:** We must remember that $\pi = 3.1416$. For any circle, the ratio of the circumference of the circle to its diameter is 3.1416. Since this ratio is always the same for all circles, it is called a constant. This constant has been given the name pi (the Greek letter π) and is used in many formulas concerned with circles.

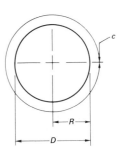

Figure 9.7

RULES

To find the circumference of a circle using the diameter, use the formula:

$$c = \pi D$$

To find the circumference of a circle using the radius, use the formula:

$$c = 2\pi R$$

To find the diameter of a circle, use the formula:

$$D = \frac{c}{\pi}$$

To find the radius of a circle, use the formula:

$$R = \frac{c}{2\pi}$$

For example, to calculate the circumference of the 5″-diameter wheel shown in Figure 9.8, we follow the rule for finding the circumference of a circle using the diameter:

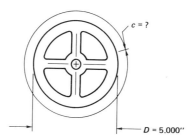

Figure 9.8

$$c = \pi D$$

We substitute the known values into the formula:

$$c = 3.1416 \times 5$$

We then multiply to find the circumference:

$$c = 15.708″, \text{ rounded off}$$

Arcs

The length of an arc has the same ratio to the circumference of a circle as the central angle (φ, the Greek letter phi) of that arc has to 360°:

$$\frac{\text{arc}}{\text{circumference}} = \frac{\text{central angle}}{360°}$$

Recall from Chapter 7 that a central angle is an angle whose vertex is at the center of a circle and whose sides are radii of the circle. Some useful formulas are derived from this proportional relationship. These formulas are given in the following rules, in reference to Figure 9.9.

RULES

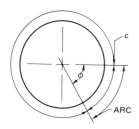

Figure 9.9

To find the measurement of an arc, use the formula:

$$\text{arc} = \frac{c \times \phi}{360°}$$

To find the measurement of the central angle of an arc, use the formula:

$$\phi = \frac{\text{arc} \times 360°}{c}$$

To find the circumference of a circle, use the formula:

$$c = \frac{\text{arc} \times 360°}{\phi}$$

The following example shows how to use these rules to calculate the length of an arc.

EXAMPLE

Problem

Calculate the measurement of the arc of the 40° angle on the 4.5″-diameter circle shown in Figure 9.10.

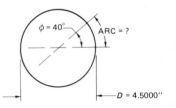

Figure 9.10

Analysis

First calculate the circumference of the circle by using the formula:

$$c = \pi D$$

Then calculate the arc measurement by using the formula:

$$\text{arc} = \frac{c \times \phi}{360°}$$

Solution

Step 1a: Substitute the known values into the formula for finding the circumference

$$c = 3.1416 \times 4.5$$

Step 1b: Multiply to find the circumference

$$c = 14.137″, \text{ rounded off}$$

Step 2: Substitute the known values into the formula for finding the arc measurement

$$\text{arc} = \frac{14.137 \times 40}{360}$$

Step 3: Perform the operations in the numerator

$$\text{arc} = \frac{565.49}{360}$$

Step 4: Divide to find the arc measurement

Answer

$$arc = 1.571''$$

TANGENT RELATIONSHIPS

To deal with circular relationships, we must understand the concept of tangents. As shown in Figure 9.11, a *tangent line* is a straight line that touches a circle or curve at only one point. *Tangent curves* or *tangent circles* are curves or circles that touch each other at only one point. The points at which lines, curves, or circles are tangent are called *tangent points*. In Figure 9.11, the tangent points are labeled TP.

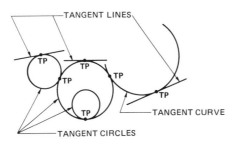

Figure 9.11

The concept of tangents is important to machinists because they work with both straight and curved surfaces. The points at which tangent surfaces flow into other tangent surfaces are the tangent points. In Figure 9.12, arrows point to the tangent points.

Figure 9.12

In the shop, improper control of straight and curved surfaces at a point of tangency will lead to awkward-looking intersections. Such intersections are to be avoided unless, of course, they are in the print specifications. Machinists can maintain the desired control over the point of tangency by recognizing some basic facts. Lines that are tangent to circles or curves are always perpendicular to the radius of those circles or curves at the tangent point, as shown in Figure 9.13a. The radii of tangent curves and circles are *colinear* (on the same straight line) at the tangent point, as shown in Figure 9.13b.

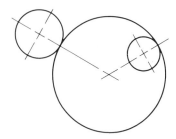

Figure 9.13a   **Figure 9.13b**

A common shop problem that requires recognition of these geometric situations is illustrated in Figure 9.14. The figure shows how two lines (or straight surfaces) that are tangent to a common circular surface may intersect. The figure shows how, in this situation, two equal right triangles can be set up by drawing a center line.

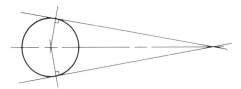

Figure 9.14

Tangent surfaces are also important when determining overall surface dimensions. As Figure 9.15 shows, the tangent points at which curved surfaces flow into straight or other curved surfaces become the intersecting points for the central angle of the curved surface (arc). The central angle in each case is always the supplement of the angle formed by the tangent lines of the curve:

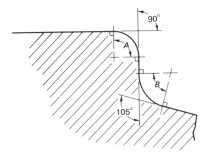

Figure 9.15

$\angle A$ = central angle = 90° (supplement of 90°)

$\angle B$ = central angle = 75° (supplement of 105°)

Since we know the central angle, we could calculate the length of the curved surfaces if we knew the radii of the curves.

For example, we may want to determine the length of the curved surface (arc) shown in Figure 9.16. Since the angle of the tangent line is 135°, we know that the central angle (ϕ) of the curved surface is 45°, the supplement of 135°. We also know that the radius is 1.250″ and that $\pi = 3.1416$.

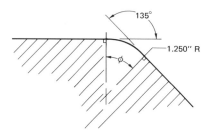

Figure 9.16

To calculate the circumference of the imaginary circle of which the curved surface is a part, we use the formula for finding the circumference:

$$c = 2\pi R$$

We substitute the known values into the formula:

$$c = 2 \times 3.1416 \times 1.250$$

We multiply these values to find the circumference:

$$c = 7.854″$$

Now we calculate the length of the curved surface by using the formula for finding the length of an arc:

$$\text{arc} = \frac{c \times \phi}{360°}$$

We then substitute the known values into the formula:

$$\text{arc} = \frac{7.854 \times 45}{360}$$

We next perform the operations indicated in the numerator:

$$\text{arc} = \frac{353.43}{360}$$

Finally, we divide to find the length of the arc:

$$\text{arc} = 0.982″$$

The following example shows how to calculate the length of a curved surface (arc) in a shop-related problem.

EXAMPLE

Problem

Calculate the arc measurement x of the bend shown in Figure 9.17.

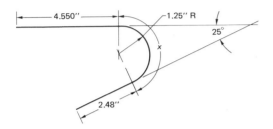

Figure 9.17

Analysis

We know from the figure that $r = 1.25''$. First calculate the central angle (ϕ) of the curved surface. Then calculate the circumference of the imaginary circle of which the curved surface is a part. Finally, calculate the length of the curved surface, which is an arc of the imaginary circle.

Solution

Step 1:   Calculate ϕ, the supplement of the 25° angle shown in the figure

$$\phi = 180° - 25° = 155°$$

Step 2:   Calculate the circumference of the imaginary circle that includes arc measurement x

$$c = 2\pi r$$
$$= 2 \times 3.1416 \times 1.25 = 7.854''$$

Step 3:   Calculate the length of the curved surface by using the formula for finding the length of an arc

$$x = \frac{c \times \phi}{360°}$$

$$= \frac{7.854 \times 155}{360} = \frac{1217.37}{360} = 3.382$$

Answer

$$x = 3.382''$$

Bending Metals

Bending metals creates a special problem because the surface dimensions change during bending. Thus, the linear measurements before and after the bending of metal surfaces are different. We cannot use the surface dimensions of metals when determining bend measurements, as we did in the previous example.

Consider, for example, taking a 1″ × 1/4″ × 10″ strip of metal and bending it at the middle to form a 90° angle on a 1″ radius, as shown in Figure 9.18. Before the bend, the two flat surfaces of the strip have the same linear dimension. After the bend is made, the two surface dimensions are no longer equal.

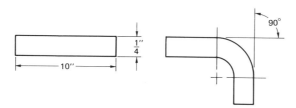

Figure 9.18

To overcome this problem, we use an imaginary line located inside the metal, called the *bend line*. The dimensions of the bend line will not change during bending. The location of the bend line varies from metal to metal because each type of metal is affected differently during bending. The line also varies with the thickness of the metal. The location of the line is always given in reference to the inside surface of the bend.

The following example shows how to apply tangent relationships to a shop-related problem involving a bend line.

EXAMPLE

Problem

Determine the overall length of stock 1/2″ thick and 2″ wide needed to make the bracket shown in Figure 9.19. Assume that the bend line is located 0.268″ from the inside of the bend.

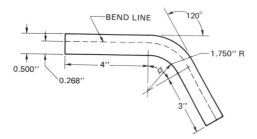

Figure 9.19

Analysis

We need to determine the central angle of the bend, the radius of the bend line, and the circumference of an imaginary circle having this radius in order to determine the arc length of the bend line, the unknown measurement.

Solution

Step 1:   Find the central angle of the bend

$\phi = 60°$, the supplement of 120°

Step 2:   Find the radius of the bend line by adding the inside radius plus the bend allowance

$R = 1.750 + 0.268 = 2.018''$

Step 3:   Find the circumference of an imaginary circle having a radius of 2.018″ by following the rule for finding the circumference of a circle

$c = 2\pi R$

$= 2 \times 3.1416 \times 2.018 = 12.679''$

Step 4:   Find the arc length of the bend line for 60° by following the rule for finding the length of an arc:

$$\text{arc} = \frac{c \times \phi}{360°}$$

$$\text{arc} = \frac{12.679 \times 60}{360} = \frac{760.74}{360} = 2.113''$$

Step 5:   Find the overall length necessary for the blank by adding together 4″ (given) plus the length of the arc plus 3″ (given)

overall length $= 3'' + 2.113'' + 4''$

Answer

overall length $= 9.113''$

ANGLE-CIRCLE RELATIONSHIPS

Up to now, we have considered the measurement of arcs in linear units. We can, however, also think of them as having angular measurements. The angular measurement of an arc is equal to the central angle of that arc.

RULE

To find the angular measurement of an arc, use the formula:

(central angle)° = (intercepted arc)°

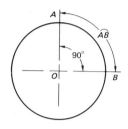

Figure 9.20

Intercept means to include between two points or curves. The arc shown in Figure 9.20 is intercepted by the radii of the circle, which form the legs of the central angle.

For example, arc *AB*, shown in Figure 9.20, is one-fourth of a circle. Its angular measurement is 90°, equal to that of its central angle, ∠*AOB*. On the other hand, if we are told that an arc has an angular measurement of 90°, we know that its central angle is 90°.

NOTE: Up to now, we have referred to angles by the capital letter at the vertex or within the angle measurement line. Another way of naming angles is by the three capital letters located at the points that form the angle. The letter in the center is always the letter at the vertex of the angle. In Figure 9.20, for example, the central angle *AOB* is also ∠*O*. We refer to an arc by the two capital letters at the end points of the arc. In Figure 9.20, the arc is called arc *AB*, or $\widehat{AB}$. The curved line over the letters is the symbol for arc.

Inscribed Angles

An *inscribed angle* of a circle is an angle that has its vertex on the circle and sides that are chords of the circle. The angle is drawn inside the circle. In Figure 9.21, ∠*ABC* and ∠*DEF* are inscribed angles.

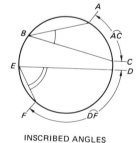

INSCRIBED ANGLES

Figure 9.21

RULE

To find the angular measurement of an inscribed angle, use the formula:

(inscribed angle)° = $\frac{1}{2}$(intercepted arc)°

For example, in Figure 9.20, if $\widehat{AC}$ = 50° and $\widehat{DF}$ = 120°, then:

$$\angle ABC = \frac{1}{2}(\widehat{AC}) = 25° \quad \text{and} \quad \angle DEF = \frac{1}{2}(\widehat{DF}) = 60°$$

The following example shows how to calculate the angular measurement of inscribed angles.

EXAMPLE

Problem

Find the angular measurements of inscribed angles A, B, and C illustrated in Figure 9.22.

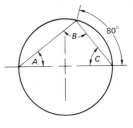

Analysis

The figure shows that $\widehat{BC} = 80°$ and that line AC is the diameter of the circle. Calculate the value of $\widehat{AB}$ and $\widehat{AC}$, the intercepted arcs and then calculate the value of the inscribed angles.

Figure 9.22

Solution

Step 1a: Calculate the value of $\widehat{AB}$

$$\widehat{AB} = 180° - 80° = 100°$$

Step 1b: Calculate the value of $\widehat{AC}$

$$\widehat{AC} = 180°$$

Step 2a: Calculate the values of the inscribed angles by using the formula:

$$(\text{inscribed angle})° = \frac{1}{2}(\text{intercepted arc})°$$

Step 2b: Calculate the value of $\angle A$

$$\angle A = \frac{1}{2}\widehat{BC} = \frac{1}{2}(80°) = 40°$$

Step 2c: Calculate the value of $\angle B$

$$\angle B = \frac{1}{2}\widehat{AC} = \frac{1}{2}(180°) = 90°$$

Step 2d: Calculate the value of $\angle C$

$$\angle C = \frac{1}{2}\widehat{AB} = \frac{1}{2}(100°) = 50°$$

Answer

$$\angle A = 40°, \angle B = 90°, \angle C = 50°$$

Tangent Angles

A *tangent angle* of a circle is an angle that has its vertex at a tangent point and sides that is formed by a tangent line and a chord. In Figure 9.23, $\angle CAB$ is a tangent angle and $\overset{\frown}{AC}$ is the intercepted arc.

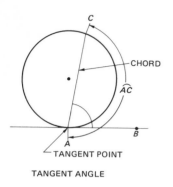

TANGENT ANGLE

Figure 9.23

RULE

To find the angular measurement of a tangent angle, use the formula:

$$(\text{tangent angle})° = \frac{1}{2}(\text{intercepted arc})°$$

For example, in Figure 9.23, if $\overset{\frown}{AC} = 150°$, then:

$$\angle CAB = \frac{1}{2}(\overset{\frown}{AC}) = 75°$$

Interior Angles

An *interior angle* of a circle is an angle that has its vertex in the interior of the circle and is formed by the intersection of two chords. In Figure 9.24, $\angle EAB$, $\angle BAC$, $\angle CAD$, and $\angle DAE$ are interior angles with their vertex at point A. Notice that $\angle EAB = \angle CAD$ and $\angle BAC = \angle DAE$ because they are vertical angles.

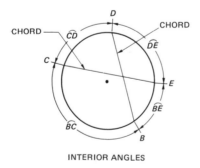

INTERIOR ANGLES

Figure 9.24

RULE

To find the angular measurement of an interior angle, use the formula:

$$(\text{interior angle})° = \frac{1}{2}(\text{intercepted arc} + \text{vertical-angle intercepted arc})°$$

For example, in Figure 9.24, if $\widehat{EB} = 50°$ and $\widehat{CD} = 85°$, then:

$$\angle EAB = \frac{1}{2}(\widehat{EB} + \widehat{CD}) = 67.5°$$

Notice that $\angle CAD$ is also $67.5°$.

Exterior Angles

An *exterior angle* of a circle has its vertex outside the circle and is formed by tangent or intersecting lines of the circle. In Figure 9.25, $\angle BAC$ is an exterior angle in each of the figures.

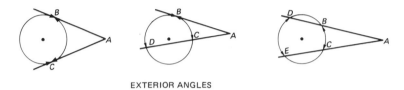

EXTERIOR ANGLES

Figure 9.25

RULE

To find the angular measurement of an exterior angle, use the formula:

$$(\text{exterior angle})° = \frac{1}{2}(\text{major arc} - \text{minor arc})°$$

For example, in Figure 9.25b, if $\widehat{BD} = 150°$ and $\widehat{BC} = 70°$, then:

$$\angle BAC = \frac{1}{2}(\widehat{BD} - \widehat{BC}) = 40°$$

TRIANGLE-CIRCLE RELATIONSHIPS

We have just looked at angles formed inside a circle (inscribed and interior angles), on a circle (tangent angles), and outside a circle (exterior angles). Here we look at inscribed circles and triangles, which are often encountered in testing and measurement situations in the shop.

Inscribed Circles

An *inscribed circle* of a triangle is a circle that is completely enclosed by a triangle whose three sides are tangents of the circle. The formulas associated with inscribed circles of triangles are the formulas for the diameter of a circle. The following basic formula can be applied to the inscribed circle of a scalene triangle, using Figure 9.26 for reference.

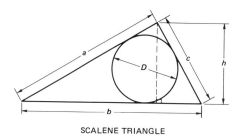

SCALENE TRIANGLE

Figure 9.26

RULE

To find the diameter of an inscribed circle of a scalene triangle, use the formula:

$$D = \frac{2bh}{(a + b + c)}$$

For example, to determine the diameter of the inscribed circle shown in Figure 9.27, we must first calculate dimension h. To calculate h, we use the projection formula for scalene triangles and the basic right-triangle formulas. These calculations are not shown here since we are already familiar with them. By using the formulas, we find that $h = 2.179''$.

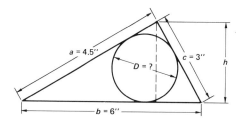

Figure 9.27

Next, we calculate the diameter of the inscribed circle by applying the formula to the measurements shown in the figure:

$$D = \frac{2bh}{(a + b + c)}$$

where $a = 4.5''$
    $b = 6''$
    $c = 3''$
    $h = 2.179''$

We then substitute the known values into the formula:

$$D = \frac{2 \times 6 \times 2.179}{(4.5 + 6 + 3)}$$

We perform the operations indicated in the numerator and denominator:

$$D = \frac{26.148}{13.5}$$

Finally, we divide to find the diameter of the inscribed circle:

$$D = 1.937''$$

This basic formula can be applied to any other type of triangle in which a circle is inscribed. However, the formula can be simplified for all the other types of triangles.

The following example shows how to apply the formula for finding the diameter of an inscribed circle of a scalene triangle in a shop-related problem.

EXAMPLE

Problem

Determine the diameter (D) of the test plug required to check the V-slot shown in Figure 9.28.

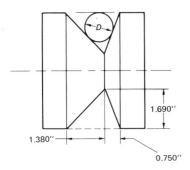

Figure 9.28

Analysis

We know from the figure that the line measuring 1.690″ goes from the vertex of an angle perpendicular to the base of an imaginary triangle to form two right triangles. We also know that:

$$b, \text{the base,} = 1.380 + 0.750 = 2.130''$$

$$h = 1.690''$$

We must first find sides a and c of the scalene triangle before we can apply the formula for finding the diameter of an inscribed circle.

Solution

Step 1a: Find a, the hypotenuse of the right triangle whose base $= 0.750''$, by using the formula

$$c = \sqrt{a^2 + b^2}$$

Step 1b: Substitute the letters (symbols) used in this problem into the formula

$$a = \sqrt{h^2 + b^2}$$

Step 1c: Substitute the known values into the formula and solve for a

$$a = \sqrt{1.690^2 + 0.750^2}$$

$$= \sqrt{2.856 + 0.563} = \sqrt{3.419} = 1.849''$$

Step 2a: Find c, the hypotenuse of the right triangle whose base $= 1.380''$, by using the formula

$$c = \sqrt{a^2 + b^2}$$

Step 2b: Substitute the letters (symbols) used in this problem into the formula

$$c = \sqrt{h^2 + b^2}$$

Step 2c: Substitute the known values into the formula and solve for c

$$c = \sqrt{1.690^2 + 1.380^2}$$
$$= \sqrt{2.856 + 1.904} = \sqrt{4.76} = 2.182''$$

Step 3a: Apply the formula for finding the diameter of an inscribed circle of a scalene triangle

$$D = \frac{2bh}{(a + b + c)}$$

Step 3b: Substitute the known values into the formula and solve for D

$$D = \frac{2 \times 2.130 \times 1.690}{1.849 + 2.130 + 2.182} = \frac{7.199}{6.161} = 1.168$$

Answer

$$D = 1.168''$$

Calculations for the inscribed circle of an isosceles triangle require only the right-triangle formulas. Here, again, *h* is usually calculated first.

RULES

To find the diameter of the inscribed circle of an isosceles triangle (Figure 9.29), use the formula:

$$D = \frac{2bh}{b + 2c}$$

To find the diameter of the inscribed circle of an equilateral triangle (Figure 9.30), use the formula:

$$D = \frac{s}{\sqrt{3}}$$

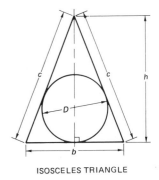

ISOSCELES TRIANGLE

Figure 9.29

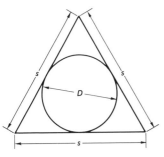

EQUILATERAL TRIANGLE

Figure 9.30

To find the diameter of the inscribed circle of a right triangle (Figure 9.31), use the formula:

$$D = (a + b) - c$$

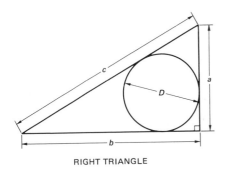

RIGHT TRIANGLE

Figure 9.31

Since the formula for the inscribed circles of right triangles in general is so simple, we will not look further at special right triangles.

Inscribed Triangles

An *inscribed triangle* of a circle is a triangle that is completely enclosed by a circle, with the vertexes of the triangle on the circle. Only two cases are important for machinists, and the rules for them follow.

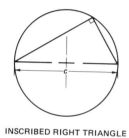

INSCRIBED RIGHT TRIANGLE

Figure 9.32

RULES

To find the hypotenuse of an inscribed right triangle (Figure 9.32), use the formula:

$$D \;=\; c$$

(Notice that the hypotenuse of an inscribed right triangle is the same as the diameter.)

To find the diameter of a circle inscribing an equilateral triangle (Figure 9.33), use the formula:

$$D \;=\; \frac{2s}{\sqrt{3}}$$

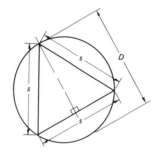

INSCRIBED EQUILATERAL TRIANGLE

Figure 9.33

To find the length of the sides of an inscribed equilateral triangle (Figure 9.33), use the formula:

$$s \;=\; \frac{D\sqrt{3}}{2}$$

INDEXING

The division of a circle into accurate angular or equal divisions has been a major concern for a long time. The division of a circle is needed, for example, in navigation, surveying, and machining procedures. *Indexing* is the procedure used in the shop to accurately divide a circle into equal parts. It is required for cutting squares, gears, and splines.

A standard device used in the shop to divide a circle into equal parts is the *indexing head,* also called the *dividing head.* An indexing head is shown in Figure 9.34. The indexing head is basically a gear box that has a 40 to 1 ratio. The

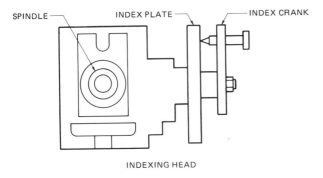

Figure 9.34

workpiece is held on the spindle head. The 40 revolutions of the index crank are controlled by the use of holes on *index plates* to divide the circular workpiece accurately. A typical plate for simple indexing is shown in Figure 9.35.

Four indexing methods—direct, simple, angular, and differential—can be used with the indexing head to divide a circle accurately. In this section, we consider the first three methods because they are the most commonly used.

INDEX PLATE

Figure 9.35

Direct Indexing

Direct indexing is indexing directly from the plate. The plate is placed on the spindle, and the spindle is then turned by hand. The spindle gear must be taken out of mesh with the worm gear on the index crank to do direct indexing. The most common plate used for direct indexing has 24 holes equally spaced on a circle concentric to the spindle. However, 30- and 36-hole plates are also available.

Direct indexing is limited to factors of 24, 30, and 36. Thus, a circle can be divided only into 2, 3, 4, 6, 8, 12, and 24 equal parts when a 24-hole plate is used.

RULE

To determine the number of holes to rotate on a direct indexing plate, divide 24, 30, or 36 by the number of equal divisions desired. If the answer is not a factor of the number of holes on the index plate, direct indexing is not possible.

For example, to use direct indexing to find the number of holes to move each time to cut 9 teeth on a gear, first choose the 36-hole indexing plate (since 9 is a factor of 36) and then divide by 9:

$$36 \div 9 = 4$$

Thus, 4 holes must be moved each time to divide a 36-hole circle into 9 equal parts. If 11 teeth are needed on the gear, direct indexing cannot be used. Since 11 is not a factor of 24, 30, or 36, the index plate cannot be rotated an even number of holes.

Simple Indexing

Simple indexing is used when direct indexing is not possible. Index plates are attached to the indexing head at the base of the crank. For simple indexing, the most common indexing plates are the Brown & Sharpe series and the Cincinnati Standard plate. The Brown & Sharpe series has the following plates:

Plate 1: 15–16–17–18–19–20
Plate 2: 21–23–27–29–31–33
Plate 3: 37–39–41–43–47–49

The Cincinnati Standard (one plate) has the following holes:

Side 1: 24–25–28–30–34–37–38–39–41–42–43
Side 2: 46–47–49–51–53–54–57–58–59–62–66

The standard ratio between the index crank and the spindle on an indexing head is 40 to 1. Thus, one turn of the index crank makes 1/40 of a turn on the spindle. Similarly, 20 turns of the index crank make 1/2 of a turn (or 20/40) on the spindle. Fractional turns of the index crank are controlled by the use of indexing circles on the index plates. To turn the index crank 2-1/3 turns, for example, we would turn the index crank 2 full turns and 7 holes on a 21-hole circle. Since 7 holes is 1/3 of 21 holes, a 1/3 turn is accomplished.

RULE

To determine the amount of rotation required on the index crank for simple indexing, divide 40 by the number (N) of equal divisions required and simplify the fraction (either to a simple fraction or to a mixed number):

$$\frac{40}{N} = \text{rotation of index crank}$$

Once the amount of rotation is determined, the answer is stated in terms of number of full turns and number of holes of desired circle. The answer to the example we just looked at is "2 turns and 7 holes on a 21-hole circle."

If the answer is a mixed number, the whole number indicates the number of complete turns that the index crank must make. All fractional answers and fractional parts of mixed numbers indicate the fractional amount of a turn required. These fractions must be changed to an equal fraction whose denominator is equal to the number of holes found on one of the circles of an indexing plate. The value of the numerator of the new fraction represents the fractional turn required in terms of holes.

For example, to find the required rotation of the index crank to machine a gear that has 35 teeth, using a Brown & Sharpe indexing plate, we first divide 40 by 35 and simplify the answer:

$$40/35 \; = \; 1\text{-}5/35 \; = \; 1\text{-}1/7$$

Thus the index crank must make a 1-1/7 turn each time. We then select a 21-hole circle because 7 is a factor of 21:

$$1/7 \; = \; 3/21$$

Thus, 3 holes on a 21-hole circle is the same as a 1/7 turn. The required rotation of the index crank is 1 turn and 3 holes on a 21-hole circle. Note that we could have used a 49-hole Brown & Sharpe plate. If we had used a Cincinnati Standard plate, we could have chosen the 28-, 42-, or 49-hole circle.

Angular Indexing

Angular indexing is the type of indexing used when the measurement on the job to be indexed is given as an angle. Since one turn of the index crank makes 1/40 of a turn on the spindle, one turn in angular terms is 1/4 of 360°, or 9°. Therefore, to turn 18° on the spindle, two turns of the index crank are necessary. When angles are expressed in minutes and seconds, an approximate value is obtained from an angular indexing table. A section of an angular indexing table is shown in Table 9.1. (For complete tables, see the Appendix and *Machinery's Handbook*.) In Table 9.1, H is the number of holes to turn and C is the number of holes on the circle. For example, the first value, .0204, is equal to 1 hole (H) on a 49-hole (C) circle.

RULES

To determine the amount of rotation of the index crank for angular measurements if the angle is measured only in degrees, divide the angle by 9° and use simple indexing to determine the required rotation:

$$\frac{\text{angle}°}{9°} \; = \; \text{rotation of index crank}$$

If the angle is measured in degrees and minutes, first convert the angle measurement to minutes and then divide by 540' (9° × 60' = 540'):

$$\frac{\text{angle}'}{540'} \; = \; \text{rotation of index crank (decimal number)}$$

Table 9.1 Section of an Angular Indexing Table

Value	H	C	Value	H	C
.0204	1	49	.0851	4	47
.0213	1	47	.0870	2	23
.0233	1	43	.0909	3	33
.0244	1	41	.0930	4	43
.0256	1	39	.0952	2	21
.0270	1	37	.0968	3	31
.0303	1	33	.0976	4	41
.0323	1	31	.1000	2	20
.0345	1	29	.1020	5	49
.0370	1	27	.1026	4	39
.0408	2	49	.1034	3	29
.0426	2	47	.1053	2	19
.0435	1	23	.1064	5	47
.0465	2	43	.1081	4	37
.0476	1	21	.1111	2	18
.0488	2	41	.1111	3	27
.0500	1	20	.1163	5	43
.0513	2	39	.1176	2	17
.0526	1	19	.1212	4	33
.0541	2	37	.1220	5	41
.0555	1	18	.1224	6	49
.0588	1	17	.1250	2	16
.0606	2	33	.1277	6	47
.0612	3	49	.1282	5	39
.0625	1	16	.1290	4	31
.0638	3	47	.1304	3	23
.0645	2	31	.1333	2	15
.0666	1	15	.1351	5	37
.0690	2	29	.1379	4	29
.0698	3	43	.1395	6	43
.0732	3	41	.1429	3	21
.0741	2	27	.1429	7	49
.0769	3	39	.1463	6	41
.0811	3	37	.1481	4	27
.0816	4	49	.1489	7	47

Reprinted from *Shop Theory*, 6th ed., by J. Anderson and E. Tatro, © 1974. With permission of Webster/McGraw-Hill.

Round the answer off to 4 decimal places.

If the angle is measured in degrees, minutes, and seconds, first convert the angle measurement to seconds and then divide by 32,400″ (9° × 60′ × 60″ = 32,400″):

$$\frac{\text{angle}''}{32,400''} = \text{rotation of index crank (decimal number)}$$

Round the answer off to 4 decimal places.

The whole part of the decimal number gives the required full turns of the index crank. The decimal part gives the fractional part of a turn. We use the angular index table (Table 9.1) to equate this decimal to a desired hole circle. Notice that only approximate values can be obtained with decimal numbers.

For example, consider the problem of milling two slots, 38° apart on centers, on an arbor. To determine the required index-crank rotation, we first divide 38° by 9° and simplify the answer:

$$\frac{38°}{9°} = 4\frac{2}{9}$$

Thus, we must make 4-2/9 turns of the index crank. We then select an 18-hole circle because 9 is a factor of 18:

$$2/9 = 4/18$$

A 2/9 turn is equal to 4 holes on an 18-hole circle. We need 4 turns and 4 holes on an 18-hole circle to mill the slots.

However, if we wish to determine the rotation required on an index crank to drill two holes 55°18′30″ apart on centers, we must first convert 55°18′30″ to seconds:

$$
\begin{aligned}
55° &= 55 \times 60 \times 60 &= 198{,}000″ \\
18′ &= 18 \times 60 &= 1{,}080″ \\
30″ & &= \underline{30″} \\
& &199{,}110″
\end{aligned}
$$

Then, we divide 199,110″ by 32,400 to find the number of turns:

$$199{,}110 \div 32{,}400 = 6.1454$$

Thus, 6.1454 turns of the index crank are needed. On the angular index table we see that 0.1454 is closest to 0.1463, the equivalent of 6 holes on a 41-hole circle. The required rotation is 6 turns and 6 holes on a 41-hole circle.

To find the error, we subtract 0.1454 from 0.1463:

$$0.1463 - 0.1454 = 0.0009$$

We then multiply by 3600, since 1° = 3600″:

$$0.009 \times 3600″ = 3.24″ \text{ (error)}$$

Metric Applications

All the concepts and formulas presented in this chapter also apply when metric units are used. Again, millimeters would be used instead of inches.

TERMS FOR REVIEW

- circle
- radius
- radii
- diameter
- chord
- circumference
- arc
- concentric circles
- tangent lines
- tangent curves
- tangent circles
- tangent points
- colinear
- bend line

- inscribed angle
- tangent angle
- interior angle
- exterior angle
- inscribed circle
- inscribed triangle
- indexing
- indexing head
- dividing head
- index plates
- direct indexing
- simple indexing
- angular indexing

EXERCISES

Exercise 9.1: Interpretation of Circles

A. Solve the following problems. Round off answers to the nearest thousandth of an inch.

1. Find the circumference (*c*) of a circle whose diameter is 6-1/4″.

2. Find the circumference (*c*) of a circle whose radius is 2.0625″.

3. Find the diameter (*D*) of a circle whose circumference is 12.75″.

4. Find the radius (*R*) of a circle whose circumference is 18.045″.

5. A 26″ bicycle wheel will travel how far in 8 revolutions?

6. If you double the size (diameter) of a wheel, will the circumference also double?

7. The pitch diameter of a spur gear is 4.125″. What is the circumference of the gear's pitch circle?

8. An old wooden wagon wheel 64″ in diameter needs an iron rim. What length of flat iron is needed?

9. What is the largest circle that can be made from a flat strip of brass 27.5″ in length?

10. Find the circumference of a 5.25″ flat belt pulley.

— 5.25″ —

11. A piece of round stock on a lathe is 2.750″ in diameter. (a) How much surface metal does your cutting tool remove in one revolution? (b) In 20 revolutions? (c) At a speed of 500 rev/min? (Note: The surface metal removed by a cutting tool in one revolution is the circumference of the round stock.)

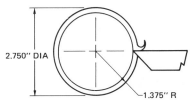

2.750″ DIA

1.375″ R

12. A 10″ grinding wheel in the finishing shop is specified for a maximum RPM of 4800 RPM. What is the surface speed in ft/min of this wheel at that RPM? (Note: Surface speed of round objects is the circumference × RPM's.)

13. If the above grinding wheel was worn down to a diameter of 9″, what would its new surface speed be in ft/min?

1. *c* = _____

2. *c* = _____

3. *D* = _____

4. *R* = _____

5. _____

6. _____

7. *c* = _____

8. _____

9. _____

10. *c* = _____

11a. _____

11b. _____

11c. _____

12. _____

13. _____

14. Calculate the arc measurement of the following circle (in inches).

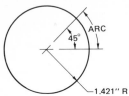

15. Determine the radius (R) of the following circle.

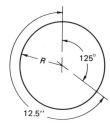

16. Determine the central angle (ϕ) that intercepts a 4″ arc on a 7.440″ diameter circle.

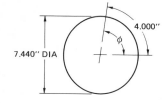

17. Calculate the radius (R) of the following illustration.

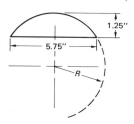

18. Determine dimension h of the following woodruff key.

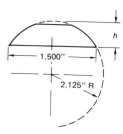

19. Calculate the thickness (*x*) of the metal used to make the cavity illustrated in the following sectional view.

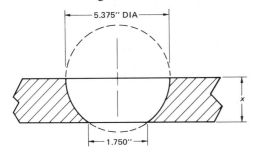

19. *x* = _____

20. Determine dimension *x* of the following illustration.

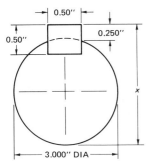

20. *x* = _____

21. Determine dimension *x* of the following flat.

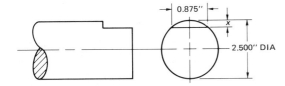

21. *x* = _____

22. Determine dimensions *x* and *y* of the keyway illustrated.

22a. *x* = _____

22b. *y* = _____

23. Calculate the widths of the flats *x* and *y* on the following ring.

23a. *x* = _____

23b. *y* = _____

Exercise 9.2: Tangent Relationships

A. Determine the unknown values in the following problem situations. Round off answers to the nearest thousandth.

1. Determine dimensions x and y and angles A and B of the following illustration.

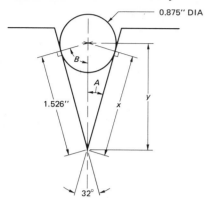

1a. x = _____

1b. y = _____

1c. $\angle A$ = _____

1d. $\angle B$ = _____

2. Determine dimensions x and y of the following illustration.

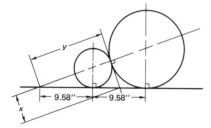

2a. x = _____

2b. y = _____

3. Calculate the total length of the surface illustrated.

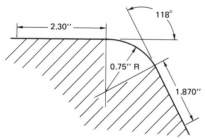

3. _____

4. Determine the total length of the following line.

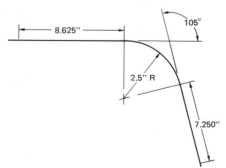

4. _____

5. Determine the overall length of the following line.

5. _____

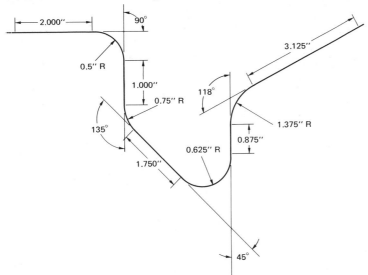

6. Calculate the arc measurement of the following bearing cap.

6. _____

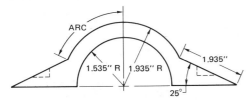

7. Calculate the arc measurement of the following tab.

7. _____

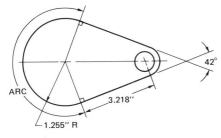

B. The following are commonly shaped parts. Determine the length of the stock necessary to make them. Round off answers to the nearest thousandth.

1. Determine the length of stock necessary to form the bracket indicated. The bend line is located 0.250″ from the inside of the bend.

1. _____

2. Determine the length of stock necessary to form the U clamp indicated. The bend line is located 0.318″ from the inside radius.

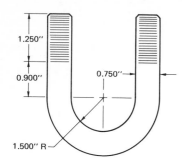

3. Determine the length of stock necessary to form the 12″ ring illustrated. The bend line is located 0.138″ from the inside radius.

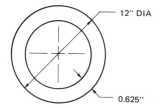

4. Determine the length of stock required to form the following link. The bend line is located 0.350″ from the inside radius.

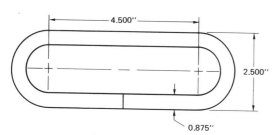

5. Calculate the overall length of stock required to make the following plate. The bend line is located 0.132″ from the inside of all the bends.

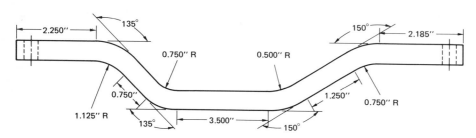

Exercise 9.3: Angle-Circle Relationships

A. Solve the following problems.

1. Calculate the angular measurement of the central angle, *A*, in the following illustration.

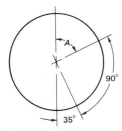

1. ∠*A* = _____

2. Calculate the angular measurement of the inscribed angle, *A*, in the following illustration.

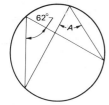

2. ∠*A* = _____

3. Calculate the angular measurement of the tangent angles *A* and *B* in the following illustration.

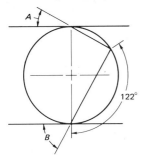

3a. ∠*A* = _____

3b. ∠*B* = _____

4. Calculate the angular measurement of the interior angles *A* and *B* in the following illustration.

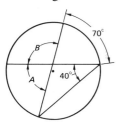

4a. ∠*A* = _____

4b. ∠*B* = _____

5. Calculate the angular measurement of the exterior angle *A* in the following illustration.

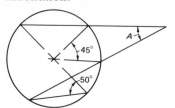

5. ∠*A* = _____

6. Determine the angular measurement of ∠*ACE*, ∠*CAE*, ∠*BDE*, ∠*CAB*, ∠*BAF*, ∠*EAB*, ∠*EBD*, and ∠*DEB* in the following illustration.

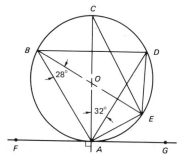

6a. ∠*ACE* = _____

6b. ∠*CAE* = _____

6c. ∠*BDE* = _____

6d. ∠*CAB* = _____

6e. ∠*BAF* = _____

6f. ∠*EAB* = _____

6g. ∠*EBD* = _____

6h. ∠*DEB* = _____

7. Determine the angular measurement of angles *A*, *B*, *C*, *D*, *E*, *F*, *G*, *H*, *I*, *J*, *K*, and *L* in the following illustration.

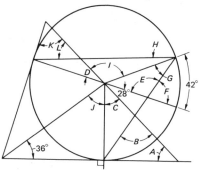

7a. ∠*A* = _____

7b. ∠*B* = _____

7c. ∠*C* = _____

7d. ∠*D* = _____

7e. ∠*E* = _____

7f. ∠*F* = _____

7g. ∠*G* = _____

7h. ∠*H* = _____

7i. ∠*I* = _____

7j. ∠*J* = _____

7k. ∠*K* = _____

7l. ∠*L* = _____

Exercise 9.4: Triangle-Circle Relationships

A. The following problem situations may be found in the machine shop. Round off answers to the nearest thousandth.

1. Determine the radius (*R*) of the inscribed circle and base (*b*) of the triangle, illustration below.

1a. *R* = _____

1b. *b* = _____

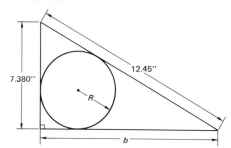

2. Determine the diameter (D) of the circle on which the centers of the three 0.250″ holes are located.

2. D = _____

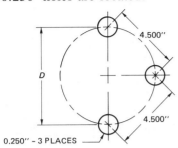

3. Determine the diameter (D) of the test plug required to check the V-slot on the following block.

3. D = _____

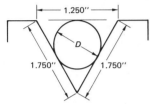

4. Determine the diameter (D) of the wire required to check the following V-thread.

4. D = _____

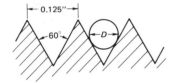

5. Determine the center-to-center distance of any two holes on the following spacer plate.

5. _____

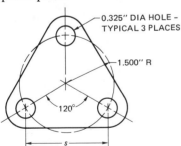

Exercise 9.5: Indexing

A. Determine the number of holes to rotate on the indexing plate to make the following equal divisions through direct indexing.

1. 12 divisions on a 24-hole plate? _____

2. 12 divisions on a 36-hole plate? _____

3. 6 divisions on a 24-hole plate? _____

4. 5 divisions on a 30-hole plate? _____

5. 3 divisions on a 36-hole plate? _____

6. 4 divisions on a 24-hole plate? _____

B. Determine the amount of rotation required of the index crank to make the following equal divisions through simple indexing. State all fractional turns in terms of the smallest circle of Brown & Sharpe plates 1, 2, and 3.

1. To cut 12 teeth on a gear? _____   2. To cut 23 teeth on a gear? _____

3. To drill 25 equal-spaced holes on a circle? ____   4. To cut a 14-groove spline? _____

5. To cut a regular hexagon? _____   6. To cut 9 slots equally spaced on a plate? _____

7. To cut a 116-tooth gear? _____   8. To cut a 136-tooth gear? _____

9. To cut the 360° graduation marks on the outer edge of a 10″ circular plate? _____

C. Determine the amount of rotation required of the index crank to make the following angles through angular indexing. Use the table in the appendix if necessary.

1. 55° _____   2. 118° _____   3. 30° _____

4. 90° _____   5. 22°30′ _____   6. 14°55′ _____

7. 38°22′ _____   8. 76°45′ _____   9. 18°42′30″ _____

10. 36°18′45″ _____

Exercise 9.6: Metric Applications

A. The following problem situations may be found in the machine shop. Round off answers to the nearest hundredth.

1. Find the circumference of a circle whose diameter is 35.5mm.   1. c = _____

2. Find the diameter of a cylinder whose circumference is 554.32mm.   2. D = _____

3. On a flat 230mm pulley, a belt is in contact with the pulley for only 160°. What length of belt is always in contact with the pulley?   3. _____

4. Determine the length of belt needed for the following pulley system.   4. _____

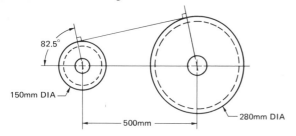

150mm DIA — 82.5° 500mm 280mm DIA

5. What is the largest diameter loop that can be made from a flat strap of metal 1,345mm long?   5. _____

6. Determine the widths of the flats x and y of the following cam.   6a. x = _____

4.35mm   6.5mm   21.65mm R   6b. y = _____

7. Determine the diameter (*D*) of a test plug required to check the 90° cut illustrated.

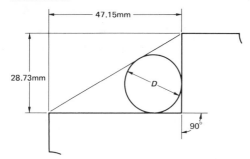

8. What is the diameter of a circle inscribed in a 65 × 65mm square?

9. What is the diameter of a circle in which a 80 × 125mm rectangle is inscribed?

7. *D* = _____

8. *D* = _____

9. *D* = _____

CHAPTER 10

TRIGONOMETRY

Learning Objectives

After studying this chapter, you should be able to:

— State the ratios that define the sine, cosine, and tangent of right-triangle leg angles

— Read trigonometry tables

— Apply trigonometric functions to solve for angular measurements

— Apply trigonometric functions to solve for linear measurements

— (Optional): Apply the sine and cosine functions to obtuse angles

— Apply the law of sines and cosines to scalene triangles

For machinists, a knowledge of trigonometric relationships is another very useful mathematical tool—probably the most useful tool of all. Most of the trigonometric relationships used by machinists are based on the right triangle. However, the trigonometric formulas that we will use differ from the right-triangle formulas we used previously. The right-triangle formulas dealt strictly with the length of the sides of right triangles. Trigonometry formulas deal with both the sides and the leg angles.

INTERPRETATION OF TRIGONOMETRY

The principles of *trigonometry* are based on the proportional relationships of similar triangles. These proportional relationships are true for all types of similar triangles. We concentrate on right triangles in this chapter, since they are the most useful for us. In an optional section at the end of the chapter, we look at obtuse and scalene triangles.

Similar Right Triangles

Right triangles that have the same leg angles are *similar right triangles*. The two right triangles illustrated in Figure 10.1 are similar because both have leg angles of 20° and 70°. Any other right triangles having leg angles of 20° and 70° are also similar to these two triangles.

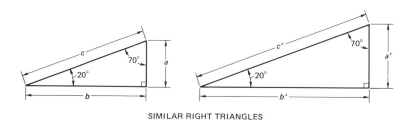

SIMILAR RIGHT TRIANGLES

Figure 10.1

We can state a proportional relationship for similar triangles—that is, the lengths of any two sides of one triangle are in exact ratio to the corresponding sides of any other similar triangle. Therefore, in Figure 10.1, the ratio of side a to side b of the triangle on the left is equal to the ratio of side a' to side b' of the triangle on the right:

$$\frac{a}{b} = \frac{a'}{b'}$$

We can state six ratios, based on the proportional relationships, for similar triangles. In reference to the triangles shown in Figure 10.1, these ratios are:

$$\frac{a}{b} = \frac{a'}{b'} \qquad \frac{a}{c} = \frac{a'}{c'} \qquad \frac{b}{c} = \frac{b'}{c'}$$

$$\frac{b}{a} = \frac{b'}{a'} \qquad \frac{c}{a} = \frac{c'}{a'} \qquad \frac{c}{b} = \frac{c'}{b'}$$

Consider, for example, the two 3–4–5 right triangles shown in Figure 10.2. Equating the six possible ratios for the two triangles, we obtain the following proportional statements:

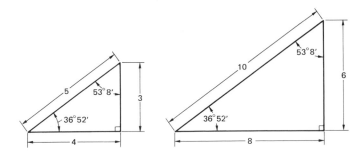

Figure 10.2

$$\frac{3}{4} = \frac{6}{8} \qquad \frac{3}{5} = \frac{6}{10} \qquad \frac{4}{5} = \frac{8}{10}$$

$$\frac{4}{3} = \frac{8}{6} \qquad \frac{5}{3} = \frac{10}{6} \qquad \frac{5}{4} = \frac{10}{8}$$

Ratios of Right-Triangle Legs

Trigonometry is the mathematical application of the ratios of the lengths of the legs of right triangles, called trigonometric functions. Thoroughly understanding these ratios is very important in using them properly to solve problems in the shop. To illustrate how these ratios are used, consider a 30°–60° right triangle, as shown in Figure 10.3. In Chapter 8 (Triangles), we found that the leg opposite the 30° angle

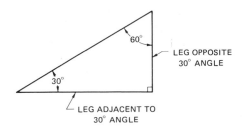

Figure 10.3

for all 30°–60° right triangles is always one-half the length of the hypotenuse. Thus, for the 30° angle of 30°–60° right triangles, the ratio of the leg opposite to the hypotenuse is:

$$\frac{\text{leg opposite}}{\text{hypotenuse}} = 0.5000$$

This ratio will always be true for any 30° angle of a 30°–60° right triangle, no matter how small or large the triangle. Further, for the 30° angle, the ratio of its adjacent leg to the hypotenuse (see Figure 10.3) is:

$$\frac{\text{leg adjacent}}{\text{hypotenuse}} = 0.8660$$

The 30°–60° right triangle shown in Figure 10.4 is an example of the two ratios just stated. Here, for the 30° angle, the ratio of the leg opposite to the hypotenuse is:

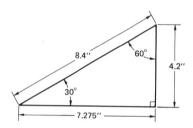

Figure 10.4

$$\frac{\text{leg opposite}}{\text{hypotenuse}} = \frac{4.2}{8.4} = 0.5000$$

The ratio of the leg adjacent to the hypotenuse is:

$$\frac{\text{leg adjacent}}{\text{hypotenuse}} = \frac{7.275}{8.4} = 0.8660$$

Notice that the legs of the right triangle are not referred to as altitude or base. Instead, they are referred to as the leg opposite or the leg adjacent to one of the leg angles. These terms are used because the terms *altitude* and *base* are relative to the position of the triangle. If the position of the triangle is changed, the legs change position—the same legs are no longer the altitude and the base of the triangle. However, if the legs are referred to as the legs opposite or adjacent to an angle, the position of the triangle does not make any difference.

Consider the 20°–70° right triangle, shown in Figure 10.5, as an illustration of how these terms are applied. As can be seen, each leg can be referred to as an

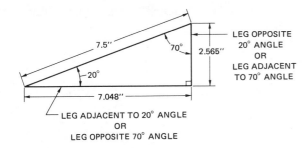

Figure 10.5

opposite leg or an adjacent leg, depending on which leg angle is considered. Some of the trigonometric ratios for the triangle shown in Figure 10.5 are as follows:

— For the 20° angle, ratio of leg opposite to hypotenuse:

$$\frac{\text{leg opposite}}{\text{hypotenuse}} = \frac{2.565}{7.5} = 0.3420$$

— For the 70° angle, ratio of leg opposite to hypotenuse:

$$\frac{\text{leg opposite}}{\text{hypotenuse}} = \frac{7.048}{7.5} = 0.9397$$

— For the 20° angle, ratio of leg adjacent to hypotenuse:

$$\frac{\text{leg adjacent}}{\text{hypotenuse}} = \frac{7.048}{7.5} = 0.9397$$

— For the 70° angle, ratio of leg adjacent to hypotenuse:

$$\frac{\text{leg adjacent}}{\text{hypotenuse}} = \frac{2.565}{7.5} = 0.3420$$

— For the 20° angle, ratio of leg opposite to leg adjacent:

$$\frac{\text{leg opposite}}{\text{leg adjacent}} = \frac{2.565}{7.048} = 0.3639$$

— For the 70° angle, ratio of leg opposite to leg adjacent:

$$\frac{\text{leg opposite}}{\text{leg adjacent}} = \frac{7.048}{2.565} = 2.7478$$

Trigonometric Functions

The ratios of the leg angles are called the *trigonometric functions* of the angles. The functions can be defined as follows:

— The *sine* (sin) of an angle is the ratio of the leg opposite to the hypotenuse:

$$\sin = \frac{\text{leg opposite}}{\text{hypotenuse}}$$

— The *cosine* (cos) of an angle is the ratio of the leg adjacent to the hypotenuse:

$$\cos = \frac{\text{leg adjacent}}{\text{hypotenuse}}$$

— The *tangent* (tan) of an angle is the ratio of the leg opposite to the leg adjacent:

$$\tan = \frac{\text{leg opposite}}{\text{leg adjacent}}$$

— The *cotangent* (cot) of an angle is the ratio of the leg adjacent to the leg opposite:

$$\cot = \frac{\text{leg adjacent}}{\text{leg opposite}}$$

— The *secant* (sec) of an angle is the ratio of the hypotenuse to the leg adjacent:

$$\sec = \frac{\text{hypotenuse}}{\text{leg adjacent}}$$

— The *cosecant* (csc) of an angle is the ratio of the hypotenuse to the leg opposite:

$$\csc = \frac{\text{hypotenuse}}{\text{leg opposite}}$$

Notice that we usually use the abbreviations for the trigonometric functions when using formulas.

NOTE: We can use these definitions of trigonometric functions as formulas for finding the measurements of right triangles, as we will see in the section on trigonometry problems. We use them as formulas to solve both angular- and linear-measurement problems.

Remember that the function of any given angle is always the same. Thus, the values obtained for the 20° and 70° angles of the 20°–70° right triangle are exactly the values that will be obtained for any 20°–70° right triangle. In trigonometry, these functions are used to find unknown dimensions of right triangles.

Trigonometry Tables

Trigonometry tables contain all the ratios of right triangles stated as the function values of angles between 0° and 90°. Two sections of a typical trigonometric table are shown in Table 10.1. The ratios given in the table have been rounded off to five decimal places. The table is read in the following manner.

Table 10.1 Sections of a Typical Trigonometry Table

20°

M	Sine	Cosine	Tan.	Cotan.	Secant	Cosec.	M
0	.34202	.93969	.36397	2.7475	1.0642	2.9238	60
1	.34229	.93959	.36430	.7450	.0643	.9215	59
2	.34257	.93949	.36463	.7425	.0644	.9191	58
3	.34284	.93939	.36496	.7400	.0645	.9168	57
4	.34311	.93929	.36529	.7376	.0646	.9145	56
5	.34339	.93919	.36562	2.7351	1.0647	2.9122	55
6	.34366	.93909	.36595	.7326	.0648	.9098	54
7	.34393	.93899	.36628	.7302	.0650	.9075	53
8	.34421	.93889	.36661	.7277	.0651	.9052	52
9	.34448	.93879	.36694	.7252	.0652	.9029	51
10	.34475	.93869	.36727	2.7228	1.0653	2.9006	50
11	.34502	.93859	.36760	.7204	.0654	.8983	49
12	.34530	.93849	.36793	.7179	.0655	.8960	48
13	.34557	.93839	.36826	.7155	.0656	.8937	47
14	.34584	.93829	.36859	.7130	.0658	.8915	46
15	.34612	.93819	.36892	2.7106	1.0659	2.8892	45
16	.34639	.93809	.36925	.7082	.0660	.8869	44
17	.34666	.93799	.36958	.7058	.0661	.8846	43
18	.34693	.93789	.36991	.7033	.0662	.8824	42
19	.34721	.93779	.37024	.7009	.0663	.8801	41
20	.34748	.93769	.37057	2.6985	1.0664	2.8778	40
21	.34775	.93758	.37090	.6961	.0666	.8756	39
22	.34803	.93748	.37123	.6937	.0667	.8733	38
23	.34830	.93738	.37156	.6913	.0668	.8711	37
24	.34857	.93728	.37190	.6889	.0669	.8688	36
25	.34884	.93718	.37223	2.6865	1.0670	2.8666	35
26	.34912	.93708	.37256	.6841	.0671	.8644	34
27	.34939	.93698	.37289	.6817	.0673	.8621	33
28	.34966	.93687	.37322	.6794	.0674	.8599	32
29	.34993	.93677	.37355	.6770	.0675	.8577	31
30	.35021	.93667	.37388	2.6746	1.0676	2.8554	30
31	.35048	.93657	.37422	.6722	.0677	.8532	29
32	.35075	.93647	.37455	.6699	.0678	.8510	28
33	.35102	.93637	.37488	.6675	.0679	.8488	27
34	.35130	.93626	.37521	.6652	.0681	.8466	26
35	.35157	.93616	.37554	2.6628	1.0682	2.8444	25
36	.35184	.93606	.37587	.6604	.0683	.8422	24
37	.35211	.93596	.37621	.6581	.0684	.8400	23
38	.35239	.93585	.37654	.6558	.0685	.8378	22
39	.35266	.93575	.37687	.6534	.0686	.8356	21
40	.35293	.93565	.37720	2.6511	1.0688	2.8334	20
41	.35320	.93555	.37754	.6487	.0689	.8312	19
42	.35347	.93544	.37787	.6464	.0690	.8290	18
43	.35375	.93534	.37820	.6441	.0691	.8269	17
44	.35402	.93524	.37853	.6418	.0692	.8247	16
45	.35429	.93513	.37887	2.6394	1.0694	2.8225	15
46	.35456	.93503	.37920	.6371	.0695	.8204	14
47	.35483	.93493	.37953	.6348	.0696	.8182	13
48	.35511	.93482	.37986	.6325	.0697	.8160	12
49	.35538	.93472	.38020	.6302	.0698	.8139	11
50	.35565	.93462	.38053	2.6279	1.0699	2.8117	10
51	.35592	.93451	.38086	.6256	.0701	.8096	9
52	.35619	.93441	.38120	.6233	.0702	.8074	8
53	.35647	.93431	.38153	.6210	.0703	.8053	7
54	.35674	.93420	.38186	.6187	.0704	.8032	6
55	.35701	.93410	.38220	2.6164	1.0705	2.8010	5
56	.35728	.93400	.38253	.6142	.0707	.7989	4
57	.35755	.93389	.38286	.6119	.0708	.7968	3
58	.35782	.93379	.38320	.6096	.0709	.7947	2
59	.35810	.93368	.38353	.6073	.0710	.7925	1
60	.35837	.93358	.38386	2.6051	1.0711	2.7904	0
M	Cosine	Sine	Cotan.	Tan.	Cosec.	Secant	M

69°

21°

M	Sine	Cosine	Tan.	Cotan.	Secant	Cosec.	M
0	.35837	.93358	.38386	2.6051	1.0711	2.7904	60
1	.35864	.93348	.38420	.6028	.0713	.7883	59
2	.35891	.93337	.38453	.6006	.0714	.7862	58
3	.35918	.93327	.38486	.5983	.0715	.7841	57
4	.35945	.93316	.38520	.5960	.0716	.7820	56
5	.35972	.93306	.38553	2.5938	1.0717	2.7799	55
6	.36000	.93295	.38587	.5916	.0719	.7778	54
7	.36027	.93285	.38620	.5893	.0720	.7757	53
8	.36054	.93274	.38654	.5871	.0721	.7736	52
9	.36081	.93264	.38687	.5848	.0722	.7715	51
10	.36108	.93253	.38720	2.5826	1.0723	2.7694	50
11	.36135	.93243	.38754	.5804	.0725	.7674	49
12	.36162	.93232	.38787	.5781	.0726	.7653	48
13	.36189	.93222	.38821	.5759	.0727	.7632	47
14	.36217	.93211	.38854	.5737	.0728	.7611	46
15	.36244	.93201	.38888	2.5715	1.0729	2.7591	45
16	.36271	.93190	.38921	.5693	.0731	.7570	44
17	.36298	.93180	.38955	.5671	.0732	.7550	43
18	.36325	.93169	.38988	.5649	.0733	.7529	42
19	.36352	.93158	.39022	.5627	.0734	.7509	41
20	.36379	.93148	.39055	2.5605	1.0736	2.7488	40
21	.36406	.93137	.39089	.5583	.0737	.7468	39
22	.36433	.93127	.39122	.5561	.0738	.7447	38
23	.36460	.93116	.39156	.5539	.0739	.7427	37
24	.36488	.93105	.39189	.5517	.0740	.7406	36
25	.36515	.93095	.39223	2.5495	1.0742	2.7386	35
26	.36542	.93084	.39257	.5473	.0743	.7366	34
27	.36569	.93074	.39290	.5451	.0744	.7346	33
28	.36596	.93063	.39324	.5430	.0745	.7325	32
29	.36623	.93052	.39357	.5408	.0747	.7305	31
30	.36650	.93042	.39391	2.5386	1.0748	2.7285	30
31	.36677	.93031	.39425	.5365	.0749	.7265	29
32	.36704	.93020	.39458	.5343	.0750	.7245	28
33	.36731	.93010	.39492	.5322	.0751	.7225	27
34	.36758	.92999	.39525	.5300	.0753	.7205	26
35	.36785	.92988	.39559	2.5278	1.0754	2.7185	25
36	.36812	.92978	.39593	.5257	.0755	.7165	24
37	.36839	.92967	.39626	.5236	.0756	.7145	23
38	.36866	.92956	.39660	.5214	.0758	.7125	22
39	.36893	.92945	.39694	.5193	.0759	.7105	21
40	.36921	.92935	.39727	2.5171	1.0760	2.7085	20
41	.36948	.92924	.39761	.5150	.0761	.7065	19
42	.36975	.92913	.39795	.5129	.0763	.7045	18
43	.37002	.92902	.39828	.5108	.0764	.7026	17
44	.37029	.92892	.39862	.5086	.0765	.7006	16
45	.37056	.92881	.39896	2.5065	1.0766	2.6986	15
46	.37083	.92870	.39930	.5044	.0768	.6967	14
47	.37110	.92859	.39963	.5023	.0769	.6947	13
48	.37137	.92848	.39997	.5002	.0770	.6927	12
49	.37164	.92838	.40031	.4981	.0771	.6908	11
50	.37191	.92827	.40065	2.4960	1.0773	2.6888	10
51	.37218	.92816	.40098	.4939	.0774	.6869	9
52	.37245	.92805	.40132	.4918	.0775	.6849	8
53	.37272	.92794	.40166	.4897	.0776	.6830	7
54	.37299	.92784	.40200	.4876	.0778	.6810	6
55	.37326	.92773	.40233	2.4855	1.0779	2.6791	5
56	.37353	.92762	.40267	.4834	.0780	.6772	4
57	.37380	.92751	.40301	.4813	.0781	.6752	3
58	.37407	.92740	.40335	.4792	.0783	.6733	2
59	.37434	.92729	.40369	.4772	.0784	.6714	1
60	.37461	.92718	.40403	2.4751	1.0785	2.6695	0
M	Cosine	Sine	Cotan.	Tan.	Cosec.	Secant	M

68°

Courtesy of Illinois Tool Works Inc., Chicago, Illinois

1. For angles between 0° and 45°, use the functions stated at the top of the table. Read the table from the left, from the top to the bottom, for the minutes (M).

2. For angles between 45° and 90°, use the functions stated at the bottom of the table. Read the table from the right, from the bottom to the top, for the minutes (M).

3. Some columns have a whole number stated for only every fifth ratio value. Apply these whole numbers to all the other ratio values in between them.

For example, to find the sine of 20°36′, we take the following steps:

1. Find 20° at the head of the table
2. Find the sine column at the top of the table
3. Find 36′ on the left of the table (M)
4. Read across from 36′ to the sine column
5. Find the answer: sin 20°36′ = 0.35184

Remember that sin 20°36′ is the ratio of the leg opposite to the hypotenuse for a 20°36′ angle of a right triangle.

To find the tangent of 21°50′, we take the following steps:

1. Find 21° at the head of the table
2. Find the tangent (Tan.) column at the top of the table
3. Find 50′ on the left of the table
4. Read across from 50′ to the tangent column
5. Find the answer: tan 21°50′ = 0.40065

Remember that tan 21°50′ is the ratio of the leg opposite to the leg adjacent for a 21°50′ angle of a right triangle.

To find the cosine of 68°20′, we take the following steps:

1. Find 68° at the foot of the table
2. Find the cosine column at the bottom of the table
3. Find 20′ on the right of the table
4. Read across from 20′ to the cosine column
5. Find the answer: cos 68°20′ = 0.36921

Remember that cos 68°20′ is the ratio of the leg adjacent to the hypotenuse for a 68°20′ angle of a right triangle.

Each value in a trigonometry table corresponds to two angles. These angles are always the two leg angles of the triangle to which the value applies. For example:

cos 68°20′ = 0.36921

sin 21°40′ = 0.36921

where 68°20′ and 21°40′ are a pair of leg angles.

Inverse Trigonometric Functions

We have seen how to use the trigonometric table to find a function value for any given leg angle. A machinist also needs to be able to read the table in reverse. That is, when we know the value of a given function, we need to be able to find the angle to which it belongs. The angle we are trying to find is called an *arc function*. The arc functions are: *arc sine, arc cosine, arc tangent, arc cotangent, arc secant,* and *arc cosecant*. The following examples for finding arc functions relate to Table 10.1.

If we are asked to find the arc sin 0.36650, we are being asked to find the angle whose sine is 0.36650. To find the angle whose sine is 0.36650, we take the following steps:

1. Read the sine columns, either up or down, to find 0.36650

2. In this case, 0.36650 is in the column with the sine function at the top

3. Read the angle (degrees) at the head of the table and the angle (minutes) on the left of the table

4. Find the answer: arc sin 0.36650 = 21°30′

If we are asked to find the arc cos 0.35293, we are being asked to find the angle whose cosine is 0.35293. To find the angle whose cosine is 0.35293, we take the following steps:

1. Read the cosine columns, either up or down, to find 0.35293

2. In this case, 0.35293 is in the column with the cosine function at the bottom

3. Read the angle (degrees) at the base of the table and the angle (minutes) on the right of the table

4. Find the answer: arc cos 0.35293 = 69°20′

Interpolation

At times, we need to maintain a high level of accuracy. We must express angle measurements in degrees, minutes, and seconds. Without the aid of an electronic calculator with trigonometry functions, this calculation can pose a special problem. Most trigonometry tables express the functional values of angles measured only in degrees and minutes. An approximation procedure called *interpolation* is used to solve this problem. The following examples illustrate the procedure.

To find the sine of 25°28′15″, we take the following steps:

1. First, find sin 25°28′ and sin 25°29′ because sin 25°28′15″ falls between these values in the trigonometry table, and find the difference:

sin 25°28′
sin 25°28′15″ } 15″
sin 25°29′ } 60″   angle difference

2. Then find the functional-value difference between sin 25°28′ and sin 25°29′ (disregard the decimal points):

sin 25°28′ = 42999 } ?
sin 25°28′15″ = ?   } 26   functional-value difference
sin 25°29′ = 43025

3. Equate the angle-measurement differences to the functional-value differences as a proportion:

$$\frac{15}{60} = \frac{?}{26}$$

4. Solve the proportion for the unknown functional-value difference:

$$? = \frac{15 \times 26}{60} = 6.5, \text{ or } 7, \text{ rounded off}$$

5. Find the answer:

$$\sin 25°28'15'' \cong \sin 25°28' + \text{ functional-value difference}$$
$$\cong 42998 + 7$$
$$\cong 0.43005$$

Notice that we use the symbol $\cong$, which means approximately equal to. We use this symbol because our interpolated answer is an approximate value.

To find the arc sine 0.55397, we take the following steps:

1. First find the sine values that 0.55397 falls between in the trigonometry table:

$$0.55388 = \sin 33°38'$$
$$0.55397 = \sin 33°38'?''$$
$$0.55412 = \sin 33°39'$$

$?$ ⎫ 60'' angle difference

2. Then find the functional-value differences between the sin values (disregard the decimal points):

$$\sin 33°38' = 55388$$
$$\sin 33°38'?'' = 55397$$
$$\sin 33°39' = 55412$$

9 ⎫ 24 functional-value difference

3. Equate the sine-value differences to the angle-measurement differences as a proportion:

$$\frac{9}{24} = \frac{?''}{60''}$$

4. Solve the proportion for the unknown angle-measurement difference:

$$? = \frac{9 \times 60}{24} \cong 23''$$

5. Find the answer:

$$\text{arc sin } 0.55397 \cong 33°38' + \text{ angle difference}$$
$$\cong 33°38' + 23'' \cong 33°38'23''$$

Electronic Calculators

Knowing how to use the trigonometry tables is important. However, when a high degree of accuracy is needed, an electronic calculator with trigonometry functions gives more accurate figures than the interpolation procedure. Study the owner's manual that came with your electronic calculator and learn how to use the trigonometry functions correctly.

RIGHT-TRIANGLE TRIGONOMETRY

We will first use trigonometry functions to solve for unknown dimensions of right triangles. Later, we will need to formulate right-triangle problems to which we can apply all the geometric relationships covered in the previous chapters. In both cases, we will use trigonometric functions to solve for two types of measurement—angular and linear measurements.

Angle-Measurement Problems

Problems concerned with finding measurements of angles can be solved by calculating the leg angles of right triangles. In order to solve for a leg angle, we need to know the measurements of at least two sides of the triangle.

NOTE: When two sides of a right triangle are known, the third side can be found by using the Pythagorean theorem.

For example, we may want to find the measurement of $\angle A$ in the right triangle shown in Figure 10.6, where the length of side b is unknown and:

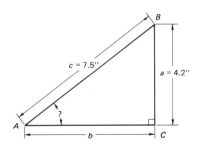

Figure 10.6

$$\text{side } a \;=\; 4.2''$$
$$\text{side } c \;=\; 7.5''$$

Since we are looking for $\angle A$, the legs of the triangle must be defined relative to $\angle A$:

side a is the leg opposite $\angle A$

side b is the leg adjacent to $\angle A$

side c is the hypotenuse

Since we know the lengths of two sides of the triangle, two functions of $\angle A$ are known:

$$\sin \angle A \;=\; \frac{\text{opp}}{\text{hyp}} \;=\; \frac{4.2''}{7.5''} \;=\; 0.5600$$

$$\csc \angle A \;=\; \frac{\text{hyp}}{\text{opp}} \;=\; \frac{7.5''}{4.2''} \;=\; 1.7857$$

We can now solve either

$$\text{arc sin } 0.5600 \;=\; \angle A \quad \text{or} \quad \text{arc csc } 1.7857 \;=\; \angle A$$

The trigonometry table gives the following values:

$$\text{arc sin } 0.5600 \;=\; 34°3'$$

$$\text{arc csc } 1.7857 \;=\; 34°3'$$

Thus, $\angle A = 34°3'$.

As expected, both functions provide the same answer. In an actual problem-solving situation, we need to use only one function. We can easily find the other unknown measurements of the right triangle shown in Figure 10.6. To find $\angle B$, we subtract the value of $\angle A$ from 90°:

$$\angle B \;=\; (90° - \angle A) \;=\; (90° - 34°3') \;=\; 55°57'$$

To find the length of leg b, we follow the rule for finding the length of a leg when the lengths of the other leg and the hypotenuse are known:

$$b \;=\; \sqrt{c^2 - a^2}$$
$$= \sqrt{7.5^2 - 4.2^2} \;=\; 6.214''$$

The following example shows how to use trigonometric functions to find the unknown measurements of a right triangle.

EXAMPLE

Problem

Find $\angle B$, $\angle A$, and side b of the right triangle shown in Figure 10.7.

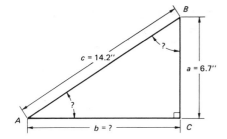

Figure 10.7

Analysis

We know from Figure 10.7 that:

$$\text{side } a = 6.7''$$

$$\text{side } c = 14.2''$$

The length of side b is unknown.

Since we are looking for $\angle B$, the legs of the triangle must be defined relative to $\angle B$:

$$\text{side } a \text{ is the leg adjacent to } \angle B$$

$$\text{side } b \text{ is the leg opposite } \angle B$$

$$\text{side } c \text{ is the hypotenuse}$$

Since the lengths of two sides of the triangle are known, two functions of $\angle B$ can be stated:

$$\cos \angle B = \frac{\text{adj}}{\text{hyp}} = \frac{6.7}{14.2} = 0.47183$$

$$\sec \angle B = \frac{\text{hyp}}{\text{adj}} = \frac{14.2}{6.7} = 2.1194$$

Use the cosine function to solve for $\angle B$.

Solution

Step 1:   Find the angle whose cosine is 0.47183

$$\text{arc cos } 0.47183 = 61°51'$$

$$\angle B = 61°51'$$

Step 2:   Find the value of $\angle A$ by subtracting the value of $\angle B$ from 90°

$$\angle A = 90° - \angle B = 90° - 61°51' = 28°9'$$

Step 3:   To find leg b, follow the rule for finding the length of a leg when the lengths of the other leg and the hypotenuse are known

$$b = \sqrt{c^2 - a^2}$$

$$= \sqrt{14.2^2 - 6.7^2} = 12.520''$$

Answer

$\angle B = 61°51'$, $\angle A = 28°9'$, leg $b = 12.520''$

We might wonder why, in the previous problem, b was not calculated first. Then, we would have been able to apply any one of the six trigonometric functions.

NOTE: If an error is made in calculating the initial value, that incorrect value can generate errors in other calculated values. It is always good practice to use only the original known values, whenever possible, to solve for unknown values.

Linear-Measurement Problems

Problems concerned with finding linear measurements can be solved by calculating the lengths of the sides of right triangles. To solve for a side, we must know the measurements of the other two sides or of a side and an angle of the triangle.

NOTE: When two sides of a triangle are known, find the third side by using the Pythagorean theorem. When only one side and a leg angle are known, apply the trigonometric functions.

The trigonometric functions can be restated to apply to the sides of a right triangle, according to the following rules.

RULES

To solve for the hypotenuse, apply one of the following formulas, depending on what measurements are known:

hypotenuse $=$ leg opposite $\div$ sine

$=$ leg opposite $\times$ cosecant

$=$ leg adjacent $\div$ cosine

$=$ leg adjacent $\times$ secant

To solve for the leg opposite a known angle, apply one of the following formulas, depending on what measurements are known:

leg opposite $=$ hypotenuse $\times$ sine

$=$ hypotenuse $\div$ cosecant

$=$ leg adjacent $\div$ cotangent

$=$ leg adjacent $\times$ tangent

To solve for the leg adjacent to a known angle, apply one of the following formulas, depending on what measurements are known:

leg adjacent $=$ hypotenuse $\times$ cosine

$=$ hypotenuse $\div$ secant

$=$ leg opposite $\times$ cotangent

$=$ leg opposite $\div$ tangent

The following examples show the procedure for finding the side measurements of a right triangle when the measurements of the hypotenuse and one angle are known. To find the length of sides *a* and *b* of the right triangle shown in Figure 10.8, where side *c* $=$ 8″ and $\angle A$ $=$ 24°, we first define the legs of the triangle relative to $\angle A$:

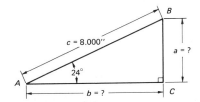

Figure 10.8

side *a* is the leg opposite $\angle A$

side *b* is the leg adjacent to $\angle A$

Then, to solve for *a*, the leg opposite $\angle A$, we follow the rule for finding the leg opposite a known angle when the hypotenuse is known:

leg opposite $=$ hypotenuse $\times$ sine of known angle

We substitute the known values:

a $=$ hyp $\times$ sin 24°
    $=$ 8 $\times$ 0.40674 $=$ 3.254″

To solve for *b*, the leg adjacent to $\angle A$, we follow the rule for finding the leg adjacent when the hypotenuse is known:

leg adjacent $=$ hypotenuse $\times$ cosine of known angle

We substitute the known values:

$$b = \text{hyp} \times \cos 24°$$
$$= 8 \times 0.91354 = 7.308''$$

Thus, side $a = 3.3254''$ and side $b = 7.308''$.

The following example shows how to use trigonometry to solve for linear measurements.

EXAMPLE

Problem

Find the length of sides a and c of the right triangle shown in Figure 10.9.

Analysis

We know from Figure 10.9 that:

$$b = 5.25''$$
$$\angle B = 35°15'$$

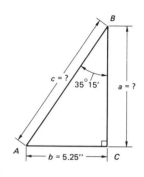

Figure 10.9

Therefore, the legs of the triangle must be defined relative to $\angle B$:

    side b is the leg opposite $\angle B$

    side c is the hypotenuse

    side a is the leg adjacent to $\angle B$

To solve for c, the hypotenuse, follow the rule for finding the length of the hypotenuse when the leg opposite is known:

$$\text{hypotenuse} = \text{leg opposite} \div \text{sine of known angle}$$

To solve for a, the leg adjacent to $\angle B$, follow the rule for finding the length of the adjacent leg when the length of the leg opposite is known:

$$\text{leg adjacent} = \text{leg opposite} \div \text{tangent of known angle}$$

Solution

    Step 1:   Find the length of c by substituting the known values into the formula for the hypotenuse

$$c = \text{leg opposite} \div \sin 35°15'$$
$$= 5.25 \div 0.57714 = 9.097''$$

    Step 2:   Find the length of a by substituting the known values into the formula for the leg adjacent

$$a = \text{leg opposite} \div \tan 35°15'$$
$$= 5.25 \div 0.70673 = 7.429''$$

Answer

$$c = 9.097'', a = 7.429''$$

Notice that we could have applied other trigonometric functions in the preceding example. However, machinists should concentrate on using the sine, cosine, and tangent functions. All shop-related trigonometry problems can be solved with these three functions, and they are the functions commonly available on electronic calculators.

Shop-Related Problems

In order to use the rules of trigonometry in shop-related problems, a machinist must be able to visualize a right triangle within the blueprint. In other words, to find the measurement of an angle, that angle must be seen as a leg angle or part of a leg angle of a right triangle. To find a linear measurement, that measurement must be seen as a side or part of a side of a right triangle.

The geometric relationships that we have studied up to now will determine whether or not the right triangles we visualize within a shop problem can be used to solve that problem. Sometimes, assuming into a problem things that are not true is very easy. Fewer mistakes are made in working shop problems by practicing the following suggestions:

1. Draw the visualized right triangle separately from the work, along with what is known about it

2. Show work alongside the illustration, including formula used, values substituted, and major calculations

The following examples illustrate the visualization process in problem solving. To find the included angle of the taper shown in Figure 10.10a, first create a right triangle by drawing a line parallel to the base of the taper. This line and the visualized right triangle are shown in Figure 10.10b. Then solve for the leg angle of the right triangle drawn separately in Figure 10.10c. This angle is the included angle of the taper.

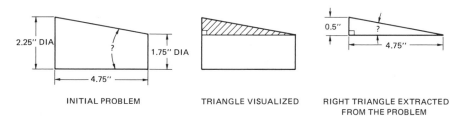

INITIAL PROBLEM	TRIANGLE VISUALIZED	RIGHT TRIANGLE EXTRACTED FROM THE PROBLEM
Figure 10.10a	Figure 10.10b	Figure 10.10c

To find the unknown measurement of the V-slot shown in Figure 10.11a, first visualize a right triangle. A right triangle can be created by drawing in the altitude of the triangle, as Figure 10.11b shows. Then solve for the unknown leg of the

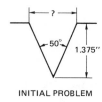

INITIAL PROBLEM

Figure 10.11a

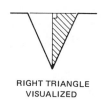

RIGHT TRIANGLE
VISUALIZED

Figure 10.11b

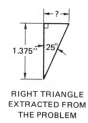

RIGHT TRIANGLE
EXTRACTED FROM
THE PROBLEM

Figure 10.11c

right triangle drawn separately in Figure 10.11c. Double this value to find the total unknown measurement.

The problem illustrated in Figure 10.12a involves a tangent circle. To find the unknown measurement, a right triangle is created in Figure 10.12b by extending the diameter line and drawing in a radius. This right triangle is drawn separately in Figure 10.12c, where we can then solve for the hypotenuse. Returning to Figure 10.12b, we can see that adding the length of the radius to the length of the hypotenuse provides the total unknown measurement.

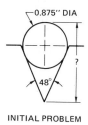

INITIAL PROBLEM

Figure 10.12a

RIGHT TRIANGLE
VISUALIZED

Figure 10.12b

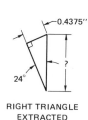

RIGHT TRIANGLE
EXTRACTED
FROM THE PROBLEM

Figure 10.12c

The following examples show how to visualize a right triangle in shop-related problems and how to use right-triangle trigonometry to solve them.

EXAMPLE

Problem

Determine the length of the tapered portion (x) of the idler arbor shown in Figure 10.13a.

Analysis

Visualize a right triangle whose hypotenuse is one side of the tapered portion of the idler arbor and whose base is x, as shown in Figure 10.13b. Find one side and one leg angle in order to use right-triangle trigonometry to find x.

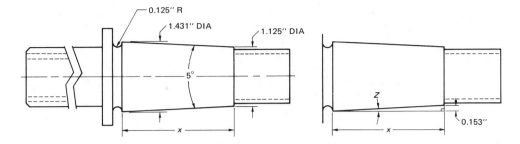

Figure 10.13a   **Figure 10.13b**

Solution

Step 1:   Find one side of the visualized triangle by subtracting the small-end diameter from the large-end diameter and dividing by 2 (remember that because of the center line we are working with given measurements divided by 2)

$$\frac{1.431 \ - \ 1.125}{2} \ = \ 0.153''$$

Step 2:   Find $\angle Z$ opposite the side measuring 0.153″ by dividing the 5° included angle shown in Figure 10.13a by 2

Note: Because the center line divides the included angle in half, $\angle Z =$ 1/2(5°).

$$\angle Z \ = \ 5° \ \div \ 2 \ = \ 2.5°$$

Step 3:   To find x, the leg adjacent to a known angle, use right-triangle trigonometry

$$\text{leg adj} \ = \ \frac{\text{leg opp}}{\tan \angle Z}$$

$$= \ \frac{0.153}{\tan 2.5°} \ = \ \frac{0.153}{0.4366} \ = \ 3.504''$$

Answer

$$x \ = \ 3.504''$$

EXAMPLE

Problem

Determine the test measurement (x) on the dovetail shown in Figure 10.14a.

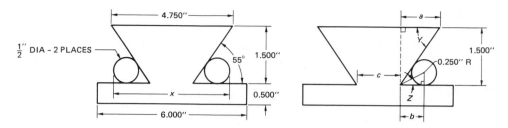

Figure 10.14a   Figure 10.14b

Analysis

First visualize a right triangle with a leg equal to the radius (0.250″) of the test plug and use right-triangle trigonometry to find the leg adjacent to the known angle. Then visualize a right triangle with a side equal to 1.500″, given in Figure 10.14a, and use right-triangle trigonometry to find the leg adjacent to the known angle. Finally, apply the found dimensions to determine x.

Solution

Step 1: Since the total angular measurement shown in Figure 10.14a is 55°, the angle opposite the 0.250″ leg $\angle(Z)$ is half of that, or 27°30′. Use right-triangle trigonometry to solve for b (Figure 10.14b), the leg adjacent to the known angle

$$b = \frac{\text{leg opp}}{\tan \angle Z}$$

$$= \frac{0.250}{\tan 27°30'} = \frac{0.250}{0.52057} = 0.480''$$

Step 2: The angle opposite the 1.500″ leg of the second triangle ($\angle Y$) is 55° because it is an alternate angle. Use right-triangle trigonometry to solve for a (Figure 10.14b), the leg adjacent to the known angle

$$a = \frac{\text{leg opp}}{\tan \angle Y}$$

$$= \frac{1.500}{\tan 55} = \frac{1.500}{1.4281} = 1.050''$$

Step 3: Find c (Figure 10.14b) by subtracting the found dimension a from the given dimension

$$c = 4.750 - 2(1.050)$$
$$= 2.650''$$

Step 4: Find x (remember that the diameter is twice the radius)

$$x = c + 2b + \text{plug diameter}$$
$$= 2.650 + 0.960 + 0.500 = 4.110''$$

Answer

$$x = 4.110''$$

Sine Bars

The *sine bar* is a tool used in the machine shop to give accuracy to work with angle measurements. Using a sine bar is one of the ways in which machinists apply trigonometry in the shop. A typical sine bar is illustrated in Figure 10.15. There are many different types.

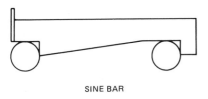

SINE BAR

Figure 10.15

The sine bar consists of a hardened, accurately ground bar and two cylindrical plugs. The cylindrical plugs are attached near the ends of the bar. The length of the sine bar is the distance between the centers of the plugs. The sine bar is constructed with attention to a high degree of accuracy on three measurements:

1. The cylindrical plugs are accurately ground to equal diameters
2. The plugs are accurately located on the bar so that their centers are (most commonly) exactly 5″ or 10″ apart
3. The center line between the plugs is exactly parallel to the top surface of the bar

Simple right-triangle setups are easy to create with a sine bar, as shown in Figure 10.16. The sine bar, with its known length, becomes the hypotenuse of the right triangle. Generally, the difference in the height of the plugs is controlled by the use of gage blocks.

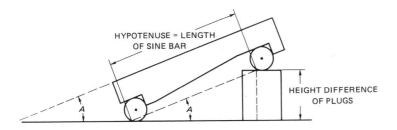

HYPOTENUSE = LENGTH OF SINE BAR

HEIGHT DIFFERENCE OF PLUGS

Figure 10.16

Working with a sine bar creates only two types of trigonometry problems: (1) finding the leg angle *A* or (2) determining the difference in plug height needed to create a desired leg angle A (see Figure 10.16). In each case, the sine function is used:

$$\sin \angle A = \frac{\text{height difference of plugs}}{\text{length of sine bar}}$$

For example, to determine $\angle A$ of the 5″ sine bar shown in Figure 10.17, we first note the information given in the illustration:

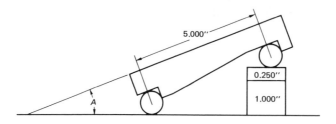

Figure 10.17

height difference = 1.250″

length of sine bar = 5.000″

We follow the rule for finding $\sin \angle A$:

$$\sin \angle A = \frac{\text{height difference of plugs}}{\text{length of sine bar}}$$

We substitute the known values into the formula:

$$\sin \angle A = \frac{1.250}{5.000} = 0.2500$$

We know, therefore, that:

$$\angle A = \text{arc sin } 0.2500$$

In the trigonometry tables, the angle whose sine is 0.2500 is:

$$\angle A = 14°29'$$

The following example shows how to solve another shop-related problem by using the sine bar.

EXAMPLE

Problem

Determine the height (h) of the gage blocks shown in Figure 10.18 required to form a 25°30′ angle with a 5″ sine bar.

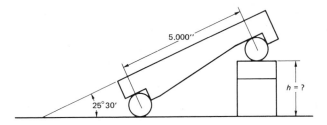

Figure 10.18

Analysis

From the illustration, we know that:

$$\text{sine bar} = 5.000''$$
$$\text{angle} = 25°30'$$

Follow the rule for finding the sine:

$$\text{sine of known angle} = \frac{\text{height difference of plugs}}{\text{length of sine bar}}$$

Solution

Step 1: Restate the formula in terms of the height difference of the plugs

$$h = \text{length of sine bar} \times \text{sine of known angle}$$

Step 2: Substitute the known values into the formula

$$h = 5 \times \sin 25°30'$$
$$= 5 \times 0.4305$$

Answer

$$h = 2.153''$$

OBLIQUE-TRIANGLE TRIGONOMETRY

Up to now, we have applied trigonometric functions only to right triangles. However, trigonometric functions have more applications. They can also be applied to the most difficult oblique triangles, the scalene triangles—assuming, of course, we have enough information. Applications of this type do not occur as often as the right-triangle type. The situations we consider here can also be resolved by using the projection formula in combination with right-triangle trigonometry. For these reasons, this section is considered optional.

To apply trigonometry to a scalene triangle, we must know at least three of the triangle's measurements. One of these measurements must be the length of one of its sides. The other two can be either sides or angles.

Functional Values of Obtuse Angles

At times, in order to apply trigonometric formulas to a scalene triangle, we must find the sine and cosine values of obtuse angles. Remember that obtuse angles are angles greater than 90° and less than 180°. The sine and cosine values of obtuse angles are generally not given in trigonometry tables. However, they can be obtained from these tables by using the relationship of supplementary angles. The following are a few examples of that relationship for the sine and cosine functions:

$$\sin 120° = \sin 60°$$
$$\sin 112° = \sin 68°$$
$$\sin 135° = \sin 45°$$
$$\cos 120° = -\cos 60°$$
$$\cos 112° = -\cos 68°$$
$$\cos 135° = -\cos 45°$$

The sine and cosine values of an obtuse angle can be found by looking up the sine and cosine values of its supplementary angle. The cosine value, however, becomes negative.

RULE

To find the sine and cosine values of an obtuse angle A, use the formulas:

$$\sin \angle A = \sin (180° - \angle A)$$
$$\cos \angle A = -\cos (180° - \angle A)$$

We apply these relationships to the previous examples as follows:

$$\sin 120° = \sin (180° - 120°)$$
$$= \sin 60° = 0.86603$$

$$\sin 112° = \sin (180° - 112°)$$
$$= \sin 68° = 0.92718$$

$$\sin 135° = \sin (180° - 135°)$$
$$= \sin 45° = 0.70711$$

$$\cos 120° = -\cos (180° - 120°)$$
$$= -\cos 60° = -0.5000$$

$$\cos 112° = -\cos (180° - 112°)$$
$$= -\cos 68° = -0.37461$$

$$\cos 135° = -\cos (180° - 135°)$$
$$= -\cos 45° = -0.70711$$

Law of Sines

The *law of sines* expresses a proportional relationship between the sines of the angles of a triangle to their opposite sides. The law of sines states the following relationships (in reference to Figure 10.19):

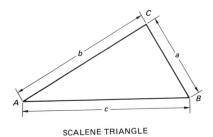

SCALENE TRIANGLE

Figure 10.19

$$\frac{a}{\sin \angle A} = \frac{b}{\sin \angle B} = \frac{c}{\sin \angle C}$$

Each of these relationships is the ratio between the sine of an interior angle and the side opposite that angle. Thus, these relationships can be applied only when we know (1) an angle, (2) the side opposite that angle, and (3) one other angle or side.

For example, suppose we want to find the unknown measurements (angles and sides) of the scalene triangle shown in Figure 10.20. Remember that in order to apply trigonometry to a scalene triangle, we must know at least three of its measurements. Figure 10.20 shows that:

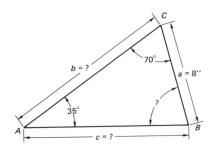

Figure 10.20

$$\angle A = 35°$$
$$a = 8''$$
$$\angle C = 70°$$

where a is the side opposite $\angle A$. The unknown measurements are $\angle B$, side c (the side opposite $\angle C$), and b (the side opposite $\angle B$).

To find $\angle B$, we add the values of angles A and C and subtract the sum from 180°:

$$\angle B = 180° - (\angle A + \angle C)$$
$$= 180 - (35 + 70) = 180 - 105 = 75$$

To find side c, we apply the law of sines:

$$\frac{c}{\sin \angle C} = \frac{a}{\sin \angle A}$$

We substitute the known values:

$$\frac{c}{\sin 70°} = \frac{8}{\sin 35°}$$

We restate the proportion by cross multiplying and dividing:

$$c = \frac{8 \times \sin 70°}{\sin 35°}$$

We substitute the known values for the sines (from the trigonometry tables):

$$c = \frac{8 \times 0.93969}{0.57358}$$

We perform the operations indicated in the numerator and denominator to find the value of c:

$$c = \frac{7.518}{0.57358} = 13.106''$$

To find side b, we again apply the law of sines:

$$\frac{b}{\sin \angle B} = \frac{a}{\sin \angle A}$$

We substitute the known values:

$$\frac{b}{\sin 75°} = \frac{8}{\sin 35°}$$

We restate the problem by cross multiplying and dividing:

$$b = \frac{8 \times \sin 75°}{\sin 35°}$$

We substitute the values for the sines (from the trigonometry tables):

$$b = \frac{8 \times 0.96593}{0.57358}$$

Finally, we perform the operations indicated in the numerator and denominator:

$$b = \frac{7.7274}{0.57358} = 13.472''$$

The following examples illustrate how to use trigonometry to find the unknown measurements of scalene triangles.

EXAMPLE

Problem
Find the unknown angles and side of the scalene triangle shown in Figure 10.21.

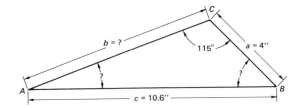

Figure 10.21

Analysis
The illustration shows that:

$$\angle C = 115°$$
$$c = 10.6''$$
$$a = 4''$$

where c is the side opposite $\angle C$ and a is the side opposite $\angle A$. The unknown measurements are $\angle A$, $\angle B$, and b, the side opposite $\angle B$. Use the law of sines to find the unknown angles and side.

Solution
Step 1a: To solve for $\angle A$, apply the law of sines:

$$\frac{a}{\sin \angle A} = \frac{c}{\sin \angle C}$$

Step 1b: Substitute the known values into the formula

$$\frac{4}{\sin \angle A} = \frac{10.6}{\sin 115°}$$

Step 1c: Cross multiply and divide to restate the problem in terms of $\angle A$

$$\sin \angle A = \frac{4 \times \sin 115°}{10.6}$$

Step 1d: Substitute the value for sin 115° (which equals sin 65°)

$$\sin \angle A = \frac{4 \times 0.90631}{10.6}$$

Step 1e: Carry out the operations indicated in the numerator and denominator

$$\sin \angle A = \frac{3.625}{10.6} = 0.34200$$

Step 1f: Use the trigonometry tables to find the angle whose sine is 0.34200

$$\angle A = \text{arc sin } 0.34200 = 20°$$

Step 2:   To find $\angle B$, subtract the sum of $\angle A$ plus $\angle C$ from 180°

$$\angle B = 180° - (\angle A + \angle C) = 180° - 135° = 45°$$

Step 3a: To solve for b, apply the law of sines

$$\frac{b}{\sin \angle B} = \frac{c}{\sin \angle C}$$

Step 3b: Substitute the known values into the formula

$$\frac{b}{\sin 45°} = \frac{10.6}{\sin 115°}$$

Step 3c: Cross multiply and divide to restate the problem in terms of b

$$b = \frac{10.6 \times \sin 45°}{\sin 115°}$$

Step 3d: Substitute the values for sin 45° and sin 115°

$$b = \frac{10.6 \times 0.70711}{0.90631}$$

Step 3e: Perform the operations indicated in the numerator and denominator

$$b = \frac{7.495}{0.90631} = 8.270''$$

Answer

$$\angle A = 20°, \angle B = 45°, b = 8.270''$$

EXAMPLE

Problem

Find $\angle C$ of the scalene triangle shown in Figure 10.22.

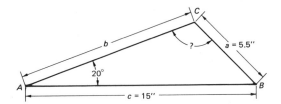

Figure 10.22

Analysis

We know from the diagram that:

$$a = 5.5''$$

$$c = 15''$$

$$\angle A = 20°$$

Apply the law of sines to find $\angle C$. Since Figure 10.22 shows that $\angle C$ is an obtuse angle, the trigonometric relationship of supplementary angles must be used to find the value of $\angle C$.

Solution

Step 1:   Apply the law of sines

$$\frac{c}{\sin \angle C} = \frac{a}{\sin \angle A}$$

Step 2:   Substitute the known values into the formula

$$\frac{15}{\sin \angle C} = \frac{5.5}{\sin 20°}$$

Step 3:   Cross multiply and divide to restate the problem in terms of $\angle C$

$$\sin \angle C = \frac{15 \times \sin 20°}{5.5}$$

Step 4:   Substitute the value of sin 20° from the trigonometry table

$$\sin \angle C = \frac{15 \times 0.34202}{5.5}$$

Step 5:   Perform the operations indicated in the numerator and denominator

$$\sin \angle C = \frac{5.130}{5.5} = 0.93278$$

Step 6:   In the trigonometry tables, find the angle whose sine is 0.93278

$$\angle C = \text{arc sin } 0.93278 = 68°52'$$

Step 7:   Since Figure 10.22 shows that $\angle C$ is an obtuse angle, $\angle C$ must be the supplement of 68°52′

$$\angle C = 180° - 68°52'$$

Answer

$$\angle C = 111°8'$$

The following example shows how to use oblique-triangle trigonometry (the law of sines) to solve a shop-related problem.

EXAMPLE

Problem

Determine the coordinate measure (x) of the adjustment bracket shown in Figure 10.23a.

Analysis

Use the law of sines to find the center-to-center measurement a (Figure 10.23b). Then use right-triangle trigonometry to solve for leg x of the visualized right triangle shown in Figure 10.23b.

Solution

Step 1:   Determine $\angle B$

$$\angle B = 180° - 48° - 74° = 58°$$

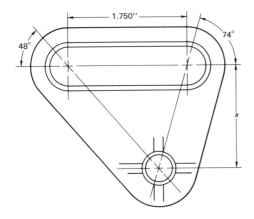

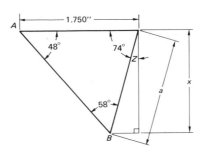

Figure 10.23a   **Figure 10.23b**

Step 2:   Use the law of sines to solve for a, where b, the side opposite the 58° angle, equals 1.750″

$$\frac{a}{\sin \angle A} = \frac{b}{\sin \angle B}$$

$$a = \frac{b(\sin \angle A)}{\sin \angle B}$$

$$= \frac{1.750 \times \sin 48°}{\sin 58°} = \frac{1.750 \times 0.74314}{0.84805} = 1.534″$$

Step 3:   Solve for $\angle Z$, the complement of $\angle C$

$$\angle Z = 90° - 74° = 16°$$

Step 4:   Use right-triangle trigonometry to solve for x

$$x = \text{hyp} \times \cos \angle Z$$

$$= 1.534 \times \cos 16° = 1.534 \times 0.96126 = 1.475″$$

Answer

$$x = 1.475″$$

Law of Cosines

The *law of cosines* can be applied in many situations to which the law of sines cannot be applied. Remember that these situations can also be resolved by using the projection formula and right-triangle trigonometry. The different forms of the law of cosines are stated below in reference to Figure 10.24.

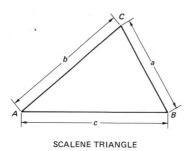

SCALENE TRIANGLE

Figure 10.24

RULES

To find side c of a scalene triangle, use the formula:

$$c^2 = a^2 + b^2 - 2ab \cos \angle C \quad \text{or} \quad c = \sqrt{a^2 + b^2 - 2ab \cos \angle C}$$

To find side a of a scalene triangle, use the formula:

$$a^2 = c^2 + b^2 - 2cb \cos \angle A \quad \text{or} \quad a = \sqrt{c^2 + b^2 - 2cb \cos \angle A}$$

To find side b of a scalene triangle, use the formula:

$$b^2 = a^2 + c^2 - 2ac \cos \angle B \quad \text{or} \quad b = \sqrt{a^2 + c^2 - 2ac \cos \angle B}$$

To find ∠C of a scalene triangle, use the formula:

$$\cos \angle C = \frac{a^2 + b^2 - c^2}{2ab}$$

To find ∠A of a scalene triangle, use the formula:

$$\cos \angle A = \frac{c^2 + b^2 - a^2}{2cb}$$

To find ∠B of a scalene triangle, use the formula:

$$\cos \angle B = \frac{a^2 + c^2 - b^2}{2ac}$$

For example, we use the following procedure to find the measurement of side *a* of the scalene triangle shown in Figure 10.25. The figure shows that:

$$\angle A = 28°$$
$$b = 10''$$
$$c = 12''$$

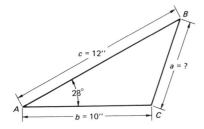

Figure 10.25

We apply the rule of the law of cosines for finding side a of a scalene triangle:

$$a = \sqrt{b^2 - c^2 - 2cb \cos \angle A}$$

We first substitute the known values into the formula:

$$a = \sqrt{10^2 + 12^2 - 2(10)(12)(\cos 28°)}$$

We then substitute the value of cos 28° from the trigonometry tables:

$$a = \sqrt{10^2 + 12^2 - 2(10)(12)(0.88295)}$$

We perform the operations indicated within the radical:

$$a = \sqrt{100 + 144 - 211.908}$$
$$= \sqrt{32.092}$$

Finally, we find the square root of 32.092 to solve for a:

$$a = 5.665''$$

The following examples are further illustrations of how to use the law of cosines to find an unknown measurement of a scalene triangle.

EXAMPLE

Problem

Find the measurement of $\angle A$ of the scalene triangle shown in Figure 10.26.

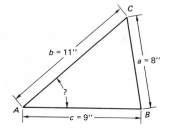

Figure 10.26

Analysis

We know from the diagram that:

$$a = 8''$$
$$b = 11''$$
$$c = 9''$$

Follow the law of cosines for finding an unknown $\angle A$:

$$\cos \angle A = \frac{c^2 + b^2 - a^2}{2bc}$$

Solution

Step 1: Substitute the known values into the formula

$$\cos \angle A = \frac{9^2 + 11^2 - 8^2}{2(9)(11)}$$

Step 2: Perform the operations indicated in the numerator and denominator

$$\cos \angle A = \frac{81 + 121 - 64}{198} = 0.69697$$

Step 3: In the trigonometry tables, find the angle whose cosine is 0.69697

$$\angle A = \text{arc cos } 0.69697$$

Answer

$$\angle A = 45°49'$$

EXAMPLE

Problem

Find the measurement of side c of the scalene triangle shown in Figure 10.27.

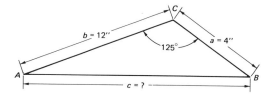

Figure 10.27

Analysis

We know from the diagram that:

$$\angle C = 125°$$
$$a = 4''$$
$$b = 12''$$

Follow the rule of the law of cosines to find the unknown side c of a scalene triangle:

$$c = \sqrt{a^2 + b^2 - 2ab \cos \angle C}$$

Since the diagram shows that $\angle C$ is an obtuse angle, we will need to follow the rule for finding the cosine of an obtuse angle:

$$\cos \angle C = -\cos (180° - \angle C)$$

Solution

Step 1:   Substitute the known values into the formula

$$c = \sqrt{4^2 + 12^2 - 2(4)(12)(\cos 125°)}$$

Step 2:   Substitute for $\cos \angle C$ the negative cosine of $55°(180° - 125°)$

$$c = \sqrt{4^2 + 12^2 - 2(4)(12)(-0.57358)}$$

Step 3:   Perform the operations indicated within the radical

Note: Remember to change the negative sign to a positive sign (negative $\times$ negative = positive).

$$c = \sqrt{16 + 144 + 55.064} = \sqrt{215.064}$$

Step 4:   Find the square root of 215.064

Answer

$$c = 14.665''$$

Metric Applications

The trigonometric concepts and relationships covered in this chapter are the same for metric-based units of measurement. The millimeter is the unit of length used. Angular measurements are given only in degrees, as the policy of this text has been. Handling angular measurement in this way makes the measurements easy to apply to trigonometric functions in electronic calculation.

TERMS FOR REVIEW

— trigonometry
— similar right triangles
— trigonometric functions
　– sine
　– cosine
　– tangent
　– cotangent
　– secant
　– cosecant
— arc functions

– arc sine
– arc cosine
– arc tangent
– arc cotangent
– arc secant
– arc cosecant
— interpolation
— sine bar
— law of sines
— law of cosines

Exercises

Exercise 10.1: Trigonometric Functions

A. Find the values that correspond to the functions of the following angles.

Angle	Sin	Cos	Tan	Cot	Sec	Csc
1. 24°	_____	_____	_____			_____
2. 37°28′	_____		_____		_____	
3. 19°52′		_____	_____	_____		
4. 42°30′		_____		_____	_____	_____
5. 76°20′	_____			_____		_____
6. 58°42′		_____		_____	_____	
7. 89°15′	_____		_____		_____	

B. Find the angle that corresponds to the value of the following functions.

	Angle	Sin	Cos	Tan	Cot	Sec	Csc
1.	_____	0.26752					
2.	_____			0.35608			
3.	_____				1.2617		
4.	_____						1.4993
5.	_____		0.79318				
6.	_____				0.77848		
7.	_____					1.8941	
8.	_____	0.85431					
9.	_____		0.12822				

C. Find the missing values.

1. sin 45°18′ = _____

2. tan 67°42′ = _____

3. arc cos 0.85551 = _____

4. csc 16°12′ = _____

5. arc cos 0.87854 = _____

6. arc sin 0.85866 = _____

7. sec 47°58′ = _____

8. cot 10°15′ = _____

9. arc cos 0.95588 = _____

10. sin 2°12′ = _____

11. cos 15°45′ = _____

12. arc sec 1.0464 = _____

13. arc csc 1.0464 = _____

14. arc cos 0.85866 = _____

Exercise 10.2: Interpolation

A. By the process of interpolation, find the functional values for the following angles.

1. sin 20°45′20″ = _____

2. cos 38°12′12″ = _____

3. cos 8°18′42″ = _____

4. tan 68°25′15″ = _____

5. sin 72°54′17″ = _____

6. sec 42°18′34″ = _____

B. By the process of interpolation, find the following angles.

1. arc sin 0.58672 = _____

2. arc tan 0.56480 = _____

3. arc sin 0.02952 = _____

4. arc cos 0.93298 = _____

5. arc cot 7.8852 = _____

6. arc cos 0.90178 = _____

C. Use an electronic calculator to check your answers to parts A and B.

Exercise 10.3: Right-Triangle Trigonometry

A. Solve for all unknown sides and angles in the following triangles. Round off all linear measurements to the nearest thousandth and angle measurements to the nearest minute.

1.

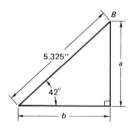

a = _____

b = _____

$\angle B$ = _____

2.

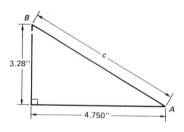

$\angle A$ = _____

$\angle B$ = _____

c = _____

3.

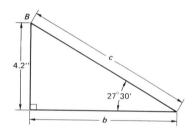

$\angle B$ = _____

b = _____

c = _____

4.

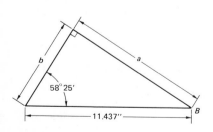

$\angle B$ = _____

a = _____

b = _____

5.

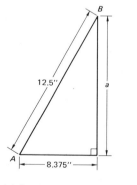

$\angle A$ = _____

$\angle B$ = _____

a = _____

6.

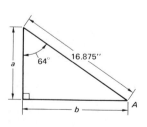

$\angle A$ = _____

a = _____

b = _____

7.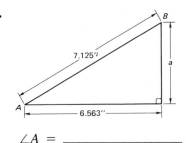

$\angle A =$ _____

$\angle B =$ _____

$a =$ _____

8.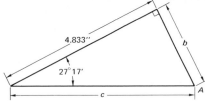

$\angle A =$ _____

$b =$ _____

$c =$ _____

B. Draw a right triangle that illustrates the information given in the following problems. Then calculate all unknown sides and angles. Round off all linear measurements to the nearest thousandth and angle measurements to the nearest minute.

1. A right triangle that has an angle of 14° and a hypotenuse of 7.25″   _____

2. A right triangle that has a leg of 5.325″ and a hypotenuse of 8.375″   _____

3. A right triangle that has legs of 4.5″ and 7.8″   _____

4. A right triangle that has an angle of 50°18′ and a leg of 4.825″ opposite that angle   _____

5. A right triangle that has an angle of 25°57′ and a leg of 8.065″ adjacent to that angle   _____

6. A right triangle that has an angle of 84°27′ and a hypotenuse of 6.475″   _____

7. A right triangle that has a leg of 2.5″ and a hypotenuse of 3.913″   _____

8. A right triangle that has an angle of 2°17′ and a leg of 0.065″ opposite that angle   _____

Exercise 10.4: Shop-Related Problems

A. The following are illustrations of possible problem situations of the shop. Round off all linear measurements to the nearest thousandth and all angle measurements to the nearest minute.

1. Determine dimensions x and y of the following illustration.

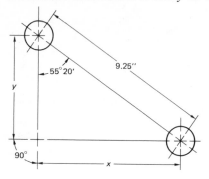

1a. x = _____

1b. y = _____

2. Determine measurements x and y of the following illustration.

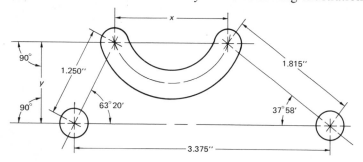

2a. x = _____

2b. y = _____

3. Determine the three center-to-center distances illustrated in the following diagram.

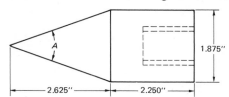

3a. _____

3b. _____

3c. _____

4. Determine the included angle A of the following tapered part.

4. $\angle A$ = _____

5. Determine the measurements x and y required for inspection of the following illustration.

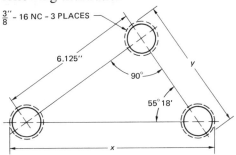

5a. $x = $ _____

5b. $y = $ _____

6. Determine the length x of the following tapered plug.

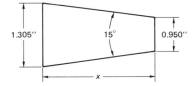

6. $x = $ _____

7. Determine measurement x of the following 1.250″ twist drill.

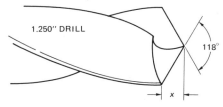

7. $x = $ _____

8. Determine the included angle A of the following tapered test plug.

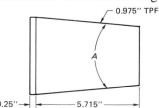

8. $\angle A = $ _____

9. Determine the included angle A and the large- and small-end diameters x and y of the following tapered sleeve.

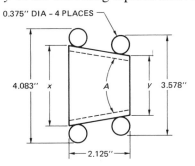

9a. $\angle A = $ _____

9b. $x = $ _____

9c. $y = $ _____

10. Determine dimensions *x* and *y* of the following adjusting plate.

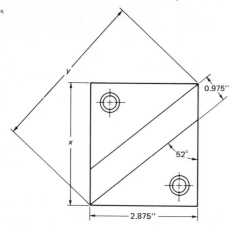

10a. *x* = _____
10b. *y* = _____

11. Determine the diameter of the test plug in the following illustration.

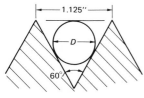

11. *D* = _____

12. Determine the radius of the test plug in the following illustration.

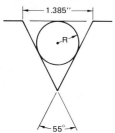

12. *R* = _____

13. Determine the test measurement *x* on the following V-block.

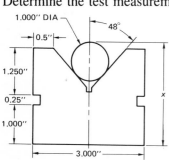

13. *x* = _____

14. Determine the layout angle *A* required to machine the following surface.

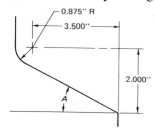

14. ∠*A* = _____

15. Determine the radius R needed to machine the following surface.

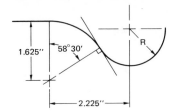

15. $R =$ _____

16. Determine the test measurement x on the following dovetail.

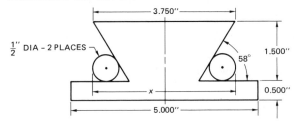

16. $x =$ _____

17. Determine the radius R of the plug used in the following illustration.

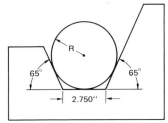

17. $R =$ _____

18. Determine angle A of the following rail guide.

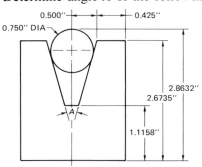

18. $\angle A =$ _____

19. Determine the included angle A and the depth of cut x on the following slotted taper.

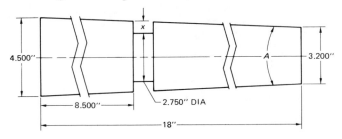

19a. $\angle A =$ _____

19b. $x =$ _____

20. For the following problems, calculate the distance between centers of the 0.375″ holes for two adjacent holes and two alternate holes. The illustration below is for part a.

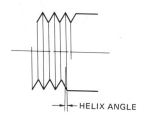

7.750″ DIA

0.375″ – 6 HOLES EQUALLY SPACED

x

y

a. Six equally spaced 0.375″ holes on a 7.750″ circle, as illustrated.
b. Eight equally spaced 0.375″ holes on an 8.250″ circle. Draw a simple illustration.
c. Ten equally spaced 0.375″ holes on a 6.375″ circle. Draw a simple illustration.
d. Five equally spaced 0.375″ holes on a 3.875″ circle. Draw a simple illustration.
e. Four equally spaced 0.375″ holes on a 9.390″ circle. Draw a simple illustration.

20a. $x =$ _____
     $y =$ _____
20b. $x =$ _____
     $y =$ _____
20c. $x =$ _____
     $y =$ _____
20d. $x =$ _____
     $y =$ _____
20e. $x =$ _____
     $y =$ _____

21. Give the depth of cut obtained when the cutting tool is fed 0.045″ into the stock by the compound when turned to the following angles (see illustration below): (a) $\angle A = 60°$, (b) $\angle A = 45°$, (c) $\angle A = 30°$, and (d) $\angle A = 52°$.

COMPOUND

90°

A

21a. _____
21b. _____
21c. _____
21d. _____

22. The *helix angle* of a screw thread is the angle the threads form with the vertical to the central axes of the shank. The helix angle can be found by the following formula:

$$\tan (\text{helix angle}) = \frac{\text{lead of screw thread}}{\pi \times \text{pitch diameter}}$$

HELIX ANGLE

22a. _____
22b. _____
22c. _____

For a single thread screw the *lead* is the same as the pitch of the thread, where the pitch = 1 divided by the number of threads per inch. Calculate the helix angle for the following threads: (a) 3/4"–10 NC with a pitch diameter of 0.6850"; (b) 3/8" – 16NC with a pitch diameter of 0.3344"; and (c) 2-1/2"– 4 NC with a pitch diameter of 2.3376".

Exercise 10.5: Sine Bars

A. Determine the measurements indicated in the following questions. Round off all linear measurements to the nearest thousandth and all angles to the nearest minute.

1. What is the angle being measured by a 5″ sine bar if the difference in heights of the ends is 3.108″?

1. _____

2. What is the angle being measured by a 10″ sine bar if the difference in heights of the ends is 4.277″?

2. _____

3. What is the difference in the heights of the ends of a 5″ sine bar if the sine bar is used to measure the following angles: (a) 30°, (b) 75°, (c) 28°15′, (d) 58°43′, and (e) 15°45′?

3a. _____

3b. _____

3c. _____

3d. _____

3e. _____

4. What is the difference in the heights of the ends of a 10″ sine bar if the sine bar is used to set up the following angles: (a) 60°, (b) 45°, (c) 61°52′, (d) 21°42′, and (e) 5°30′?

4a. _____

4b. _____

4c. _____

4d. _____

4e. _____

5. What angle is being laid out by a 5″ sine bar if the difference in the heights of the ends is 0.907″?

5. _____

Exercise 10.6: Oblique Triangles

A. Use a trigonometry table to solve for the functional values of the following angles. Round off answers to five decimal places.

1. sin 125° = _____

2. sin 162° = _____

3. sin 108° = _____

4. sin 93°52′ = _____

5. sin 112°37′ = _____

6. cos 115° = _____

7. cos 173°18′ = _____

8. cos 95°25′ = _____

9. cos 135° = _____

10. cos 104°50′ = _____

B. Use a trigonometry table to solve for the following angles. Consider all the functional values as being for an obtuse angle. Round off angles to the nearest minute.

1. arc sin 0.96894 = _____

2. arc sin 0.90814 = _____

3. arc sin 0.72136 = _____

4. arc sin 0.36569 = _____

5. arc sin 0.13341 = _____

6. arc sin 0.06105 = _____

7. arc cos −0.69406 = _____

8. arc cos −0.66697 = _____

9. arc cos −0.91671 = _____

10. arc cos −0.99255 = _____

11. arc cos −0.96448 = _____

12. arc cos −0.73135 = _____

C. Use an electronic calculator to check the functional values and angles of parts A and B.

D. Solve for the unknown dimensions of the following triangles. Use the laws of sines and cosines. Round off all linear measurements to the nearest thousandth and angles to the nearest minute.

1.

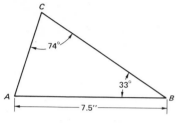

∠A = _____

a = _____

b = _____

2.

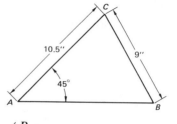

∠B = _____

∠C = _____

c = _____

3.

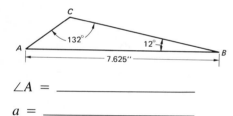

∠A = _____

a = _____

b = _____

4.

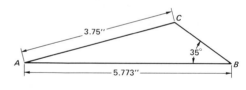

∠A = _____

∠C = _____

a = _____

5.

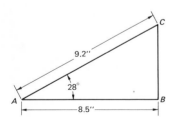

∠B = _____

∠C = _____

a = _____

6.

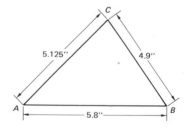

∠A = _____

∠B = _____

∠C = _____

7.

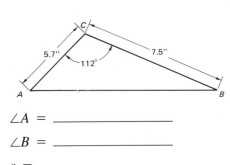

∠*A* = _____

∠*B* = _____

c = _____

8.

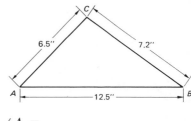

∠*A* = _____

∠*B* = _____

∠*C* = _____

E. The following are possible problem situations to be found in the shop. Solve for the indicated unknown measurements. Round off all linear measurements to the nearest thousandth and all angles to the nearest minute.

1. Solve for the radius of the test plug required in the following illustration.

1. *R* = _____

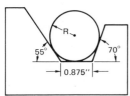

Solve for the center-to-center distance *x* and the vertical distance *y* of the following layout illustration.

2a. *x* = _____

2b. *y* = _____

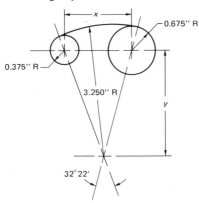

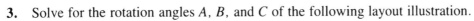 

3. Solve for the rotation angles *A*, *B*, and *C* of the following layout illustration.

3a. ∠*A* = _____

3b. ∠*B* = _____

3c. ∠*C* = _____

4. Determine measurement x of the following illustration.

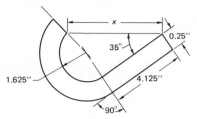

4. $x =$ _____

5. Determine test measurement x of the following guide roller.

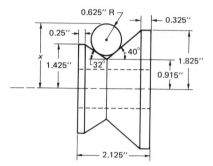

5. $x =$ _____

Exercise 10.7: Metric Applications

A. Solve the following typical shop problems. Round off all linear measurements and angular measurements to the nearest hundredth position.

1. Use an electronic calculator to find the functional values of the following angles. Round off the functional values to five decimal places.

    a. sin 18.39° = _____   **b.** tan 89.50° = _____

    c. cos 65.25° = _____   **d.** tan 6.85° = _____

    e. cos 30.33° = _____   **f.** sin 15.43° = _____

    g. cos 45.91° = _____   **h.** sin 75.23° = _____

2. Using an electronic calculator, find the angles of the following functional values in degrees, minutes, and seconds.

    a. arc tan 0.95862 = _____   **b.** arc sin 0.70708 = _____

    c. arc tan 0.28320 = _____   **d.** arc cos 0.15812 = _____

    e. arc sin 0.83257 = _____   **f.** arc cos 0.86672 = _____

    g. arc sin 0.10068 = _____   **h.** arc cos 0.56172 = _____

3. What is the length of the hypotenuse of a right triangle that has a 28.35mm leg opposite a 25.8° angle?

3. _____

4. What is the length of the leg adjacent to a 15.62° angle of a right triangle that has a 41.50mm leg opposite that angle?

4. _____

5. What is the measurement of the angle of a right triangle that has a 36.25mm hypotenuse and a 20.75mm leg opposite that angle?

5. _____

6. Determine the measurements from the three centers to point O on the following layout illustration.

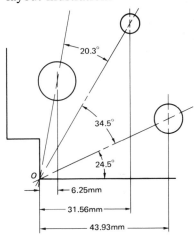

7. Determine the inspection measurements x and y for the location of the holes on the following plate.

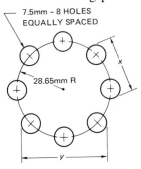

7.5mm – 8 HOLES
EQUALLY SPACED

28.65mm R

8   Determine angle A on the block illustrated.

31.75mm DIA

12.7mm

31.75mm

6.3mm

25.4mm

68.68mm

76.2mm

APPENDIX

Table A.1 American Drill and Thread Sizes and Tap Drills Necessary for 75% Maximum Thread

Drill Size — Fractional Drills	Drill Size — Number and Letter Drills	Drill Size — Decimal Equivalents	Thread Size — Size in Threads/Inch Decimal	Thread Size — OD as Decimal	Drill Size — Fractional Drills	Drill Size — Number and Letter Drills	Drill Size — Decimal Equivalents	Thread Size — Size in Threads/Inch Decimal	Thread Size — OD as Decimal
	80	.0135				37	.1040	5-44	.125
	79	.0145				36	.1065	6-32	.138
1/64		.0156			7/64		.1094		
	78	.0160				35	.1100		
	77	.0180				34	.1110		
	76	.0200				33	.1130	6-40	.138
	75	.0210				32	.1160		
	74	.0225				31	.1200		
	73	.0240			1/8		.1250		
	72	.0250				30	.1285	8-32	.164
	71	.0260				29	.1360	8-36	.164
	70	.0280				28	.1405		
	69	.0292			9/64		.1406		
	68	.0310				27	.1440		
1/32		.0312				26	.1470		
	67	.0320				25	.1495	10-24	.190
	66	.0330				24	.1520		
	65	.0350				23	.1540		
	64	.0360			5/32		.1562		
	63	.0370				22	.1570		
	62	.0380				21	.1590	10-32	.190
	61	.0390				20	.1610		
	60	.0400				19	.1660		
	59	.0410				18	.1695		
	58	.0420			11/64		.1719		
	57	.0430				17	.1730		
	56	.0465				16	.1770	12-24	.216
3/64		.0469	0-80	.060		15	.1800		
	55	.0520				14	.1820	12-28	.216
	54	.0550	1-64	.073		13	.1850		
	53	.0595	1-72	.073	3/16		.1875		
1/16		.0625				12	.1890		
	52	.0635				11	.1910		
	51	.0670	2-56	.086		10	.1935		
	50	.0700	2-64	.086		9	.1960		
	49	.0730				8	.1990		
	48	.0760				7	.2010	1/4-20	.250
5/64		.0781			13/64		.2031		
	47	.0785	3-48	.099		6	.2040		
	46	.0810				5	.2055		
	45	.0820	3-56	.099		4	.2090		
	44	.0860				3	.2130	1/4-28	.250
	43	.0890	4-40	.112	7/32		.2187		
	42	.0935	4-48	.112		2	.2210		
3/32		.0937				1	.2280		
	41	.0960				A	.2340		
	40	.0980				B	.2380		
	39	.0995				C	.2420		
	38	.1015	5-40	.125		D	.2460		

Drill Size			Thread Size		Drill Size			Thread Size	
Fractional Drills	Number and Letter Drills	Decimal Equivalents	Size in Threads/ Inch Decimal	OD as Decimal	Fractional Drills	Number and Letter Drills	Decimal Equivalents	Size in Threads/ Inch Decimal	OD as Decimal
1/4	E	.2500			15/32		.4687		
	F	.2570	5/16-18	.3125	31/64		.4844	9/16-12	.5625
	G	.2610			1/2		.5000		
17/64		.2656			33/64		.5156	9/16-18	.5625
	H	.2660			17/32		.5312	5/8-11	.6250
	I	.2720	5/16-24	.3125	35/64		.5469		
	J	.2770			9/16		.5625		
	K	.2810			37/64		.5781	5/8-18	.6250
9/32		.2812			19/32		.5937		
	L	.2900			39/64		.6094		
	M	.2950			5/8		.6250		
19/64		.2969			41/64		.6406		
	N	.3020			21/32		.6562	3/4-10	.7500
5/16		.3125	3/8-16	.3750	43/64		.6719		
	O	.3160			11/16		.6875	3/4-16	.7500
	P	.3230			45/64		.7031		
21/64		.3281			23/32		.7187		
	Q	.3320	3/8-24	.3750	47/64		.7344		
	R	.3390			3/4		.7500		
11/32		.3438			49/64		.7656	7/8-9	.8750
	S	.3480			25/32		.7812		
	T	.3580			51/64		.7969		
23/64		.3594			13/16		.8125	7/8-14	.8750
	U	.3680	7/16-14	.4375	53/64		.8281		
3/8		.3750			27/32		.8437		
	V	.3770			55/64		.8594		
	W	.3860			7/8		.8750	1-8	1.000
25/64		.3906	7/16-20	.4375	57/64		.8906		
	X	.3970			29/32		.9062		
	Y	.4040			59/64		.9219		
13/32		.4062			15/16		.9375	1-14	1.000
	Z	.4130			61/64		.9531		
27/64		.4219	1/2-13	.5000	31/32		.9687		
7/16		.4375			63/64		.9844		
29/64		.4531	1/2-20	.5000	1		1.000		

Table A.2 Angular Indexing Table

Value	H	C	Value	H	C	Value	H	C	Value	H	C	Value	H	C
.0204	1	49	.1224	6	49	.2258	7	31	.3333	6	18	.4359	17	39
.0213	1	47	.1250	2	16	.2308	9	39	.3333	7	21	.4375	7	16
.0233	1	43	.1277	6	47	.2326	10	43	.3333	9	27	.4390	18	41
.0244	1	41	.1282	5	39	.2340	11	47	.3333	11	33	.4419	19	43
.0256	1	39	.1290	4	31	.2353	4	17	.3333	13	39	.4444	8	18
.0270	1	37	.1304	3	23	.2381	5	21	.3404	16	47	.4444	12	27
.0303	1	33	.1333	2	15	.2414	7	29	.3415	14	41	.4468	21	47
.0323	1	31	.1351	5	37	.2424	8	33	.3448	10	29	.4483	13	29
.0345	1	29	.1379	4	29	.2432	9	37	.3469	17	49	.4490	22	49
.0370	1	27	.1395	6	43	.2439	10	41	.3478	8	23	.4500	9	20
.0408	2	49	.1429	3	21	.2449	12	49	.3488	15	43	.4516	14	31
.0426	2	47	.1429	7	49	.2500	4	16	.3500	7	20	.4545	15	33
.0435	1	23	.1463	6	41	.2500	5	20	.3514	13	37	.4595	17	37
.0465	2	43	.1481	4	27	.2553	12	47	.3529	6	17	.4615	18	39
.0476	1	21	.1489	7	47	.2558	11	43	.3548	11	31	.4634	19	41
.0488	2	41	.1500	3	20	.2564	10	39	.3590	14	39	.4651	20	43
.0500	1	20	.1515	5	33	.2581	8	31	.3617	17	47	.4667	7	15
.0513	2	39	.1538	6	39	.2593	7	27	.3636	12	33	.4681	22	47
.0526	1	19	.1579	3	19	.2609	6	23	.3659	15	41	.4694	23	49
.0541	2	37	.1613	5	31	.2632	5	19	.3673	18	49	.4706	8	17
.0555	1	18	.1622	6	37	.2653	13	49	.3684	7	19	.4737	9	19
.0588	1	17	.1628	7	43	.2667	4	15	.3704	10	27	.4762	10	21
.0606	2	33	.1633	8	49	.2683	11	41	.3721	16	43	.4783	11	23
.0612	3	49	.1666	3	18	.2703	10	37	.3750	6	16	.4815	13	27
.0625	1	16	.1702	8	47	.2727	9	33	.3784	14	37	.4828	14	29
.0638	3	47	.1707	7	41	.2759	8	29	.3793	11	29	.4839	15	31
.0645	2	31	.1724	5	29	.2766	13	47	.3810	8	21	.4848	16	33
.0666	1	15	.1739	4	23	.2777	5	18	.3830	18	47	.4865	18	37
.0690	2	29	.1765	3	17	.2791	12	43	.3846	15	39	.4872	19	39
.0698	3	43	.1795	7	39	.2821	11	39	.3871	12	31	.4878	20	41
.0732	3	41	.1818	6	33	.2857	14	49	.3878	19	49	.4884	21	43
.0741	2	27	.1837	9	49	.2857	6	21	.3888	7	18	.4894	23	47
.0769	3	39	.1852	5	27	.2903	9	31	.3902	16	41	.4898	24	49
.0811	3	37	.1860	8	43	.2927	12	41	.3913	9	23	.5000	8	16
.0816	4	49	.1875	3	16	.2941	5	17	.3939	13	33	.5000	9	18
.0851	4	47	.1892	7	37	.2963	8	27	.3953	17	43	.5000	10	20
.0870	2	23	.1905	4	21	.2973	11	37	.4000	6	15	.5102	25	49
.0909	3	33	.1915	9	47	.2979	14	47	.4000	8	20	.5106	24	47
.0930	4	43	.1935	6	31	.3000	6	20	.4043	19	47	.5116	22	43
.0952	2	21	.1951	8	41	.3023	13	43	.4054	15	37	.5122	21	41
.0968	3	31	.2000	3	15	.3030	10	33	.4074	11	27	.5128	20	39
.0976	4	41	.2000	4	20	.3043	7	23	.4082	20	49	.5135	19	37
.1000	2	20	.2041	10	49	.3061	15	49	.4103	16	39	.5151	17	33
.1020	5	49	.2051	8	39	.3077	12	39	.4118	7	17	.5161	16	31
.1026	4	39	.2069	6	29	.3103	9	29	.4138	12	29	.5172	15	29
.1034	3	29	.2093	9	43	.3125	5	16	.4146	17	41	.5185	14	27
.1053	2	19	.2105	4	19	.3158	6	19	.4186	18	43	.5217	12	23
.1064	5	47	.2121	7	33	.3171	13	41	.4194	13	31	.5238	11	21
.1081	4	37	.2128	10	47	.3191	15	47	.4211	8	19	.5263	10	19
.1111	2	18	.2162	8	37	.3226	10	31	.4242	14	33	.5294	9	17
.1111	3	27	.2174	5	23	.3243	12	37	.4255	20	47	.5306	26	49
.1163	5	43	.2195	9	41	.3256	14	43	.4286	9	21	.5319	25	47
.1176	2	17	.2222	6	27	.3265	16	49	.4286	21	49	.5333	8	15
.1212	4	33	.2222	4	18	.3333	5	15	.4324	16	37	.5349	23	43
.1220	5	41	.2245	11	49				.4348	10	23	.5366	22	41

Value	H	C	Value	H	C	Value	H	C	Value	H	C	Value	H	C
.5385	21	39	.6296	17	27	.7209	31	43	.8108	30	37	.9000	18	20
.5405	20	37	.6316	12	19	.7222	13	18	.8125	13	16	.9024	37	41
.5454	18	33	.6326	31	49	.7234	34	47	.8140	35	43	.9032	28	31
.5484	17	31	.6341	26	41	.7241	21	29	.8148	22	27	.9048	19	21
.5500	11	20	.6364	21	33	.7273	24	33	.8163	40	49	.9070	39	43
.5510	27	49	.6383	30	47	.7297	27	37	.8181	27	33	.9090	30	33
.5517	16	29	.6410	25	39	.7317	30	41	.8205	32	39	.9130	21	23
.5532	26	47	.6452	20	31	.7333	11	15	.8235	14	17	.9149	43	47
.5555	10	18	.6471	11	17	.7347	36	49	.8261	19	23	.9184	45	49
.5555	15	27	.6486	24	37	.7368	14	19	.8276	24	29	.9189	34	37
.5581	24	43	.6500	13	20	.7391	17	23	.8293	34	41	.9231	36	39
.5610	23	41	.6512	28	43	.7407	20	27	.8298	39	47	.9259	25	27
.5625	9	16	.6522	15	23	.7419	23	31	.8333	15	18	.9268	38	41
.5641	22	39	.6531	32	49	.7436	29	39	.8367	41	49	.9302	40	43
.5652	13	23	.6552	19	29	.7442	32	43	.8372	36	43	.9310	27	29
.5676	21	37	.6585	27	41	.7447	35	47	.8378	31	37	.9333	14	15
.5714	12	21	.6596	31	47	.7500	12	16	.8387	26	31	.9355	29	31
.5714	28	49	.6666	10	15	.7500	15	20	.8421	16	19	.9362	44	47
.5745	27	47	.6666	12	18	.7551	37	49	.8462	33	39	.9375	15	16
.5757	19	33	.6666	14	21	.7561	31	41	.8485	28	33	.9388	46	49
.5789	11	19	.6666	18	27	.7568	28	37	.8500	17	20	.9394	31	33
.5806	18	31	.6666	22	33	.7576	25	33	.8511	40	47	.9412	16	17
.5814	25	43	.6666	26	39	.7586	22	29	.8519	23	27	.9444	17	18
.5854	24	41	.6735	33	42	.7619	16	21	.8537	35	41	.9459	35	37
.5862	17	29	.6744	29	43	.7647	13	17	.8571	18	21	.9474	18	19
.5882	10	17	.6757	25	37	.7674	33	43	.8571	42	49	.9487	37	39
.5897	23	39	.6774	21	31	.7692	30	39	.8605	37	43	.9500	19	20
.5918	29	49	.6809	32	47	.7742	24	31	.8621	25	29	.9512	39	41
.5926	16	27	.6829	28	41	.7755	38	49	.8649	32	37	.9524	20	21
.5946	22	37	.6842	13	19	.7760	36	47	.8666	13	15	.9535	41	43
.5957	28	47	.6875	11	16	.7777	21	27	.8696	20	23	.9565	22	23
.6000	9	15	.6897	20	29	.7777	14	18	.8719	27	31	.9574	45	47
.6000	12	20	.6923	27	39	.7805	32	41	.8718	34	39	.9592	47	49
.6047	26	43	.6939	34	49	.7826	18	23	.8723	41	47	.9630	26	27
.6060	20	33	.6957	16	23	.7838	29	37	.8750	14	16	.9655	28	29
.6087	14	23	.6969	23	33	.7872	37	47	.8776	43	49	.9677	30	31
.6098	25	41	.6977	30	43	.7879	26	33	.8780	36	41	.9697	32	33
.6111	11	18	.7000	14	20	.7895	15	19	.8788	29	33	.9730	36	37
.6122	30	49	.7021	33	47	.7907	34	43	.8824	15	17	.9744	38	39
.6129	19	31	.7027	26	37	.7931	23	29	.8837	38	43	.9756	40	41
.6154	24	39	.7037	19	27	.7949	31	39	.8888	16	18	.9767	42	43
.6170	29	47	.7059	12	17	.7959	39	49	.8888	24	27	.9787	46	47
.6190	13	21	.7073	29	41	.8000	12	15	.8919	33	37	.9796	48	49
.6207	18	29	.7097	22	31	.8000	16	20	.8936	42	47			
.6216	23	37	.7143	15	21	.8049	33	41	.8947	17	19			
.6250	10	16	.7143	35	49	.8065	25	31	.8966	26	29			
.6279	27	43	.7179	28	39	.8085	38	47	.8974	35	39			
						.8095	17	21	.8980	44	49			

Reprinted from *Shop Theory*, 6th ed., by J. Anderson and E. Tatro, © 1974. With permission of Webster/McGraw-Hill.

Table A.3 Geometric Formulas and Relationships

1. Vertical Angles

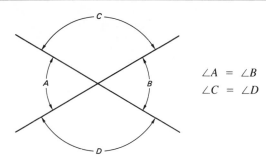

$$\angle A = \angle B$$
$$\angle C = \angle D$$

2. Alternate Angles

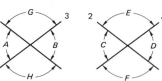

Line 1 parallel to line 2
Line 3 parallel to line 4
$$\angle A = \angle B = \angle C = \angle D$$
$$\angle G = \angle H = \angle E = \angle F$$

3. Interior Angles of a Polygon

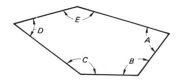

$s = (N-2)180°$
$s = $ sum of interior angles
$N = $ number of sides

4. Right Triangle Formulas

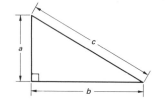

$$c = \sqrt{a^2 + b^2}$$
$$b = \sqrt{c^2 - a^2}$$
$$a = \sqrt{c^2 - b^2}$$

5. 45°–45° Right Triangle

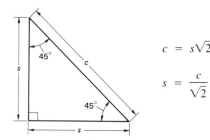

$$c = s\sqrt{2}$$
$$s = \frac{c}{\sqrt{2}}$$

6. 30°–60° Right Triangle

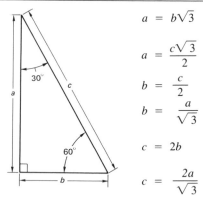

$$a = b\sqrt{3}$$
$$a = \frac{c\sqrt{3}}{2}$$
$$b = \frac{c}{2}$$
$$b = \frac{a}{\sqrt{3}}$$
$$c = 2b$$
$$c = \frac{2a}{\sqrt{3}}$$

7. Equilateral Triangle

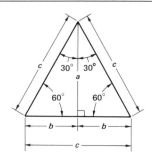

Refer to section 6.

8. Isosceles Triangle

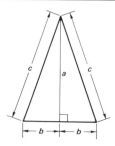

Refer to sections 4, 5, and 6.

9. Scalene Triangle (Projection Formula)

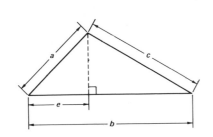 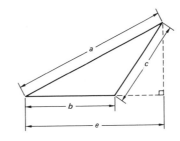

$$e = \frac{a^2 + b^2 - c^2}{2b}$$

10. Circle Measurements

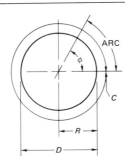

R = radius
D = diameter
c = circumference
ϕ = central angle
arc = arc measure

$c = \pi D$
$c = 2\pi R$
$D = c/\pi$
$R = c/2\pi$

$$\phi = \frac{\text{arc} \times 360°}{c} \qquad c = \frac{\text{arc} \times 360°}{\phi} \qquad \text{arc} = \frac{c \times \phi}{360°}$$

11. Chord Measurements

$$w = 2\sqrt{Dh - h^2}$$

$$h = \frac{D - \sqrt{D^2 - w^2}}{2}$$

$$D = \frac{(\frac{1}{2}w)^2 + h^2}{h}$$

12. Tangent Segments

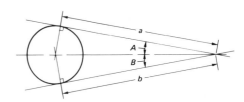

$$\angle A = \angle B$$
$$a = b$$

13. Central Angle

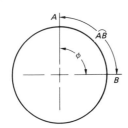

(central angle)° = (intercepted arc)°

$$\phi° = \widehat{AB}°$$

14. Inscribed Angle

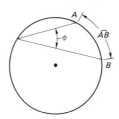

(inscribed angle)° = $\frac{1}{2}$(intercepted arc)°

$$\phi° = \frac{\widehat{AB}°}{2}$$

15. Tangent Angle

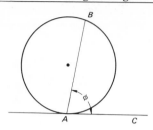

$$(\text{tangent angle})° = \frac{1}{2}(\text{intercepted arc})°$$

$$\phi° = \frac{\widehat{AB}°}{2}$$

16. Interior Angle

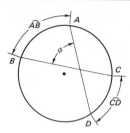

$$(\text{interior angle})° = \frac{1}{2}\left(\begin{array}{l}\text{intercepted arc} + \text{vertical} \\ \text{angle intercepted arc}\end{array}\right)$$

$$\phi° = \frac{\widehat{AB}° + \widehat{CD}°}{2}$$

17. Exterior Angle

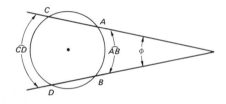

$$(\text{exterior angle})° = \frac{1}{2}(\text{major arc} - \text{minor arc})°$$

$$\phi = \frac{1}{2}(\widehat{CD}° - \widehat{AB}°)$$

18. Inscribed Circle of a Scalene Triangle

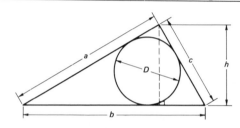

$$D = \frac{2bh}{(a + b + c)}$$

Refer to sections 4, 5, 6, and 9 for other formulas.

19. Inscribed Circle of an Isosceles Triangle

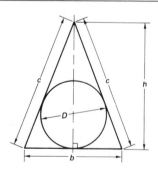

$$D = \frac{2bh}{b + 2c}$$

Refer to sections 4, 5, and 6 for other formulas.

20. Inscribed Circle of an Equilateral Triangle

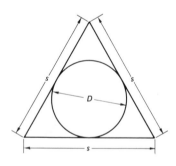

$$D = \frac{s}{\sqrt{3}}$$

$$s = D\sqrt{3}$$

21. Inscribed Circle of a Right Triangle

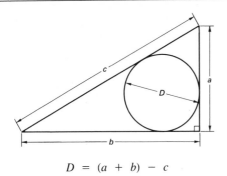

$$D = (a + b) - c$$

22. Inscribed Equilateral Triangle

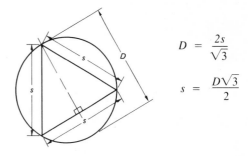

$$D = \frac{2s}{\sqrt{3}}$$

$$s = \frac{D\sqrt{3}}{2}$$

23. Regular Hexagon

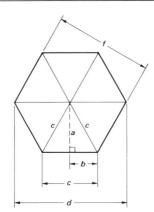

$$f = \frac{D\sqrt{3}}{2}$$

$$D = \frac{2F}{\sqrt{3}}$$

Refer to section 6 for additional formulas.

Table A.4 Trigonometric Functions and Formulas

Trigonometric Functions

$$\text{sine} = \frac{\text{leg opposite}}{\text{hypotenuse}} \qquad \text{tangent} = \frac{\text{leg opposite}}{\text{leg adjacent}} \qquad \text{secant} = \frac{\text{hypotenuse}}{\text{leg adjacent}}$$

$$\text{cosine} = \frac{\text{leg adjacent}}{\text{hypotenuse}} \qquad \text{cosecant} = \frac{\text{hypotenuse}}{\text{leg opposite}} \qquad \text{cotangent} = \frac{\text{leg adjacent}}{\text{leg opposite}}$$

Pythagorean Relationships

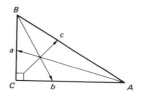

$$c = \sqrt{a^2 + b^2}$$
$$a = \sqrt{c^2 - b^2}$$
$$b = \sqrt{c^2 - a^2}$$

General Formulas for Finding Angles Stated as Specific Formulas for the Right Triangle

General Formula	Specific Formula
$\text{angle} = \text{arc sin } \dfrac{\text{leg opp}}{\text{hyp}}$	$\angle A = \text{arc sin } \dfrac{a}{c} \qquad \angle B = \text{arc sin } \dfrac{b}{c}$
$\text{angle} = \text{arc cos } \dfrac{\text{leg adj}}{\text{hyp}}$	$\angle A = \text{arc cos } \dfrac{b}{c} \qquad \angle B = \text{arc cos } \dfrac{a}{c}$
$\text{angle} = \text{arc tan } \dfrac{\text{leg opp}}{\text{leg adj}}$	$\angle A = \text{arc tan } \dfrac{a}{b} \qquad \angle B = \text{arc tan } \dfrac{b}{a}$

General Formulas for Finding Sides Stated as Specific Formulas for the Right Triangle

General Formula	Specific Formulas
leg opp = hyp × sin or leg adj × tan	$a = c \sin \angle A \qquad b = c \sin \angle B$ or $a = b \tan \angle A \qquad b = a \tan \angle B$
leg adj = hyp × cos or leg opp ÷ tan	$a = c \cos \angle B \qquad b = c \cos \angle A$ or $a = b/\tan \angle B \qquad b = a/\tan \angle A$
hyp = leg opp ÷ sin or leg adj ÷ cos	$c = a/\sin \angle A \qquad c = b/\sin \angle B$ or $c = b/\cos \angle A \qquad c = a/\cos \angle B$

ANSWERS

ANSWERS

The following are answers to odd-numbered exercises.

CHAPTER 1

Exercise 1.1: Interpretation of Fractions (p. 28)
A. **1.** 5/12　　　**3.** 73/100　　　**5.** 9/12　　　**7.** 3/4

Exercise 1.2: Types of Fractions (p. 28)
A. **1.** P　　　**3.** I　　　**5.** M　　　**7.** I
　　9. M　　　**11.** M　　　**13.** P　　　**15.** M
　　17. P　　　**19.** M

Exercise 1.3: Finding Equal Fractions (p. 28)
A. **1.** 3/4　　　**3.** 3/5　　　**5.** 11/20　　　**7.** 3/10
　　9. 1/2　　　**11.** 3/4　　　**13.** 3/10　　　**15.** 9/130
B. **1.** 1/3 foot　　**3.** 11/16 pound　　**5.** 5/6 day
C. **1.** 9　　　**3.** 44　　　**5.** 8　　　**7.** 12
　　9. 8　　　**11.** 6
D. **1.** 9/4　　　**3.** 39/4　　　**5.** 69/10　　　**7.** 21/4
　　9. 23/4
E. **1.** 2-1/3　　　**3.** 1-1/2　　　**5.** 17-3/4　　　**7.** 2-7/8
　　9. 1-3/32

Exercise 1.4: Equal Fractions and Fraction Comparisons (p. 29)
A. **1.** 2　　　**3.** 2　　　**5.** 2　　　**7.** 10

B. 1/8, 5/32, 3/16, 7/32, 17/64, 5/16, 3/8, 13/32, 7/16, and 1/2

C. **1.** 8　　　**3.** 15　　　**5.** 32　　　**7.** 50
　　9. 8　　　**11.** 50
D. **1.** yes　　　**3.** 15/16″　　　**5.** yes　　　**7a.** 9/16″
　　7b. 35/64″　　**7c.** 17/32″　　**7d.** 33/64″　　**7e.** 1/2″
　　7f. 31/64″　　**7g.** 15/32″　　**7h.** 29/64″　　**7i.** 7/16″

Exercise 1.5: Addition and Subtraction (p. 30)
A. **1.** 1-1/2　　　**3.** 1-1/16　　　**5.** 1-31/32　　　**7.** 15/16
　　9. 5-13/16　　**11.** 17-15/16
B. **1.** 3/8　　　**3.** 1/8　　　**5.** 5/8　　　**7.** 13/20
　　9. 3-3/8　　　**11.** 1-8/25　　**13.** 1-3/4　　　**15.** 9-7/8
C. **1.** 3-9/16″　　**3.** 5-3/4″　　**5a.** 1-11/32″　　**5b.** 1-15/32″
　　5c. 2-5/16″　　**7a.** 1-3/16″　　**7b.** 2-15/32″　　**7c.** 2-25/32″
　　7d. 3-21/32″　　**7e.** 2-9/64″　　**9a.** 7/8″　　**9b.** 1-27/32″
　　9c. 2-23/32″　　**9d.** 3-13/32″　　**11a.** 1-13/16″　　**11b.** 2-15/32″
　　11c. 2-27/32″　　**11d.** 5″　　**11e.** 1-5/8″　　**11f.** 1-1/8″
　　11g. 3-3/16″　　**11h.** 3-3/16″
D. **1.** 4-13/16″　　**3.** 19/64″　　**5.** 1-7/16″　　**7a.** 17/32″
　　7b. 3-43/64″　　**7c.** 1/2″　　**7d.** 4″　　**7e.** 2-25/32″
　　7f. 1-25/32″

Exercise 1.6:   Multiplication and Division (p. 35)

A.	**1.**	3-3/4	**3.**	7-7/8	**5.**	16-11/16	**7.**	9/32
	9.	1-7/8	**11.**	3/8	**13.**	35/48	**15.**	9/20
B.	**1.**	15-1/6	**3.**	18-1/3	**5.**	7/8	**7.**	36-7/8
C.	**1.**	4-21/32″	**3a.**	1-1/2″	**3b.**	2-1/4″	**3c.**	1-1/4″
	3d.	1-7/8″	**5a.**	2-7/16″	**5b.**	5-5/8″	**5c.**	7-5/16″
	7a.	1-1/4″	**7b.**	1-9/16″	**7c.**	3-15/16″	**7d.**	45/64″

CHAPTER 2

Exercise 2.1:   Interpretation of Decimals (p. 55)

A.	**1.**	0.3	**3.**	0.009	**5.**	0.06	**7.**	0.18
	9.	0.1475	**11.**	20.15	**13.**	8.2	**15.**	1.008
B.	**1.**	7/10	**3.**	9/1000	**5.**	19/100	**7.**	6-3/10
	9.	17-468/1000	**11.**	118-5/10				

Exercise 2.2:   Comparing Decimals (p. 55)

A.   **1.**   0.5″, 0.5156″, 0.5312″, 0.5469″, 0.5625″, 0.5781″, 0.5937″, 0.6094″, and 0.625″

   3.   0.1285″, 0.1200″, 0.1160″, 0.1130″, 0.1110″, 0.1100″, 0.1065″, 0.1040″, 0.1015″, 0.0995″, and 0.0980″

B.	**1.**	8.158	**3.**	18.540	**5.**	7.536	**7.**	7.005
	9.	2.2						

Exercise 2.3:   Arithmetic Operations (p. 56)

A.	**1.**	47.54	**3.**	2109.967	**5.**	214.016	**7.**	1276.81206
B.	**1.**	6.77	**3.**	$64.85	**5.**	1.9192	**7.**	1.915
C.	**1.**	$135.36	**3.**	0.24624	**5.**	1.818		
D.	**1.**	5.562	**3.**	9.488	**5.**	44.578	**7.**	734
E.	**1.**	7.923″	**3.**	5.612″	**5a.**	3.032″	**5b.**	4.532″
	7.	1.308″DIA	**9a.**	1.285″	**9b.**	3.520″	**9c.**	4.470″
	9d.	2.975″	**9e.**	6.357″	**9f.**	9.739″	**9g.**	11.764″
	9h.	12.714″	**9i.**	3.194″	**9j.**	2.570″	**9k.**	6.764″
	9l.	10.814″	**11a.**	3.590″	**11b.**	3.925″		

Exercise 2.4:   Conversions (p. 60)

A.	**1.**	0.75	**3.**	0.375	**5.**	0.0781	**7.**	0.0313
	9.	0.0156	**11.**	25.625	**13.**	18.3125	**15.**	5.875
B.	**1.**	3-7/10	**3.**	1/4	**5.**	1/8	**7.**	4-33/100
	9.	5-3/16	**11.**	3-3/4				
C.	**1.**	14/16	**3.**	44/60	**5.**	4/64	**7.**	4-7/8
	9.	7-8/32						

CHAPTER 3

Exercise 3.1:   Dimensioning (p. 79)

A.	**1.**	0.252/0.248	**3.**	3.088/3.085	**5.**	0.7515/0.7485	**7.**	0.0665/0.0655
	9.	8-41/64/8-39/64						
B.	**1a.**	0.005″	**1b.**	0.001″	**3a.**	0.018″	**3b.**	0.002″
C.	**1a.**	0.0055″	**1b.**	0.0005″	**3a.**	0.004″	**3b.**	0.001″

Exercise 3.2:   Reading Fractional and Decimal Scales (p. 80)

A.	**1.**	1/2″	**3.**	2-3/4″	**5.**	4-1/4″	**7.**	7/16″
	9.	2-15/16″	**11.**	4-9/16″				
B.	**1.**	7/16″	**3.**	2-7/16″	**5.**	4-25/32″	**7.**	15/64″
	9.	2-11/64″	**11.**	4-5/8″				
C.	**1.**	0.5″	**3.**	3.8″	**5.**	0.25″	**7.**	1.81″
	9.	3.55″	**11.**	4.81″				

Exercise 3.3: Reading Scales from Inch Marks (p. 81)

A.	**1.** 39/64″	**3.** 1-59/64″	**5.** 3-8/64″
B.	**1.** 11/16″	**3.** 1-9/16″	**5.** 2-3/4″

Exercise 3.4: Micrometers (p. 82)

A.	**1.** 0.639″	**3.** 0.007″	**5.** 0.366″	**7.** 0.437″
	9. 0.193″			
B.	**1.** 0.3326″	**3.** 0.1878″	**5.** 0.4927″	

Exercise 3.5: Depth Micrometers (p. 83)

A.	**1.** 0.567″	**3.** 0.930″	**5.** 0.789″

Exercise 3.6: Vernier Calipers (p. 83)

A.	**1.** 3.238″	**3.** 3.666″	**5.** 0.030″	**7.** 0.520″

Exercise 3.7: Gage Blocks (p. 84)

A.
1. 0.1002″ + 0.108″ + 0.150″ + 1.000″
3. 0.1001″ + 0.149″ + 0.300″ + 4.000″ + 3.000″
5. 0.1002″ + 0.148″ + 0.750″ + 4.000″

CHAPTER 4

Exercise 4.1: Interpretation of Ratios (p. 112)

A.	**1.** 3/7	**3.** 6/1	**5.** 6/10
B.	**1.** = = =	**3.** = = = = = = =	**5.** = = = = = = = = = =

Exercise 4.2: Reducing Ratios (p. 112)

A.	**1.** 15.8	**3.** 0.318	**5.** 0.199	
B.	**1.** 0.6	**3.** 0.5625	**5.** 1.11152	**7.** 0.56995

Exercise 4.3: Proportions (p. 112)

A.	**1.** yes	**3.** no	**5.** no	**7.** no
	9. no			
B.	**1.** 12	**3.** 64	**5.** 0.881	**7.** 5.571
	9. 67.407			

Exercise 4.4: Percents (p. 113)

A.	**1.** $48.00	**3.** 20%	**5.** 1300	**7.** 9.28
	9. 120%	**11.** 113.08	**13.** 177.27%	**15.** 20%
B.	**1a.** 46.2 hr.	**1b.** 10.56 hr.	**3.** 280 lbs. and 120 lbs.	**5.** $300,000
	7. $347.60	**9.** 12.5 lbs.		

Exercise 4.5: Tapers (p. 114)

A.	**1.** 0.225″	**3.** 0.700″DIA	**5.** 0.723″DIA

Exercise 4.6: TPF and TPI Specifications (p. 114)

A.	**1.** 0.04187″	**3.** 0.775″DIA	**5.** 1.841″DIA	
B.	**1a.** 0.06977″	**1b.** 0.83724″	**3.** 5.700″	**5.** 9.477″

Exercise 4.7: Simple Gear and Pulley Systems (p. 116)

A.	**1a.** 1.5/1	**1b.** 1/2	**1c.** 1/3	**1d.** 2/1
	1e. 1/1.33	**1f.** 1/1.5	**1g.** 1/4	**1h.** 3/1
	3a. D to B	**3b.** F to C	**3c.** B to E	**3d.** A to F
	3e. F to E	**3f.** C to B		

Exercise 4.8: Size and RPM Ratios (p. 117)

A.
1a.	1/2.5	**1b.**	2.5/1	**3a.**	1/1.25	**3b.**	1.25/1
5a.	1/2.14	**5b.**	2.14/1				

B.
1.	682 RPM	**3.**	120 teeth	**5a.**	1043 RPM	**5b.**	1.44/1
5c.	clockwise	**5d.**	1043 RPM	**5e.**	1.44/1	**5f.**	counterclockwise
7.	10.125″DIA	**9a.**	20 and 32	**9b.**	40 and 64	**9c.**	50 and 80
9d.	60 and 96						

Exercise 4.9: Compound Gear and Pulley Systems (p. 120)

A.
1a.	200 RPM	**1b.**	1.67/1	**1c.**	3.75/1	**1d.**	6.25/1
3a.	122 RPM	**3b.**	2.5/1	**3c.**	2.70/1	**3d.**	6.76/1
5a.	9681 RPM	**5b.**	38.72/1	**7a.**	192 RPM	**7b.**	clockwise
7c.	3.75/1	**7d.**	3.75/1	**7e.**	counterclockwise	**7f.**	3.75/1
7g.	clockwise						

CHAPTER 5

Exercise 5.1: Interpretation of Formulas (p. 159)

A. **1.** Formulas are statements that express the relationship between one value and one or more other values.

Exercise 5.2: Formula Notations (p. 159)

A.
1.	9	**3.**	72.25	**5.**	116.403	**7.**	0.766
9.	29.713						

B.
1.	8	**3.**	13	**5.**	5.721	**7.**	14.352
9.	0.769						

C. **1.** Square and division.
3. Square root, multiplication, and division.
5. Square, addition, subtraction, multiplication, and division.

Exercise 5.3: Sequence of Operations (p. 159)

A. **1.** Multiply, then divide.
3. Multiply, then determine square root.
5. In the numerator, multiply; in the denominator, add; then divide the numerator by the denominator.

Exercise 5.4: Problem Solving (p. 160)

A. **1.** Inspect the problem; identify values given directly and indirectly; check for familiar ways of applying formulas.

Exercise 5.5: Cutting Speeds and Feeds (p. 160)

A.
1.	28.6 FPM	**3.**	12.5 min	**5.**	15 min	**7.**	1210 RPM
9.	86 RPM	**11a.**	457.9 FPM	**11b.**	359.8 FPM		

Exercise 5.6: Threads (p. 161)

A.
1a.	0.050″	**1b.**	0.0625″	**1c.**	0.050″	**1d.**	0.050″
1e.	0.0909″	**1f.**	0.0833″	**1g.**	0.0556″	**1h.**	0.0313″
1i.	0.025″	**1j.**	0.0417″	**3a.**	0.063″	**3b.**	0.125″
5a.	0.0139″	**5b.**	0.0139″	**5c.**	0.0722″	**5d.**	0.1443″
5e.	0.8028″	**5f.**	0.7307″	**7a.**	0.050″	**7b.**	0.0590″
7c.	0.0406″	**7d.**	0.0271″	**7e.**	0.0325″	**7f.**	0.0232″
7g.	0.0541″	**7h.**	0.1299″	**9a.**	0.0341″	**9b.**	0.0219″
9c.	0.0682″	**9d.**	0.1228″	**9e.**	0.1535″	**9f.**	0.0307″
11a.	0.0444″ and 0.5166″	**11b.**	0.0361″ and 0.6386″	**11c.**	0.0361″ and 0.7636″	**11d.**	0.0412″ and 0.8903″
11e.	0.0525″ and 0.6447″	**11f.**	0.0289″ and 0.5109″	**13a.**	0.125″	**13b.**	1.750″
13c.	0.250″	**15a.**	0.125″	**15b.**	0.750″		

Exercise 5.7: Gears (p. 163)

A.	**1a.**	0.2244″	**1b.**	0.3696″	**1c.**	0.1745″	**1d.**	0.5712″

A.
- **1a.** 0.2244″
- **1e.** 0.3491″
- **3a.** 6″ and 6.25″
- **5.** 5.833″
- **7d.** 6.167″
- **9b.** 3.208″

- **1b.** 0.3696″
- **1f.** 0.1309″
- **3b.** 8.913″ and 9.422″
- **7a.** 9.000″
- **7e.** 108 teeth
- **9c.** 9.947″

- **1c.** 0.1745″
- **1g.** 0.0982″
- **3c.** 7.958″ and 8.754″
- **7b.** 6.000″
- **7f.** 72 teeth
- **9d.** 3.382″

- **1d.** 0.5712″
- **1h.** 0.750″
- **3d.** 1.778″ and 1.889″
- **7c.** 9.167″
- **9a.** 5.5″
- **11.** 3.625″

CHAPTER 6

Exercise 6.1: Units of Measurement (p. 171)

A.
- **1.** 30mm
- **9.** 884mm

- **3.** 97mm
- **11.** 965mm

- **5.** 252mm

- **7.** 319mm

B.
- **1.** 2000m
- **9.** 3500mm

- **3.** 8m

- **5.** 0.581cm

- **7.** 1.752km

C.
- **1.** (b) 12mm

- **3.** (c) 18mm

- **5.** (c) 60mm

Exercise 6.2: Shop-Related Problems (p. 172)

A.
- **1a.** 6.72mm
- **3c.** 41.32mm
- **5c.** 66.69mm
- **5g.** 69.52mm DIA
- **7c.** 25.08mm

- **1b.** 95.5mm
- **3d.** 101.03mm
- **5d.** 98.19mm
- **5h.** 55.47mm
- **7d.** 6.415mm

- **3a.** 51.5mm
- **5a.** 42.72mm
- **5e.** 29.52mm DIA
- **7a.** 99mm

- **3b.** 8.2mm
- **5b.** 57.89mm
- **5f.** 6.22mm
- **7b.** 37.5mm

CHAPTER 7

Exercise 7.1: Interpretation of Angles (p. 192)

Exercise 7.2: Angular Calculations (p. 192)

A.
- **1.** 64°5′
B.
- **1.** 45°
- **9.** 34°39′15″
C.
- **1.** 90°
D.
- **1.** 18°
- **9.** 14°10′
E.
- **1.** 45.5°
F.
- **1.** 42°45′

- **3.** 80°49′17″
- **3.** 38°
- **11.** 77°29′30″
- **3.** 36°40′30″
- **3.** 22°30′
- **11.** 18°26′45″
- **3.** 33.783°
- **3.** 89°20′

- **5.** 110°30′55″
- **5.** 71°35′

- **5.** 254°4′12″
- **5.** 90°

- **5.** 16.676°
- **5.** 39°15′11″

- **7.** 78°49′30″
- **7.** 14°42′

- **7.** 41°47′36″
- **7.** 60°

- **7.** 68.395°
- **7.** 73°46′48″

Exercise 7.3: Metric Angular Measurements (p. 193)

A.
- **1a.** 84°
- **2c.** 137.22°
- **3e.** 17.58°
- **5a.** 63.55°

- **1c.** 147.7°
- **2e.** 74.17°
- **4a.** 19.345°
- **5c.** 81.64°

- **1e.** 226.35°
- **3a.** 46.5°
- **4c.** 26.416°
- **5e.** 60.28°

- **2a.** 31.5°
- **3c.** 125.69°
- **4e.** 22.5°

Exercise 7.4: Types of Angles (p. 193)

A.   **1a.**   **1b.**   **1c.** 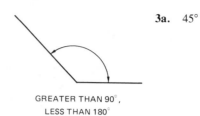   **3a.** 45°

LESS THAN 90°

GREATER THAN 90°,
LESS THAN 180°

3b. $\angle A + \angle B = 90°$ **5a.** $\angle A = \angle C = \angle E = \angle G$ **5b.** $\angle B = \angle D = \angle F = \angle H$ **7a.** 540°
7b. 51°24′

Exercise 7.5: Shop-Related Problems (p. 195)

A.   **1.** 11°   **3.** 62°25′   **5a.** 25°   **5b.** 65°
      5c. 115°   **7a.** 146°   **7b.** 104°   **7c.** 138°
      9a. 136°   **9b.** 318°30′

CHAPTER 8

Exercise 8.1: Right Triangles (p. 222)

A.   **1.** 10   **3.** 10.954   **5.** 8.352   **7.** 15.943
B.   **1.** 1.457″   **3.** 13.781″   **5.** 1.266′   **7a.** 4.012″
      7b. 6.512″   **9.** 8.436′

Exercise 8.2: Special Right Triangles (p. 224)

A.   **1.** $x = 7.550″$ **3.** $x = 4.188″$ **5.** $\angle A = 30°$
          $y = 10.677″$ $y = 7.253″$ $\angle B = 60°$
                                                               $x = 1.299″$

B.   **1.** 2.475″   **3a.** 1.805″   **3b.** 3.750″   **5.** 2.418″
      7a. 12.728″   **7b.** 12.728″

Exercise 8.3: Oblique Triangles (p. 227)

A.   **1.** 8.660″   **3.** 8.429″   **5.** 8.341″   **7.** 11.696″
      9. $x = 10.448″$; $y = 3.146″$; $z = 8.550″$
B.   **1.** 0.108″   **3a.** 1.689″   **3b.** 1.400″   **5a.** 0.808″
      5b. 1.766″

Exercise 8.4: Other Geometric Figures (p. 229)

A.   **1.** 11.314″   **3.** 20.427″   **5.** 2.511″
B.   **1a.** 0.181″   **1b.** 1.237″   **3a.** 45°   **3b.** 135°
      3c. 45°

Exercise 8.5: Metric Applications (p. 230)

A.   **1.** 95.11mm   **3.** 191.23mm   **5.** 31.64mm   **7a.** 18.56mm
      7b. 31.23mm

CHAPTER 9

Exercise 9.1: Interpretation of Circles (p. 261)

A.   **1.** 19.635″   **3.** 4.058″   **5.** 653.451″   **7.** 12.959″
      9. 8.754″ DIA   **11a.** 8.639″   **11b.** 172.780″   **11c.** 4319.5″
      13. 11,310 ft/min **15.** 3.048″R   **17.** 3.931″R   **19.** 2.542″
      21. 0.079″   **23a.** 1.936″   **23b.** 2.332″

Exercise 9.2: Tangent Relationships (p. 264)

A.	**1a.**	1.526″	**1b.**	1.587″	**1c.**	16°	**1d.** 74°
	3.	4.982″	**5.**	13.085″	**7.**	4.863″	
B.	**1.**	5.999″	**3.**	34.639″	**5.**	12.408″	

Exercise 9.3: Angle-Circle Relationships (p. 267)

A.	**1.**	55°	**3a.**	29°	**3b.**	61°	**5.**	27°30′
	7a.	46°	**7b.**	77°	**7c.**	44°	**7d.**	28°
	7e.	105°	**7f.**	75°	**7g.**	33°	**7h.**	21°
	7i.	110°	**7j.**	54°	**7k.**	62°	**7l.**	49°

Exercise 9.4: Triangle-Circle Relationships (p. 268)

A.	**1a.**	2.478″R	**1b.**	10.027″	**3.**	0.860″ DIA	**5.** 2.598″

Exercise 9.5: Indexing (p. 269)

A.	**1.** 2 holes	**3.** 4 holes	**5.** 12 holes
B.	**1.** 3 turns and 5 holes on a 15-hole circle		**3.** 1 turn and 9 holes on a 15-hole circle
	5. 6 turns and 10 holes on a 15-hole circle		**7.** 10 holes on a 29-hole circle
	9. 2 holes on an 18-hole circle		
C.	**1.** 6 turns and 2 holes on an 18-hole circle		**3.** 3 turns and 5 holes on a 15-hole circle
	5. 2 turns and 8 holes on a 16-hole circle		**7.** 4 turns and 5 holes on a 19-hole circle
	9. 2 turns and 3 holes on a 39-hole circle		

Exercise 9.6: Metric Applications (p. 270)

A.	**1.** 111.53mm	**3.** 321.14mm	**5.** 428.13mm DIA	**7.** 20.67mm DIA
	9. 148.41mm DIA			

CHAPTER 10

Exercise 10.1: Trigonometric Functions (p. 309)

A.
1. sin 24° = 0.40674; cos 24° = 0.91354; tan 24° = 0.44523; csc 24° = 2.4586
3. cos 19°52′ = 0.94049; tan 19°52′ = 0.36134; cot 19°52′ = 2.7675
5. sin 76°20′ = 0.97169; cot 76°20′ = 0.24316; csc 76°20′ = 1.0291
7. sin 89°15′ = 0.99991; tan 89°15′ = 76.390; sec 89°15′ = 76.396

B.	**1.** 15°31′	**3.** 38°24′	**5.** 37°31′	**7.** 58°08′
	9. 82°38′			
C.	**1.** 0.71080	**3.** 31°11′	**5.** 28°32′	**7.** 1.4935
	9. 17°05′	**11.** 0.96245	**13.** 72°52′	

Exercise 10.2: Interpolation (p. 310)

A.	**1.** 0.35438	**3.** 0.98950	**5.** 0.95582
B.	**1.** 35°55′29″	**3.** 1°41′30″	**5.** 7°13′40″

Exercise 10.3: Right-Triangle Trigonometry (p. 311)

A.
1.	a = 3.563″	b = 3.957″	$\angle B$ = 48°
3.	$\angle B$ = 62°30′	b = 8.068″	c = 9.096″
5.	$\angle A$ = 47°56′	$\angle B$ = 42°04′	a = 9.280″
7.	$\angle A$ = 22°55′	$\angle B$ = 67°05′	a = 2.774″

B.

1.

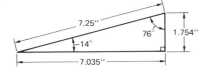

3.

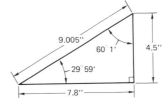

5.

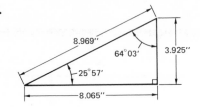

7.

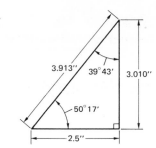

Exercise 10.4: Shop-Related Problems (p. 311)

A.   **1a.** 7.608″   **1b.** 5.261″   **3a.** 1.840″   **3b.** 1.495″
　　 3c. 1.910″   **5a.** 7.825″   **5b.** 4.616″   **7.** 0.376″
　　 9a. 16°25′   **9b.** 3.383″   **9c.** 2.770″   **11.** 0.650 DIA
　　 13. 2.773″   **15.** 0.985″R   **17.** 2.158″R   **19a.** 4°08′
　　 19b. 0.568″   **21a.** 0.023″   **21b.** 0.032″   **21c.** 0.039″
　　 21d. 0.028″

Exercise 10.5: Sine Bars (p. 317)

A.   **1.** 38°26′   **3a.** 2.500″   **3b.** 4.830″   **3c.** 2.367″
　　 3d. 4.273″   **3e.** 1.357″   **5.** 10°27′

Exercise 10.6: Oblique Triangles (p. 317)

A.   **1.** 0.81915   **3.** 0.95106   **5.** 0.92310   **7.** −0.99317
　　 9. −0.70711
B.   **1.** 104°19′   **3.** 133°50′   **5.** 172°20′   **7.** 133°57′
　　 9. 156°27′   **11.** 164°41′
D.   **1.** $\angle A = 73°$; a = 7.461″; b = 4.249″
　　 3. $\angle A = 36°$; a = 6.031″; b = 2.133
　　 5. $\angle B = 85°02′$; $\angle C = 66°58′$; a = 4.336″
　　 7. $\angle A = 39°15′$; $\angle B = 28°45′$; c = 10.989″

E.   **1.** 0.717″R   **3a.** 54°42′   **3b.** 39°24′   **3c** 85°54′
　　 5. 2.311″

Exercise 10.7: Metric Applications (p. 320)

A.   **1a.** 0.31548   **1c.** 0.41866   **1e.** 0.86313   **1g.** 0.69579
　　 2a. 43.79°   **2c.** 15.81°   **2e.** 56.36°   **2g.** 5.78°
　　 3. 65.14mm   **5.** 34.92°   **7a.** 13.24mm   **7b.** 18.11mm

INDEX

INDEX